SENIOR AUTHORS

James Burnett
Calvin Irons

PROGRAM CONSULTANTS

Diana Lambdin
Frank Lester, Jr.
Kit Norris

CONTRIBUTING AUTHORS

Debi DePaul
Beth Lewis
Peter Stowasser
Allan Turton

STUDENT JOURNAL

CONTENTS

MODULE 1

MODULE 2

MODULE 3

MODULE 4

MODULE 5

MODULE 6

CONTENTS

STEPPING STONES RESOURCES – PRINT

The *ORIGO Stepping Stones* program has been created to provide a smarter way to teach and learn mathematics. It has been developed by a team of experts to provide a world-class math program.

STUDENT JOURNAL

Engaging student pages accompany each lesson within *ORIGO Stepping Stones*. In the Student Journals for Grades 1–5, there are two pages for each lesson. Following are the features of the Grade 4 Student Journal as a part of the whole program.

STEP 1
Step In provides guided discussion of enquiry. This often sets the scene for the lesson.
Teachers can project this piece of the lesson and step through each question or point one at a time.

Module and lesson

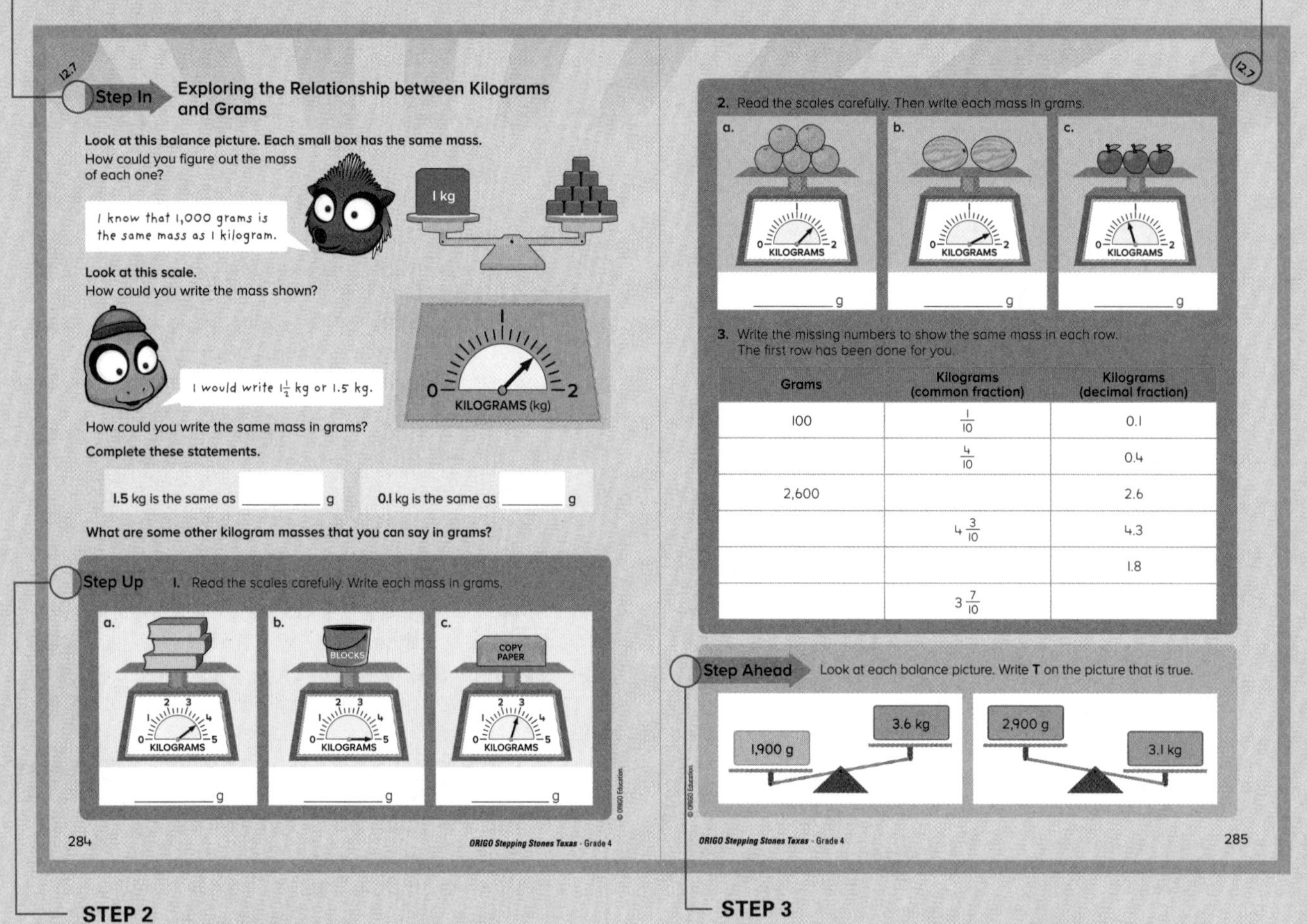

12.7

Step In Exploring the Relationship between Kilograms and Grams

Look at this balance picture. Each small box has the same mass.
How could you figure out the mass of each one?

Look at this scale.
How could you write the mass shown?

How could you write the same mass in grams?
Complete these statements.

1.5 kg is the same as ________ g   **0.1** kg is the same as ________ g

What are some other kilogram masses that you can say in grams?

Step Up 1. Read the scales carefully. Write each mass in grams.

a. ________ g b. ________ g c. ________ g

284 *ORIGO Stepping Stones Texas* · Grade 4

12.7

2. Read the scales carefully. Then write each mass in grams.

a. ________ g b. ________ g c. ________ g

3. Write the missing numbers to show the same mass in each row.
The first row has been done for you.

Grams	Kilograms (common fraction)	Kilograms (decimal fraction)
100	$\frac{1}{10}$	0.1
	$\frac{4}{10}$	0.4
2,600		2.6
	$4\frac{3}{10}$	4.3
		1.8
	$3\frac{7}{10}$	

Step Ahead Look at each balance picture. Write **T** on the picture that is true.

ORIGO Stepping Stones Texas · Grade 4 285

STEP 2
Step Up provides individual work based on the discussion above.

STEP 3
Step Ahead puts a little twist on each lesson to develop higher-order thinking skills.

Financial Literacy

ORIGO's *Stepping Into Financial Literacy* is an online channel that addresses the Personal Financial Literacy standards of the *Texas Essential Knowledge and Skills* for Mathematics. For your convenience, the student pages from this resource are provided at the back of this journal (pages 297–303).

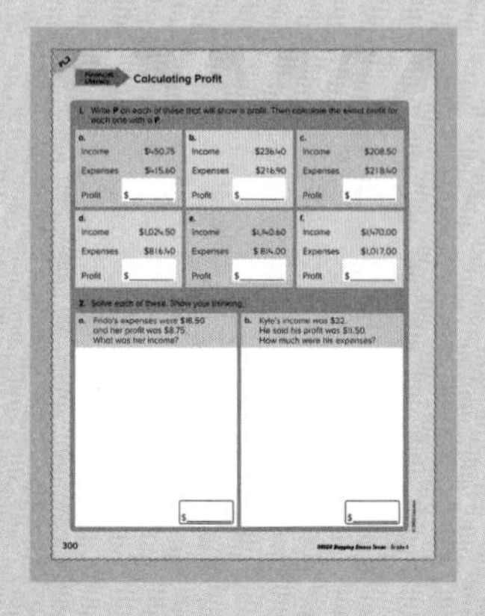

INTRODUCTION

PRACTICE BOOK

Regular and meaningful practice is a hallmark of ***ORIGO Stepping Stones***. Each module in this book has perforated pages that practice content previously learned to maintain concepts and skills, and pages that practice computation to promote fluency.

ADDITIONAL RESOURCES – PRINT

The Number Case provides teachers with ready-made resources that are designed to develop students' understanding of number.

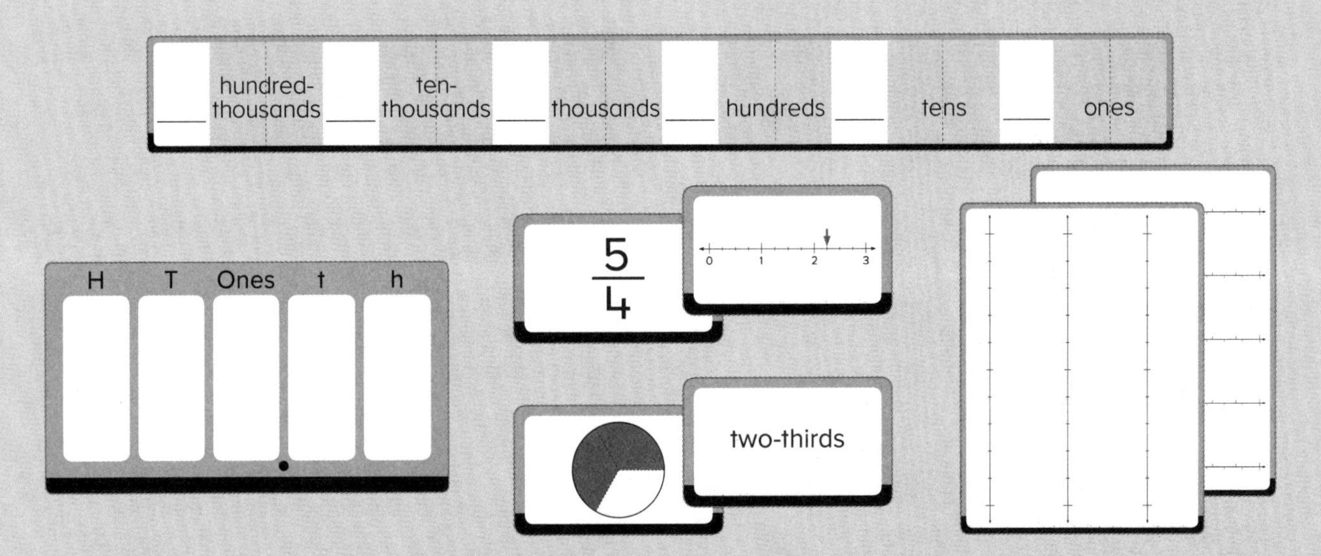

ADDITIONAL RESOURCES – ONLINE CHANNELS

These are some of the innovative teaching channels integrated into the teacher's online program.

ALGORITHM

Algorithms are rules used for completing tasks or for solving problems. There are standard algorithms for calculating answers to addition, subtraction, multiplication, and division problems.

For example:

$$\begin{array}{r} \scriptstyle 1 \\ 364 \\ +\underline{218} \\ 582 \end{array} \qquad \begin{array}{r} \scriptstyle 8\ 15 \\ 6\not{9}\not{5} \\ -\underline{327} \\ 368 \end{array}$$

ANGLE

An **acute angle** is an angle that is less than 90 degrees (90°). An **obtuse angle** is an angle that is greater than 90 degrees (90°) but less than 180 degrees (180°). A **right angle** is an angle that is equal to 90 degrees (90°).

CAPACITY

Capacity is the amount that something can hold.

COMPARING

When read from left to right, the symbol **>** means is **greater than**, and the symbol **<** means is **less than**.

For example: $2 < 6$ means 2 is less than 6

COMPOSITE NUMBER

A **composite number** is a whole number that has more than two whole number factors.

DECIMAL FRACTION

Decimal fractions are fractions in which the denominator is 10, 100, or 1,000, etc. but are always written using decimal points.

For example: $\frac{3}{10}$ can be written as 0.3

and $\frac{28}{100}$ can be written as 0.28

DECIMAL POINT

A **decimal point** indicates which digit is in the ones place. It is positioned immediately to the right of the ones digit.

For example, in this numeral, 3 is in the ones place.

23.85

A digit's **decimal place** is its position on the right-hand side of the decimal point. The first decimal place to the right of the decimal point is the tenths place. The next place is called hundredths. For example, in the numeral 23.85, 8 is in first decimal place so is called 8 tenths.

DEGREE

A **degree** is one unit of angle measure. There are 360 degrees in a full turn around a point. The symbol used to show degrees is °.

EXPANDED NOTATION

A method of writing numbers as the sum of the values of each digit.

FACTOR

Factors are whole numbers that evenly divide another whole number. For example, 4 and 5 are both factors of 20 and 20 is a multiple of both 4 and 5.

A **prime factor** is a factor that is also a prime number.

FLUID OUNCE

A **fluid ounce** is a unit of capacity. There are 16 fluid ounces in one pint. The short way to write fluid ounce is fl oz.

FRACTION

Fractions describe equal parts of a whole. In this common fraction symbol, 2 is the **numerator** and 3 is the **denominator**.

$\frac{2}{3}$

The denominator shows the total number of equal parts (3). The numerator shows the number of those parts (2).

A **common denominator** is one that two or more fractions have in common.

Proper fractions are common fractions that have a numerator that is less than the denominator.

For example, $\frac{2}{5}$ is a proper fraction.

Equivalent fractions are fractions that cover the same amount of area on a shape or are located on the same point on a number line.

For example, $\frac{1}{2}$ is equivalent to $\frac{2}{4}$.

Improper fractions are common fractions that have a numerator that is greater than or equal to the denominator.

For example, $\frac{7}{5}$ is an improper fraction.

LENGTH

Customary Units of Length		Metric Units of Length	
12 inches	1 foot	10 millimeters	1 centimeter
3 feet	1 yard	100 centimeters	1 meter
1,760 yards	1 mile	1,000 meters	1 kilometer

LINE

A straight **line** continues in both directions forever. It never ends.

A **line segment** has a start point and an end point. It is part of a straight line that continues in both directions forever.

LINE OF SYMMETRY

A **line of symmetry** splits a whole shape into two parts that are the same shape and the same size.

LIQUID VOLUME (CAPACITY)

Customary Units of Liquid Volume		Metric Units of Liquid Volume	
8 fluid ounces	1 cup	1,000 milliliters	1 liter
2 cups	1 pint	1,000 liters	1 kiloliter
2 pints	1 quart		
4 quarts	1 gallon		

MASS (WEIGHT)

Customary Units of Mass		Metric Units of Mass	
16 ounces	1 pound	1,000 grams	1 kilogram

MIXED NUMBER

A **mixed number** is any number written as a whole number followed by a fraction.

For example, $1\frac{2}{5}$ is a mixed number.

MULTIPLE

Multiples of a number can be found by multiplying that number by other whole number. For example, multiples of 4 are 4, 8, 12, and 16.

PARALLEL LINES

Parallel lines are straight lines that are the same distance apart along their entire length.

PERIMETER

A **perimeter** is the boundary of a shape and the total length of that boundary.

For example, the perimeter of this rectangle is 20 inches.

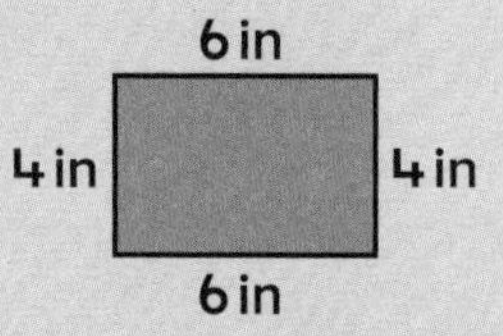

PERPENDICULAR LINES

Perpendicular lines are straight lines that make a right angle with each other.

PRIME NUMBER

A **prime number** is any whole number greater than zero that has exactly two unique factors – itself and 1.

RAY

A **ray** is part of a line that begins at a point and continues in one direction forever.

SQUARE NUMBER

A **square number** is one that can be shown as a square when arranged with dots. For example 1, 4, and 9 are the first three square numbers.

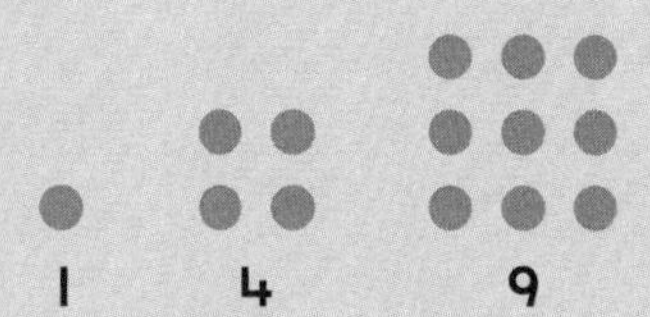

STEM-AND-LEAF PLOT

A graph where data is organized by separating place values with a vertical line. For example, 13, 18, and 23 are shown as below.

Stem	Leaf	
1	3	8
2	3	

GLOSSARY

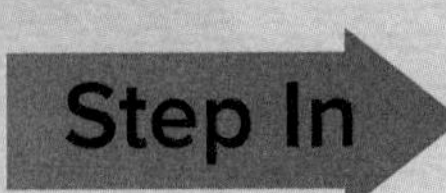

Reading and Writing Six-Digit Numbers (without Teens and Zeros)

Imagine you start at 90,000 and skip count by 1,000. What numbers would you say?

What number would you say after 99,000?

Write 100,000 in this place-value chart.

Thousands			Ones		
H	T	O	H	T	O

What do you notice about each group of three places?

Look at the number on this abacus.

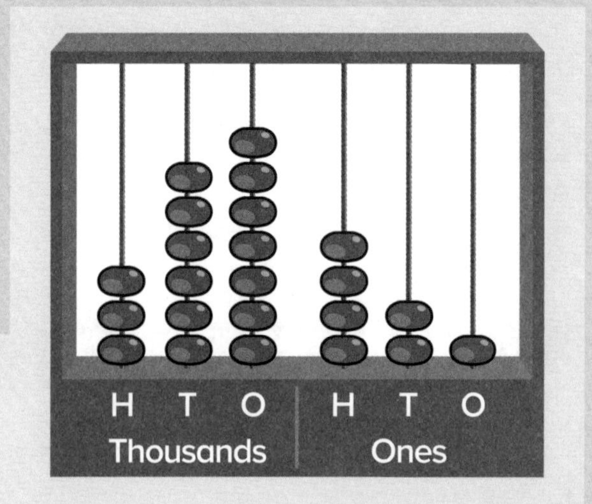

How do you know where to write the digits on this expander?

How do you read the first three digits of the number?

How do you read the whole number?

Step Up

1. Draw extra beads on the abacus to match the number on the expander.

a.

H T O H T O
Thousands Ones

2 6 4 thousands 5 2 3

b.

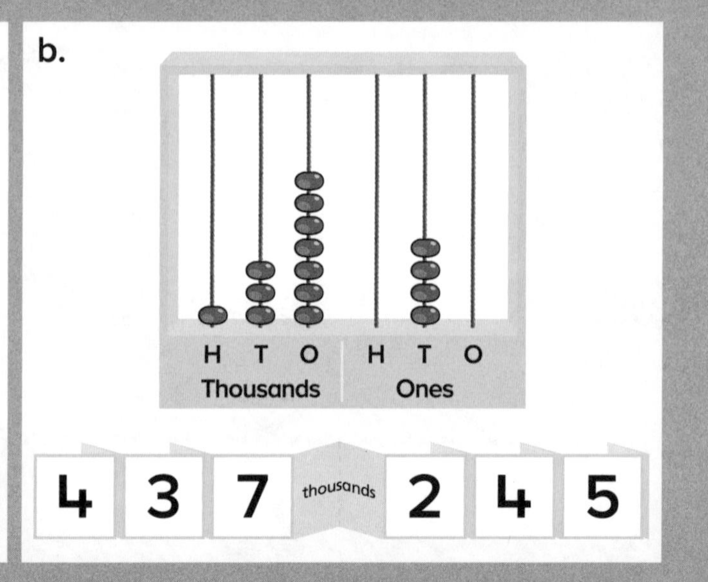

2. Look at the abacus. Write the matching number on the expander.

a.

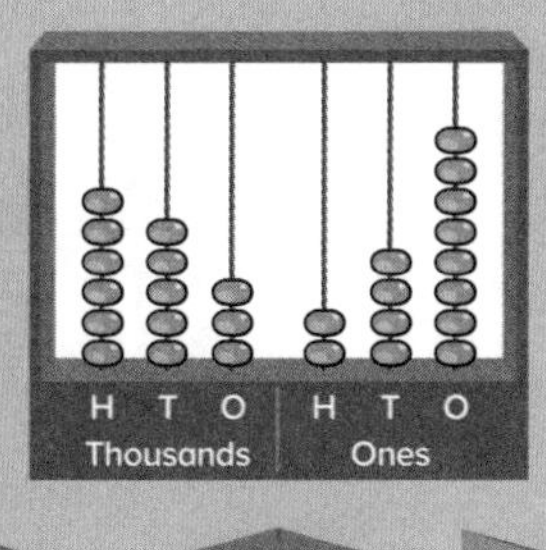

b.

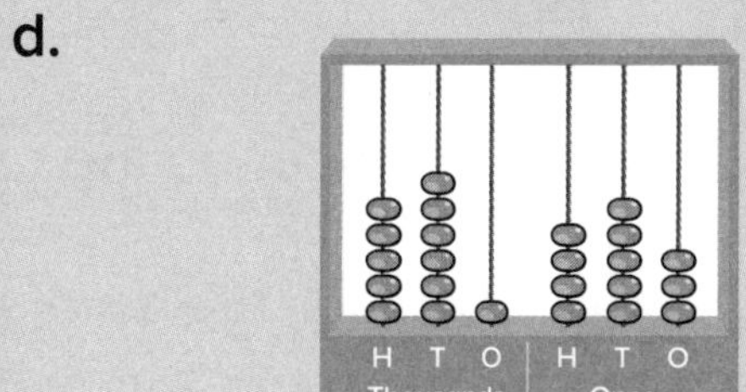

c.

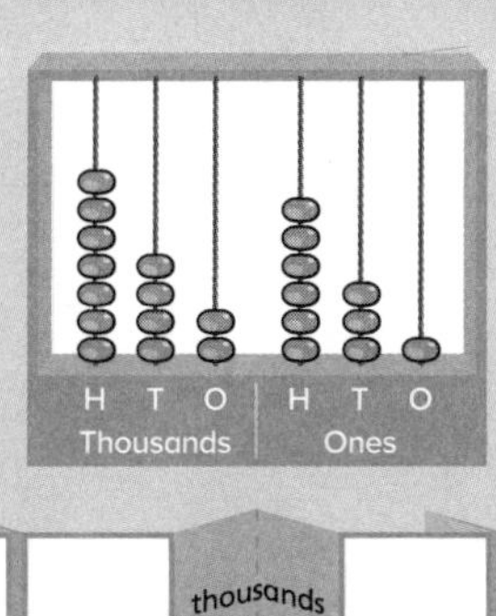

d.

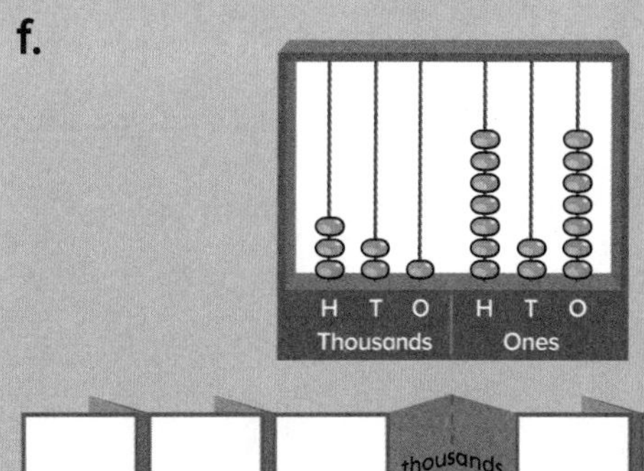

e.

H T O H T O
Thousands Ones

thousands

f.

H T O H T O
Thousands Ones

thousands

Step Ahead

Read the number on the expander. Then loop the abacus that shows a number that is 1,000 more.

4 3 5 thousands 2 4 9

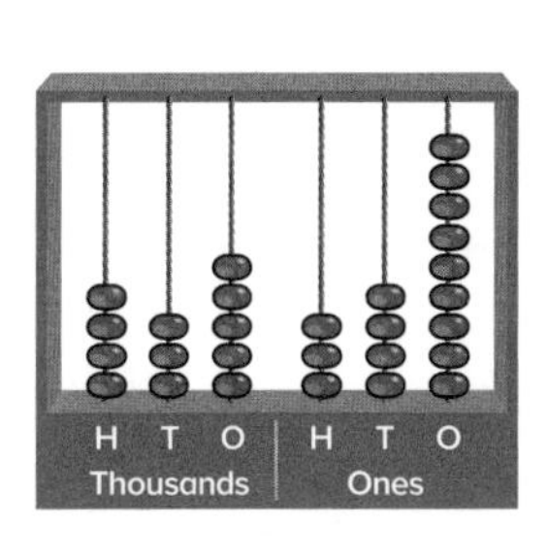

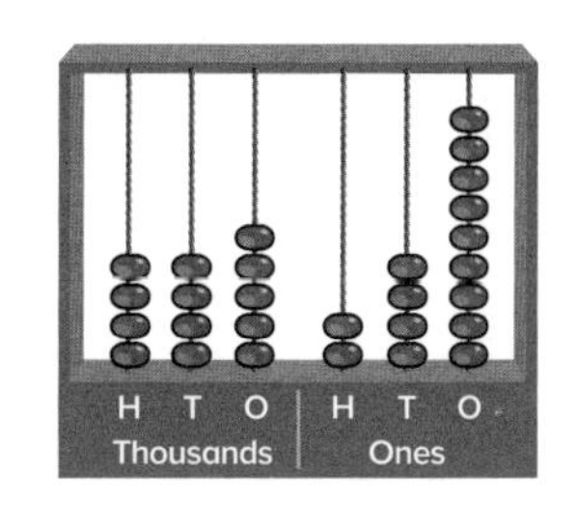

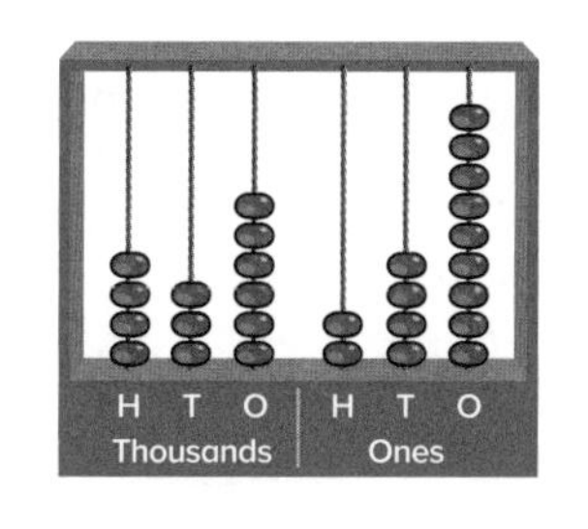

Step In: Reading and Writing Six-Digit Numbers on Expanders and in Words

Imagine you used all three of these cards to show a single number.

700,000

8,000 | 50,000

Where would you write the digits for the number on the expander below? How do you know?

How would you read the number on the open expander?

The first three digits are all thousands, so you can put these places together and read the number of thousands.

Write the same number on this expander.

How would you read the number?

Step Up

1. Write the matching number on the expander. Then write the number in words.

a.

5 hundred thousands

2 hundreds

thousands

____

____

b.

6 hundred thousands

7 ten thousands

thousands

____

____

2. Calculate the values and write the matching number on the expander. Then write the number in words.

a.

5 × 100

thousands

____

____

____

b.

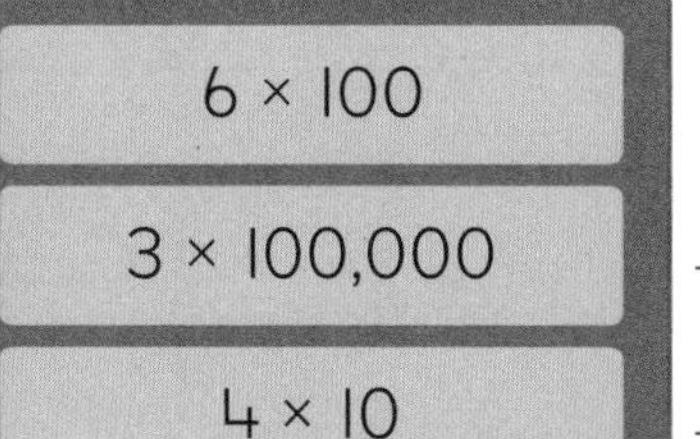

thousands

____

____

____

c.

7 × 1

8 × 100,000

thousands

____

____

____

Step Ahead Figure out the total number shown by each set of cards. Write the numbers on the expanders below.

a. 500 | 40,000 | 6,000 | 300,000

thousands

b. 30 | 100,000 | 2,000 | 50,000

thousands

Step In — Reading and Writing Six-Digit Numbers (with Teens and Zeros)

Write digits on the expander to match the number shown on the abacus.

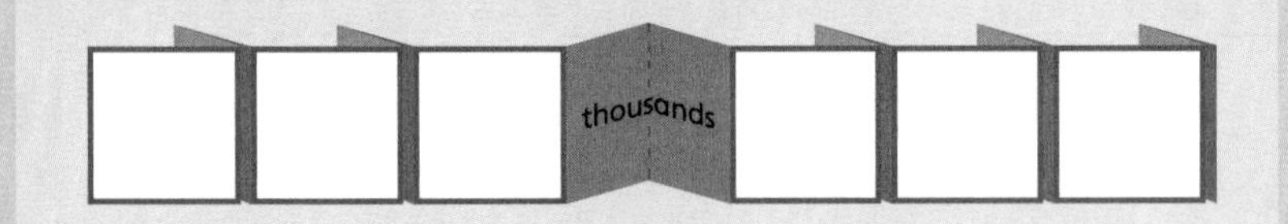

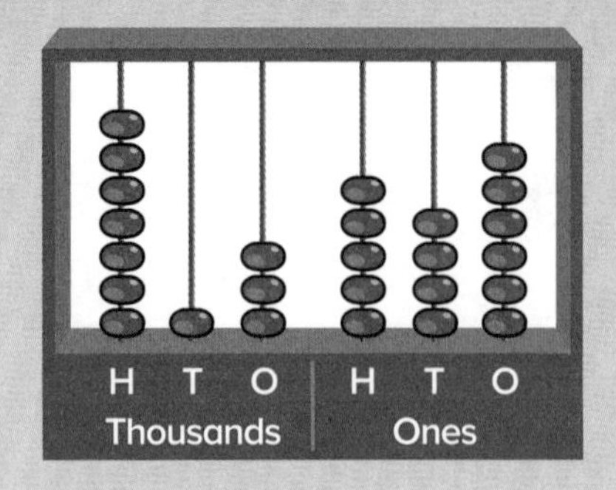

How could the expander help you figure out how to say the number name?

Write the number name.

What would you write on the expander below to match this abacus?

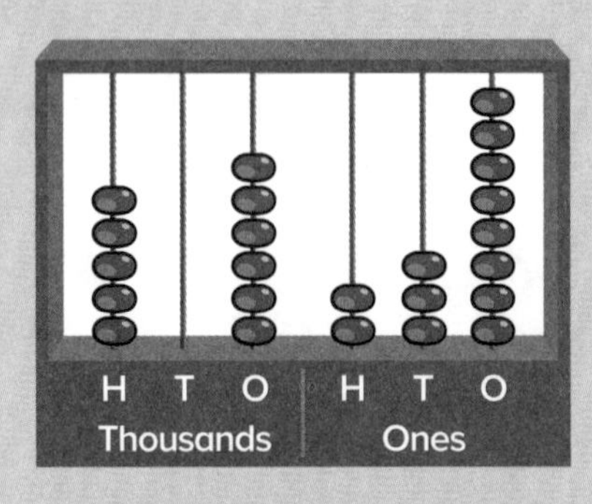

How would you say the number name?
How could the expander help you?

Step Up

1. Look at the abacus. Write the matching number on the expander. Then write the number in words.

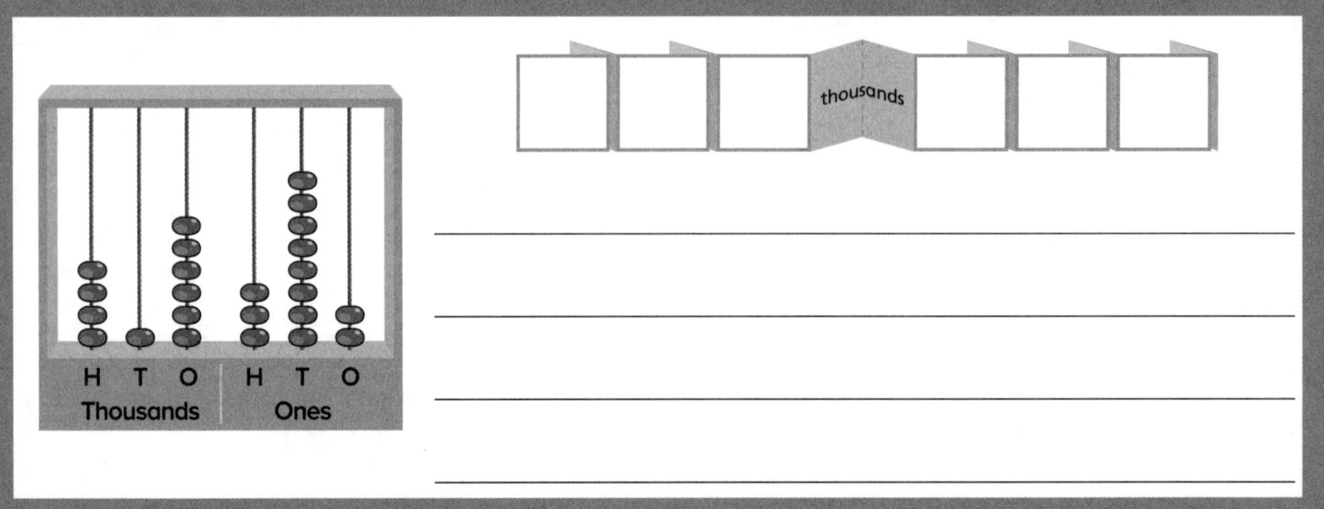

2. Write the matching numerals and number names. Draw beads on each blank abacus for the number shown.

a.

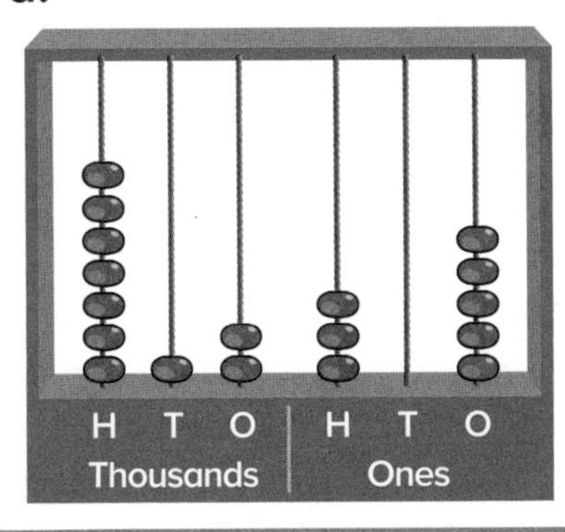

b.

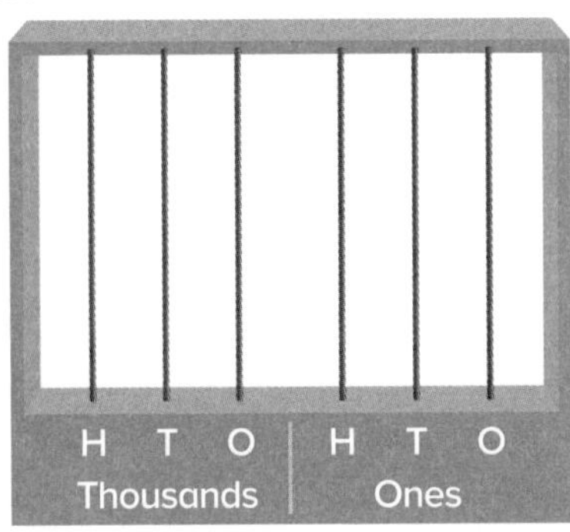

584,300

c.

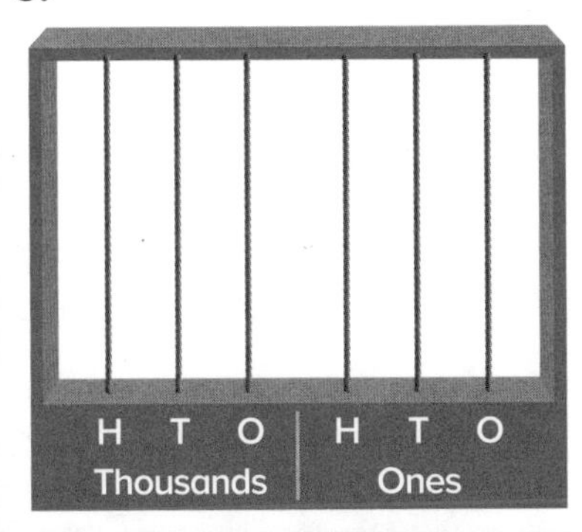

one hundred thousand
fifty-four

Step Ahead Write the value shown by the **3** in each number. The first one has been done for you.

a. 463,759  3,000

b. 815,243 ______

c. 604,350 ______

d. 390,111 ______

e. 436,725 ______

f. 775,230 ______

Step In Writing Six-Digit Numbers Using Expanded Notation

Read the number on the expander.

How would you describe the value of each digit?

Write the missing numbers to show the number using expanded notation.

(____ × 100,000) + (____ × 10,000) + (____ × 100) + (____ × 10) + (____ × 1)

Which value has not been expanded?

You do not have to expand the value of the zero in the thousands place.

Ashley expanded the same number in a different way.

5(100, 000) + 6(10,000) + 8(100) + 1(10) + 2(1)

What is the same about each method?
What is different?

Which method do you prefer? Why?
How would you use Ashley's method to write 704,251 using expanded notation?

The symbol for multiplication can be confused with the letter 'x'. Sometimes it is clearer if the multiplication symbol is left out.

5(100,000) means the same as 5 × 100,000.

Step Up

1. Write the missing numbers to show each six-digit number using expanded notation.

a. 360,712

(____ × 100,000) + (____ × 10,000) + (____ × 100) + (____ × 10) + (____ × 1)

b. 803,649

(____ × 100,000) + (____ × 1,000) + (____ × 100) + (____ × 10) + (____ × 1)

2. Write the number that has been expanded.

a. $(2 \times 100{,}000) + (4 \times 1{,}000) + (9 \times 100) + (8 \times 10) + (1 \times 1)$ ______

b. $6(100{,}000) + 8(10{,}000) + 6(1{,}000) + 4(100) + 5(1)$ ______

c. $4(100{,}000) + 9(1{,}000) + 5(10)$ ______

3. Write each number using expanded notation.

a. 625,386 ______

b. 190,714 ______

c. 530,500 ______

d. 800,487 ______

Step Ahead These place values have been written in the incorrect order. Figure out and write each number that has been expanded.

a. $(7 \times 10) + (4 \times 100{,}000) + (1 \times 10{,}000) + (9 \times 100) + (3 \times 1)$ ______

b. $6(100{,}000) + 8(1) + 4(10) + 6(1{,}000)$ ______

Step In Locating Six-Digit Numbers on a Number Line

Start at 7. Say each number on the card.

How do the numbers change?
Say the same pattern again starting at 3.

What number belongs at each mark on this number line?

How do you know?

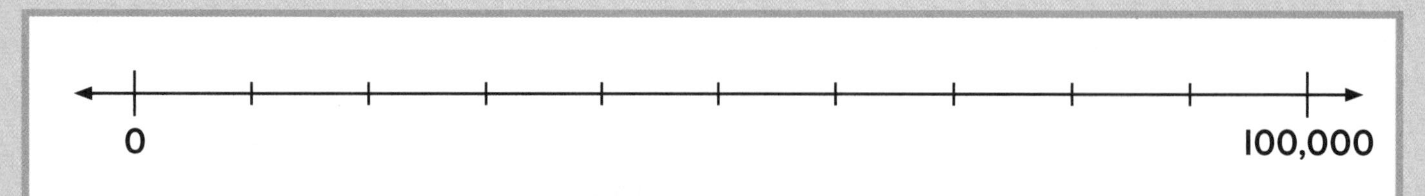

Look closely at this part of the same number line.

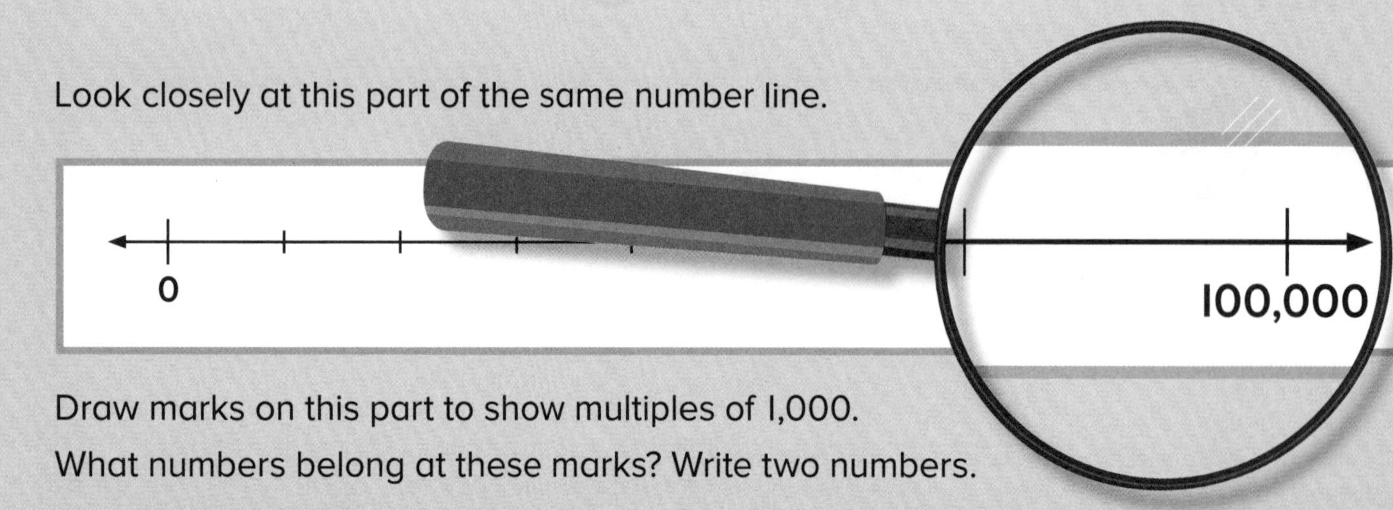

Draw marks on this part to show multiples of 1,000.

What numbers belong at these marks? Write two numbers.

Step Up

1. Draw a line to connect each number to its position on the number line.

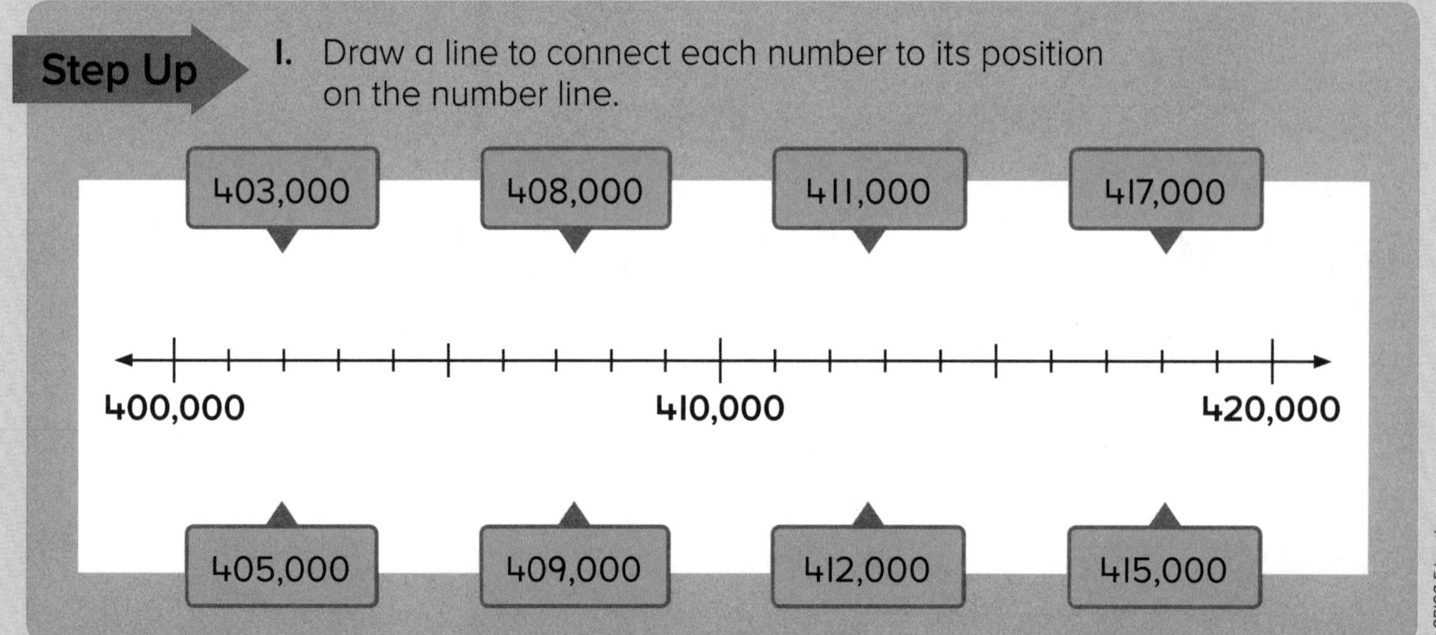

Look at each number line carefully. Write the number that is shown by each arrow.

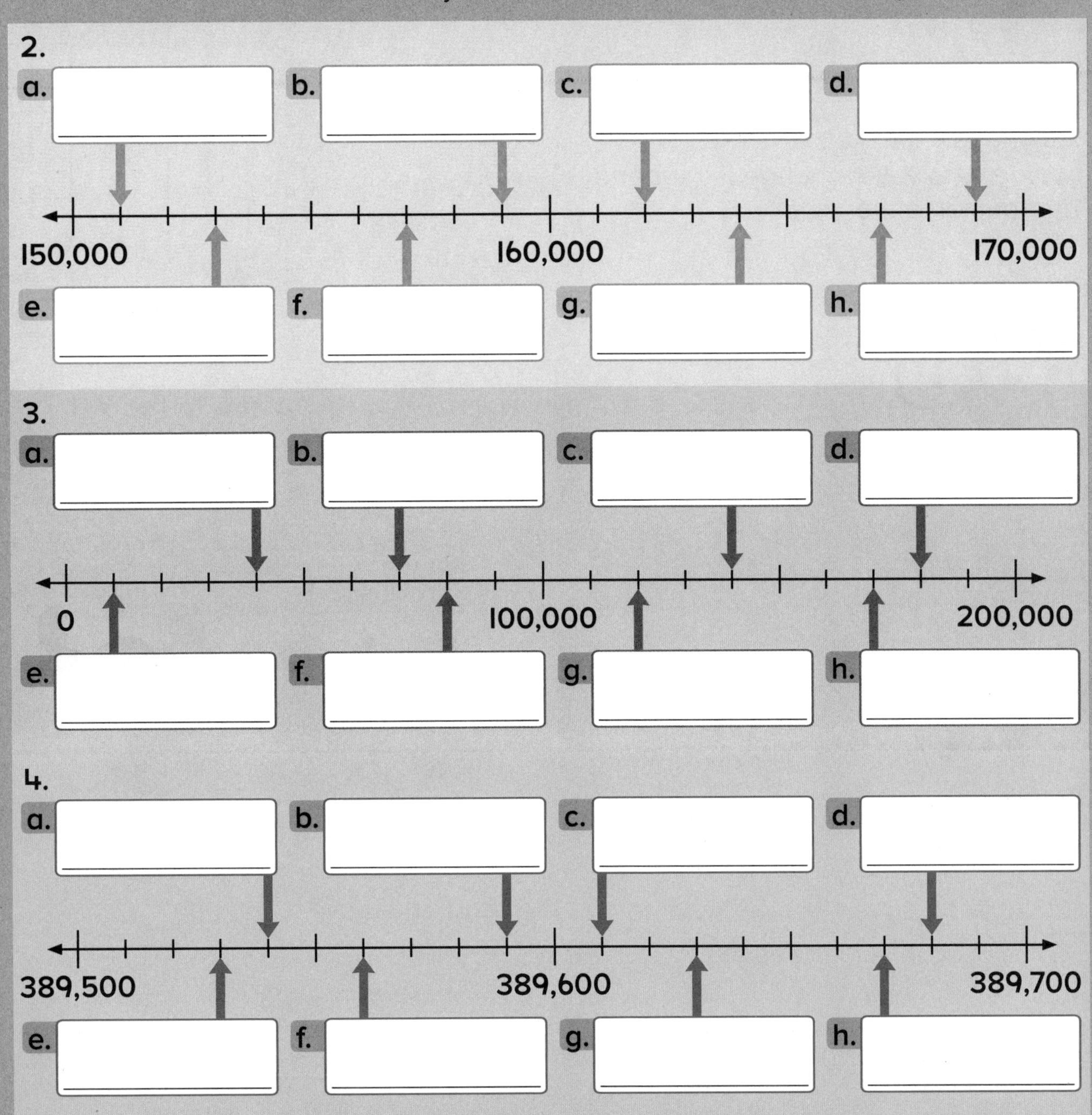

Step Ahead

Odometers measure distance. These are odometer readings from vehicles that have just been serviced. If they are serviced every 50,000 miles, write the next service reading.

a.

b.

Step In Working with Place Value

What number is shown on this abacus?

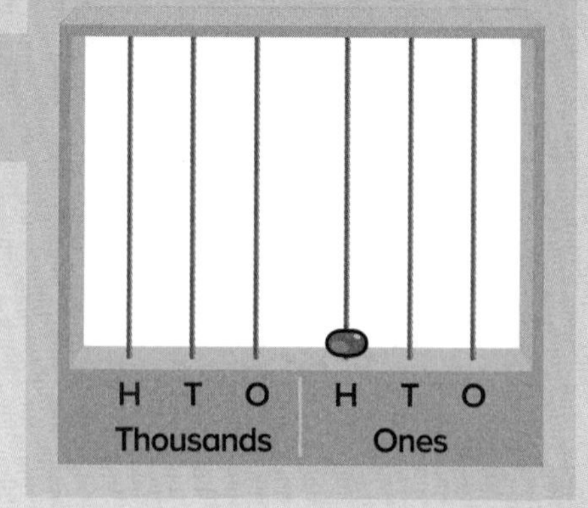

How does the value change if the bead is moved to the rods on either side?

The value is 10 times **more** if moved one rod to the **left**.
The value is 10 times **less** if moved one rod to the **right**.

What does this chart show?

1,000 is 10 times more than 100, or 100 times more than 10. What else do you notice?

Thousands			Ones		
H	T	O	H	T	O

×10 ×10 ×10 ×10 ×10

What happens if you start at the left side of the chart and move to the right?

How would each value of each place change?

Step Up

1. Color the ⬭ beside the statement that is true. Draw beads on the abacus to help your thinking.

- ⬭ 1,000 is 100 **times** more than 10.
- ⬭ 100 is 10 **times** more than 1.
- ⬭ 10,000 is 10 **times** more than 100.
- ⬭ 1,000 is 10 **times** more than 10.

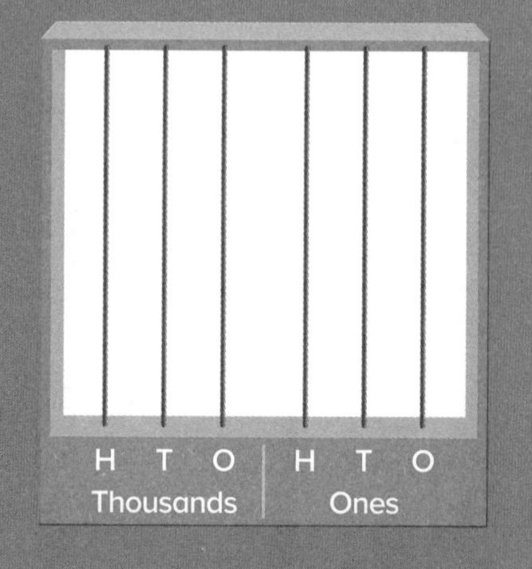

2. Mechanical odometers start with all of the places at zero and change as the car travels. These odometers show the distance in miles that different cars have traveled. Write what the odometers would show if the cars travel more miles.

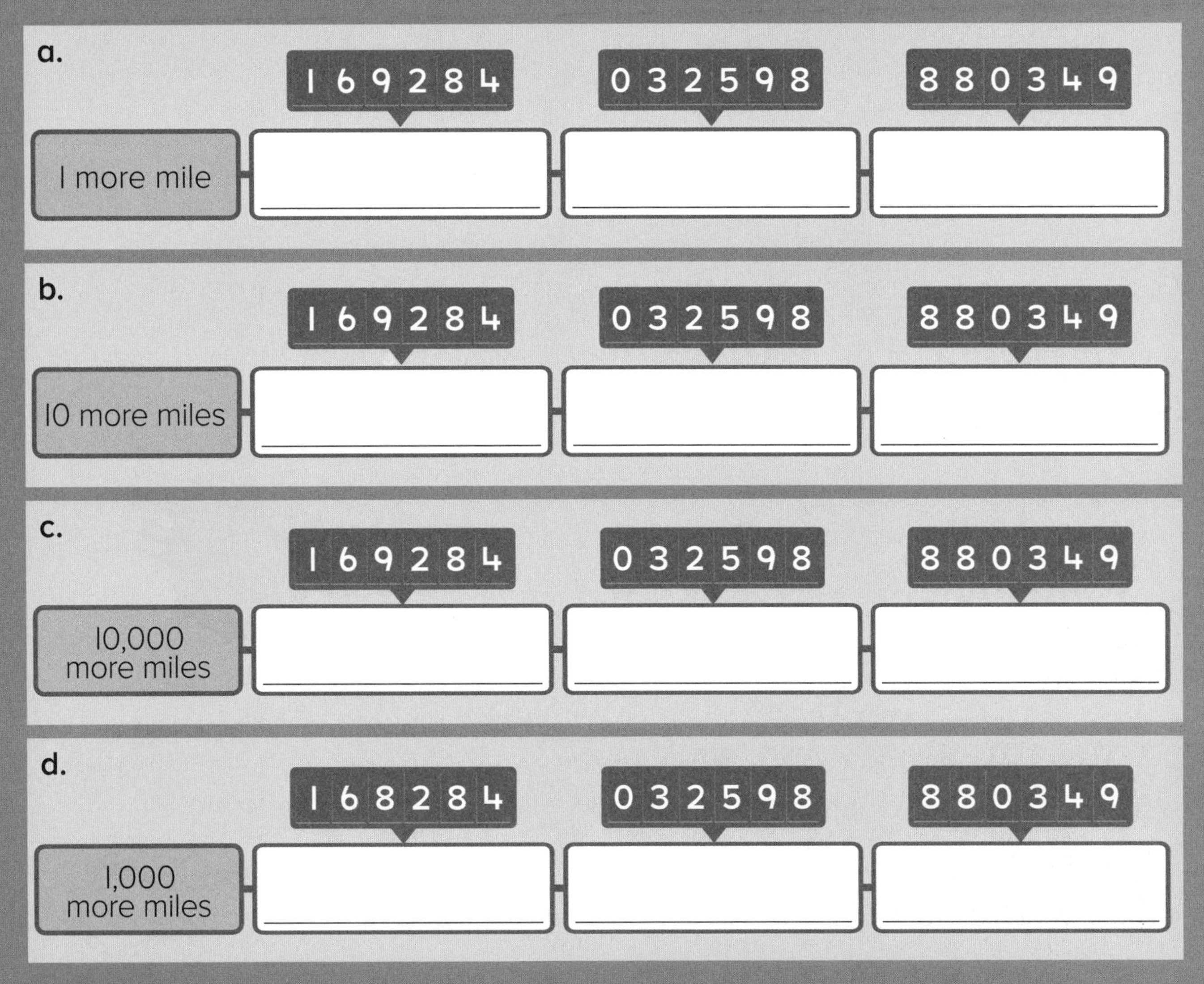

Step Ahead Look at this odometer.

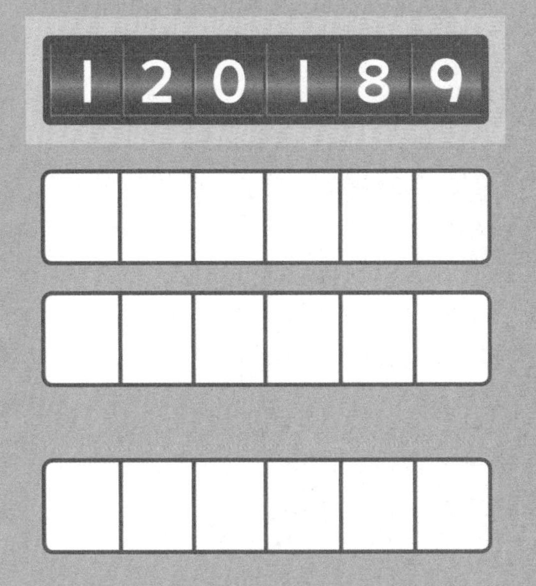

1. If the vehicle travels another 12 miles, what will the odometer show?

2. a. What is the greatest number that the odometer can show?

   b. Think about what the odometer will do if the vehicle travels one mile more than the greatest number. Write what you will see.

Step In Comparing and Ordering Six-Digit Numbers

These tables show the approximate populations of ten cities.

City	Population
Billings, MT	104,170
Cary, NC	135,234
Everett, WA	103,019
Fargo, ND	105,549
Green Bay, WI	104,057

City	Population
Lansing, MI	114,297
McKinney, TX	131,117
Palm Bay, FL	103,190
Springfield, MA	153,060
Sunnyvale, CA	140,081

How can you figure out which city has the greatest population?
Which city has the least population?

Does Springfield or McKinney have the greater population?
How could you use this number line to help you decide?

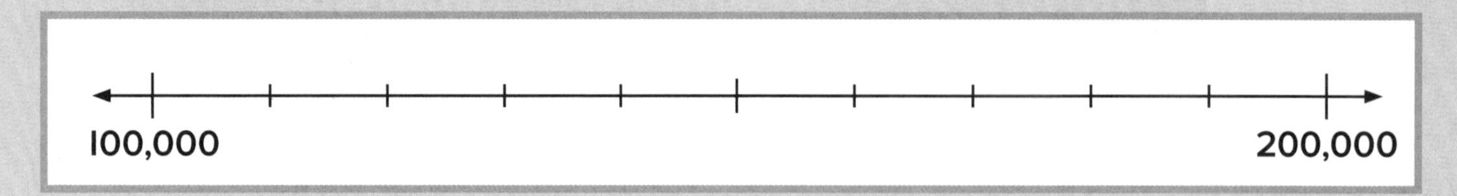

Which cities have populations that are greater than 120,000?
How can you figure it out? What helps you decide?

I looked at the digit in the ten thousands place.

Step Up

1. Write the population of each city. Then write **<** or **>** to complete each sentence. You can use the number line to help your thinking.

a. Sunnyvale ______ ◯ ______ Lansing

b. Billings ______ ◯ ______ Fargo

c. Everett ______ ◯ ______ Palm Bay

d. McKinney ______ ◯ ______ Cary

This table shows approximate populations of another six cities.
Use this table for Questions 2 to 4.

City	Population
Cape Coral, FL	154,305
Charleston, SC	120,083
Flint, MI	102,434
High Point, NC	104,371
Kansas City, KS	145,786
Lafayette, LA	120,623

2. a. Which city has the **greatest** population?

b. Which city has the **least** population?

3. Write the population of each city. Then write **<** or **>** to complete each sentence.

a. Charleston Flint

b. Kansas City Cape Coral

c. High Point Flint

d. Lafayette Charleston

e. Charleston Cape Coral

f. Kansas City High Point

4. Write the city names in order from **least** to **greatest** population.

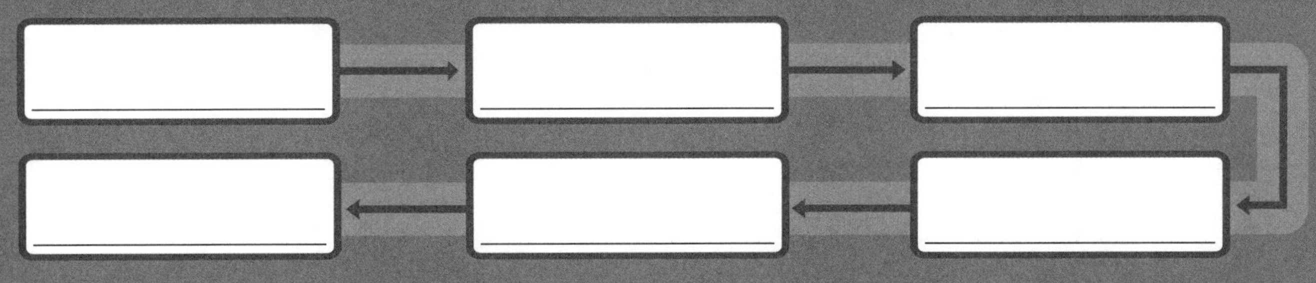

Step Ahead Look at the population table at the top of this page. Which cities have a population that is greater than 110,000 but less than 150,000?

Step In Rounding Six-Digit Numbers

This table shows the annual home game attendance totals for some NFL teams.

Team	Total
Dallas	704,345
NY Giants	641,184
Green Bay	623,577
Washington	617,767
NY Jets	615,656

Which team had the greatest total attendance?

Which teams had a total of more than 630,000 spectators?

Which teams had about 620,000 spectators?
How can you figure this out? Which digits will you look at to help you decide?

On this number line, draw an arrow to show the total attendance at the NY Giants home games.

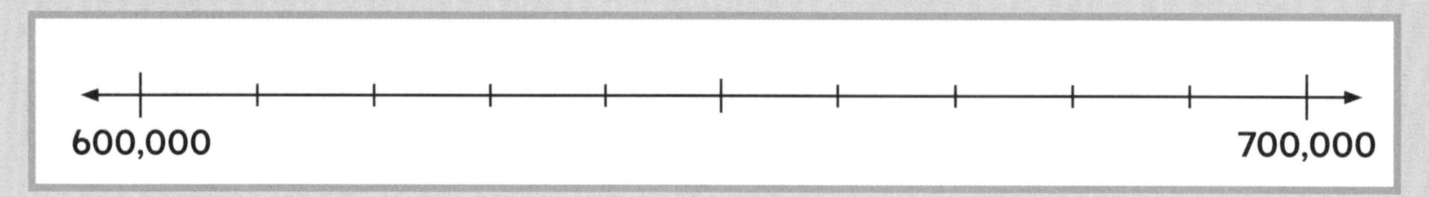

If you had to round this number to the nearest **ten thousand**, what number would you write?

Step Up

Use the table and number line above to help you complete these.

1. Round the total attendance for these teams to the nearest **hundred thousand**.

   a. Dallas ______ b. NY Giants ______

2. Round the total attendance for these teams to the nearest **ten thousand**.

   a. NY Jets ______ b. Green Bay ______

3. Round the total attendance for these teams to the nearest **thousand**.

   a. Washington ______ b. Dallas ______

This table shows the annual home game attendance totals for some more NFL teams. Use this table for Questions 4 to 7.

Team	Total
Seattle	545,577
Chicago	498,864
New England	550,048
Denver	614,977
Houston	573,271

4. Which teams had a total of more than 550,000 spectators attend their home games?

____

____

____

5. Round the total attendance for these teams to the nearest **hundred thousand**.

a. Houston ____________ **b.** New England ____________

6. Round the total attendance for these teams to the nearest **ten thousand**.

a. Denver ____________ **b.** Seattle ____________

7. Round the total attendance for these teams to the nearest **thousand**.

a. Chicago ____________ **b.** New England ____________

8. Round each number to the nearest ten, hundred, and thousand.

	Nearest Ten	Nearest Hundred	Nearest Thousand
432,068			
809,506			
565,271			

Step Ahead

Use each digit once.
Write the number that is closest to 250,000. ____________

3

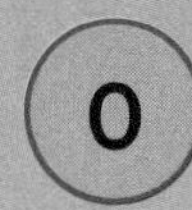

6

Step In Reviewing Multiplication and Addition Patterns

This table shows costs in a long-term parking garage.

If the cost for any single day is the same, what is the cost of parking for 8 days?

How could you figure it out?

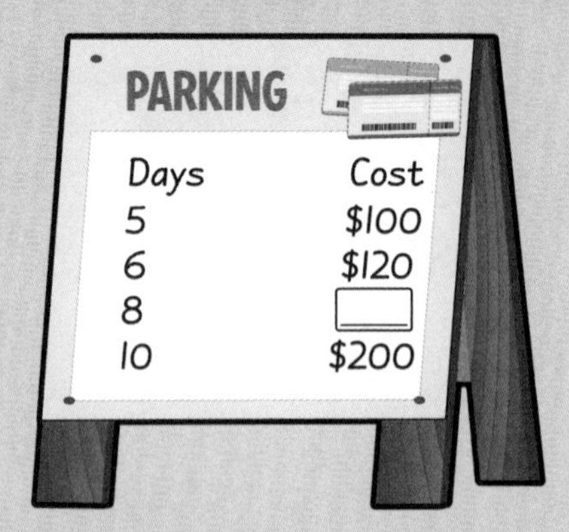

Diana drew this table to show how to calculate the cost for the number of days shown on the display board.

What should she write to complete the table?

What process can you use to figure out the cost for **any** number of days?

Days	Process	Cost
5	5 × $20	$100
6		$120
8		
10		$200

To figure out the cost for any number of days I could write: Days x $20 = Cost. I could shorten the equation by using letters instead of words: D x $20 = C.

Step Up

1. This table shows costs at a different long-term parking garage.

a. If the cost for any single day is the same, what is the cost for one day? $ ______

b. Complete the table.

c. Write an equation to show the process for figuring out the cost for any number of days.

______

Days	Process	Cost
5	5 × $	$75
6		$90
8		$120
10		$150

2. This table shows the cost of renting a car.

a. If the cost for any single day is the same, what is the cost for one day? $ ______

b. Complete the table.

c. Write an equation to show the process for figuring out the cost for any number of days.

____

Days	Process	Cost
2		$160
4		$320
5		$400
6		

3. This table shows the cost of buying concert tickets online. A service fee is included that is the same for all ticket prices.

a. How much is the service fee? $ ______

b. Complete the table.

c. Write an equation for figuring out the cost for any ticket price.

____

d. What is the total cost for a $100 ticket price? $ ______

Ticket Price ($)	Process	Cost ($)
15		17
22		24
31		33
50		52

Step Ahead Complete the table to solve this problem.

David has $8 dollars in savings. He earns $10 each week if he completes his chores.

a. How much could he save after seven weeks? $ ______

b. Write the process for figuring out the total savings for any number of weeks.

____

Week	Process	Savings
0		$8
1		$18
2		$28
3		$38

Step In Using Input-Output Tables

A factory cuts circles from sheets of paper to make stickers.

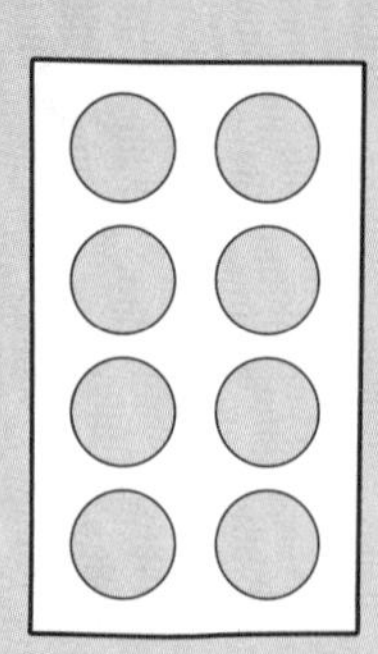

For each sheet of paper they put in a machine they get a certain number of stickers out of it.

This table shows what happens.

Sheets of Paper	1	2	3	4	5	6
Stickers	8	16	24	32	40	48

What equation could you write to describe the process between the number of sheets of paper and the number of stickers produced?

Patterns can be described in a general way by using the words input and output.

Inputs are numbers that you start with.
Outputs are the result of a change to the inputs.

What are the input numbers at the sticker factory?
What are the output numbers at the factory?

Step Up

1. A bike factory assembles 60 bikes in 2 hours, 90 bikes in 3 hours, and 120 bikes in 4 hours.

a. If the number of bikes made each hour is the same, how many bikes are made in one hour?

b. Complete the table to figure out how many bikes are assembled in 7 hours.

Hours (Input)	2	3	4	5	6	7
Bikes (Output)	60	90	120			

c. Write an equation to show the process for figuring out the number of bikes made in any number of hours.

Complete the table to help solve each problem.

2. a. There are 100 blocks in 5 boxes, 60 blocks in 3 boxes, and 80 blocks in 4 boxes.

Boxes (Input)					
Blocks (Output)					

b. How many blocks are in 9 boxes? ______

c. Write an equation to show the process for figuring out the output for any input. ______

3. a. It costs $30 to buy 2 tickets, $60 to buy 4 tickets, and $120 to buy 8 tickets.

Tickets (Input)					
Cost (Output)					

b. What is the cost of 7 tickets? $ ______

c. Write an equation to show the process for figuring out the output for any input. ______

Step Ahead Look for a pattern to solve this problem.

Red and blue counters are sold together in bags. Jerilene counted the number of red and blue counters in each bag and then wrote the results in this table.

Red Counters	15	25	19	50	35
Blue Counters	17	27	21	52	37

a. Write an equation to show the process for figuring out the number of blue counters for any number of red counters.

______

b. If there are 60 counters in total, how many counters will be red? ______

Step In Working with Number Patterns

Awan drew a simple pattern.

How many circles will he draw next?
How do you know?

Awan made a table to show the pattern.

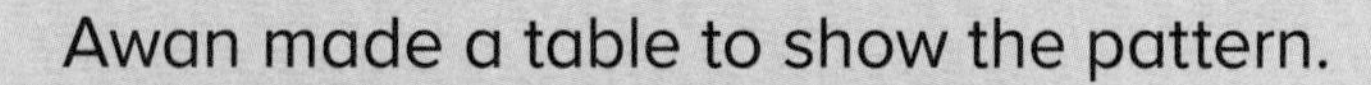

Picture (Input)	1	2	3	4	5	6
Number of Circles (Output)	3	6	9			

Complete the table.

What equation can you write to describe the relationship between the position of the picture and the number of circles?

I could write:
Picture x 3 = Circles
or
P x 3 = C

Nicole created this number pattern. 20 40 60 80 100 120

She then used the number pattern to create this table.

Position (Input)	1	2	3	4	5	6
Value (Output)	20	40	60	80	100	120

What equation can you write to describe the relationship between the position of the number in the sequence and its value? ______________

Step Up

1. a. Write this number pattern into the table.

6 12 18 24 30 36

Position (Input)	1	2	3	4	5	6
Value (Output)	6					

b. What would be the value of the 20th number in the sequence? ______________

2. a. Write this number pattern into the table.

12 24 36 48 60 72

Position (Input)	1	2	3	4	5	6
Value (Output)	12					

b. Write an equation to show the process for figuring out the value of any number in the sequence.

3. For each of these, read the relationship between the position of the number in the sequence and its value. Then complete the table to show the value for each position in the pattern.

a. Position × 30 = Value

Position (Input)	1	2	7	5	3	10
Value (Output)						

b. Position + 6 = Value

Position (Input)	1		14	9		30
Value (Output)		8			12	

c. Value = Position × 4

Position (Input)			10	6		
Value (Output)	4	20			80	36

Step Ahead

Akeema is packing jars into boxes. Each box has the same number of jars. She has 15 jars and packs them into 3 boxes. Then she grabs 40 jars and packs them into 8 boxes.

How many boxes will she need to pack 70 jars? Show your thinking.

boxes

Step In Converting between Customary Units of Measurement

This table shows the conversion of cups to fluid ounces.

Cups (c)	1	3	5	8	
Fluid Ounces (fl oz)		24	40		80

Complete the table.

How did you decide what numbers to write?
How many fluid ounces are equivalent to one cup?

What equation can you write to describe the relationship between the number of fluid ounces and the number of cups?

I could write:
Number of cups × 8 = Number of fluid ounces

I could also write:
Number of fluid ounces ÷ 8 = Number of cups

Step Up

1. Complete each table.

a.

Quarts (qt)	4		20	24	40
Gallons (gal)		3	5	6	

b.

Quarts (qt)	1		4	5	
Cups (c)		8	16	20	36

c.

Gallons (gal)		5	8		10
Pints (pt)	8	40	64	72	

2. Complete each table.

a.

Feet (ft)	1	3	6		10
Inches (in)		36	72	96	

b.

Yards (yd)	1	2	3	4	5
Inches (in)		72	108		

c.

Pounds (lb)	1	2	4	5	
Ounces (oz)		32	64		96

3. Color the ⬭ beside the statements that are true. Use the tables on pages 30 and 31 to help your thinking.

a. **2 yards**

is the same as

- ⬭ 4 feet
- ⬭ 20 inches
- ⬭ 72 inches

b. **12 cups**

is the same as

- ⬭ 3 quarts
- ⬭ 2 pints
- ⬭ 4 quarts

c. **3 pounds**

is the same as

- ⬭ 30 ounces
- ⬭ 48 ounces
- ⬭ 6 cups

Step Ahead

Jude makes quilts to sell at the market. He makes 6 quilts in one month, 12 quilts in two months, and 18 quilts in three months. How many quilts will he make in half a year? Show your thinking.

______ quilts

Step In Estimating with Addition

This table shows the number of vehicles that drove past the northern entrance of a school in one week.

	School Traffic Report – Northern Entrance						
	Sun	Mon	Tues	Wed	Thurs	Fri	Sat
Morning	195	395	354	398	405	589	217
Afternoon	235	354	409	376	437	630	289

About how many vehicles drove past the school on each school day?

Estimate the number of vehicles that drove past the school on Monday. How did you form your estimate?

I looked for a nearby ten or hundred to round each number. I then added 400 + 350 = 750.

Estimate the number of vehicles that drove past the school on Friday. Is the total more or less than 1,000? How did you decide?

There were more than 500 vehicles in the morning and in the afternoon, so the total has to be more than 1,000.

Step Up

1. Look at the table above. Estimate the total number of vehicles for each of these days. Show your thinking.

a. Wednesday

Estimate ________

b. Thursday

Estimate ________

c. Tuesday

Estimate ________

d. Saturday

Estimate ________

This table shows the number of vehicles that drove past the southern entrance of the school in one week.

	School Traffic Report – Southern Entrance						
	Sun	Mon	Tues	Wed	Thurs	Fri	Sat
Morning	127	278	305	288	414	354	185
Afternoon	204	252	349	291	394	340	109

2. Write the day on which the total number of cars that drove past the school is closest to each number below. Show your thinking.

a. About 800 vehicles

Day: ____________

b. About 700 vehicles

Day: ____________

c. About 300 vehicles

Day: ____________

d. About 600 vehicles

Day: ____________

Step Ahead

Look at the table above. Estimate the total number of cars that drove past the school in the mornings. Show your thinking.

Estimate ____________ cars

Step In Using the Standard Addition Algorithm

What does this table show?

How could you figure out the total drinks sold in Week 1?

Drink Sales		
	Week 1	Week 2
Juice	614	857
Milk	531	435

Archie used blocks to represent the sales from each type of drink. He then moved the blocks together to figure out the total.

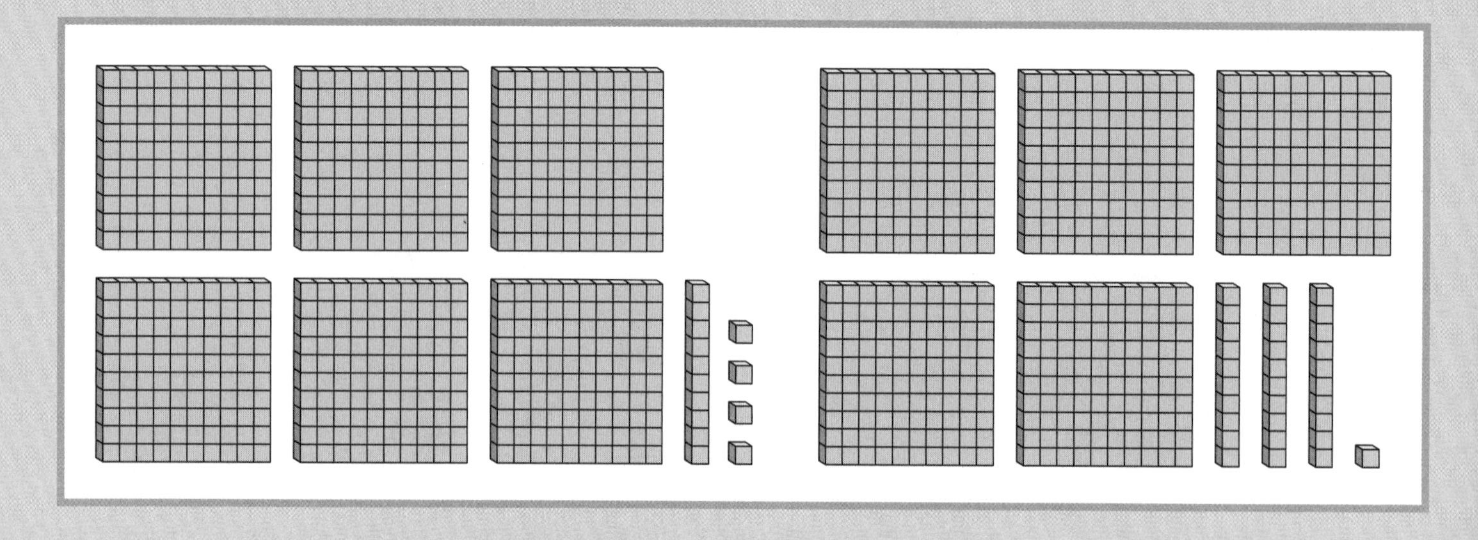

What is the total value of the blocks? How do you know?

What is another way to represent the same value?

How could you figure out the total drinks sold in Week 2?

Kuma used the standard addition algorithm to calculate the total.

What numbers should she write to complete the calculation?

		1	
	8	5	7
+	4	3	5
		9	2

How are the 12 ones represented in the algorithm?

Step Up

	Hot Food Sales				
	Week 1	Week 2	Week 3	Week 4	Week 5
Veggie Burger	1,205	748	915	1,324	1,201
Grilled Chicken Sandwich	1,317	1,055	1,230	1,197	997

Estimate the total sales for each week.
Then use the standard addition algorithm to calculate the exact total.

a. Week 1 estimate ______

	1	3	1	7
+	1	2	0	5

b. Week 2 estimate ______

	1	0	5	5
+		7	4	8

c. Week 3 estimate ______

	1	2	3	0
+		9	1	5

d. Week 4 estimate ______

e. Week 5 estimate ______

Step Ahead

Use the totals above to help calculate these.

a. Total sold in Week 1 and Week 2

______

b. Total sold in Week 3 and Week 5

______

Step In — Using the Standard Addition Algorithm (Large Numbers)

What does this table show?

Music Downloads	
Album	Downloads
Dance Mix	12,395
Country Classics	10,080
Hip Hop Anthems	8,451
Sisters of Soul	3,243

How could you figure out the total downloads for Hip Hop Anthems and Sisters of Soul?

It's a bit hard to remember all the numbers, so I would use a written method to figure out the total.

Antonia used the standard addition algorithm to calculate the total.

What steps has she done already?

What numbers should she write to complete the calculation?

What does the 11 actually represent?

	8	4	5	1
+	3	2	4	3
		6	9	4

How could you figure out the total downloads for Dance Mix and Country Classics?

I know the total will be about 22,500.

Show how you could use the standard algorithm to calculate the total.

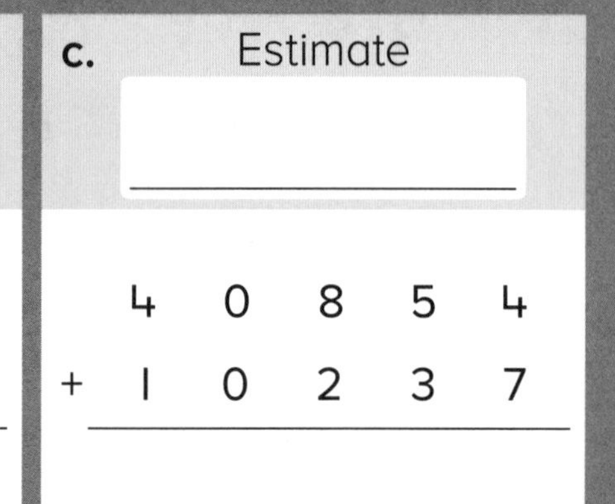

Step Up

1. Estimate each total. Then use the standard addition algorithm to calculate the exact total.

a. Estimate ______

$$\begin{array}{r} 9573 \\ +\ 5206 \\ \hline \end{array}$$

b. Estimate ______

$$\begin{array}{r} 23072 \\ +\ 4293 \\ \hline \end{array}$$

c. Estimate ______

$$\begin{array}{r} 40854 \\ +\ 10237 \\ \hline \end{array}$$

	Movie Downloads			
	January	February	March	April
Santa Paws	23,059	47,630	124,276	152,609
Dancing Dinos	14,237	25,273	125,802	74,305

2. Estimate the total downloads for each month.
Then use the standard addition algorithm to calculate the exact total.

a. January estimate ____________

b. February estimate ____________

c. March estimate ____________

d. April estimate ____________

Step Ahead

Look at the table above.
Which movie recorded the greater number of downloads? ____________

Write your estimate for each movie.
Then calculate the exact total for each.

Santa Paws	Dancing Dinos
Estimate ____________	Estimate ____________
Exact total ____________	Exact total ____________

Step In Adding Multiple Addends

This table shows the number of games sold over these three years.

How would you estimate the total games sold in these three years?

Battle Star	
Year	Number Sold
2012	935
2013	1,210
2014	742

I rounded the number sold for each year to the nearest thousand.

How could you check your estimate?

How could you calculate the exact total sales?

Andrea used the standard addition algorithm to calculate the total.

Does it matter in what order she writes the numbers to add?

What steps did she follow?

Is her answer correct? If not, what changes should she make?

	1	2	1	0
		9	3	5
+		7	4	2
	1	8	8	7

Step Up

1. Estimate each total. Then use the standard addition algorithm to calculate the exact total.

a. Estimate

	8	0	4
	3	9	6
+	2	7	5

b. Estimate

	1	4	5	2	0
		3	0	7	4
+		1	2	0	9

c. Estimate

	3	2	0	8	0
	1	4	5	2	5
+		2	4	7	3

	Game Sales		
	Battleships	**Grow a Garden**	**Dino Attack**
2012	805	13,600	117,290
2013	15,320	11,275	120,095
2014	10,160	8,032	110,910

2. Estimate the total sales for each game in your head. Then use the standard addition algorithm to calculate the exact total.

a. Battleships	**b.** Grow a Garden	**c.** Dino Attack

3. Calculate the total sales for each year. Show your thinking.

a. 2012	**b.** 2013	**c.** 2014

Step Ahead

Write the missing digits to show correct totals.

a.

	5		3	0
		3	4	
+		1	2	6
	5	8	9	7

b.

	6	0	7	1
		7	0	1
+		3	2	5
	9		9	7

c.

		5	1	8
	4	2		0
+	1	0	2	7
	2	7	4	5

Step In Estimating with Subtraction

Paul is planning a vacation.

This table shows the flight costs to some different locations.

Estimate the **difference** in cost between a flight to Las Vegas and a flight to Honolulu.

How did you form your estimate?

Estimate the difference in cost between a flight to Palm Springs and a flight to Atlanta.

What are some other estimates that you can form?

Step Up

1. Estimate the difference in cost between these flights. Show your thinking by writing the numbers you used to estimate.

a. Pittsburgh $293
Kansas City $155

Estimate $ ______

b. Philadelphia $97
Los Angeles $328

Estimate $ ______

2. Estimate the difference in cost between these flights. Show your thinking by writing the numbers you used to estimate.

a. Baltimore $252
Seattle $409

Estimate $ ______

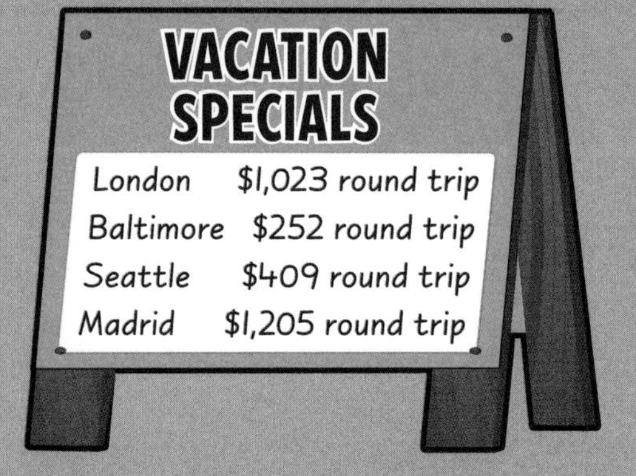

b. Madrid $1,205
Seattle $409

Estimate $ ______

c. Baltimore $252
London $1,023

Estimate $ ______

d. Madrid $1,205
London $1,023

Estimate $ ______

e. London $1,023
Seattle $409

Estimate $ ______

Write numbers in the empty spaces to make subtraction expressions that result in a difference of about 500.

a.

___ ___ 5 – ___ 2 6

b.

7 ___ 3 – ___ 8 ___

c.

9 0 ___ – 3 ___ ___

d.

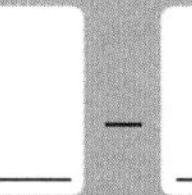

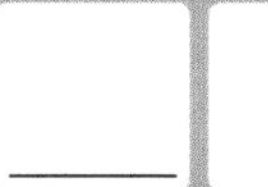

6 5 ___ – ___ ___ 1

Step In — Using the Standard Subtraction Algorithm

Imagine you had $345 and you bought this bike.
How much money would you have left over?

How do you know?

Follow these steps of the standard subtraction algorithm to calculate the difference.

Step 1

Look at the digits in each place. Can you subtract each place easily?

	H	T	O
	3	4	5
−		7	8

Step 2

You need 1 ten to help subtract the ones. Cross out 4 tens and write 3 tens.

	H	T	O
		3	
	3	~~4~~	5
−		7	8

Step 3

Cross out the ones digit and write the new number. 345 is now written as 3 hundreds, 3 tens, and 15 ones.

	H	T	O
		3	15
	3	~~4~~	~~5~~
−		7	8

Step 4

You need 1 hundred to help subtract the tens. Cross out 3 hundreds and write 2 hundreds.

	H	T	O
	2	3	15
	~~3~~	~~4~~	~~5~~
−		7	8

Step 5

Add the 10 tens that you have just broken up to the 3 tens that you already have. You now have 13 tens. Write the number.

	H	T	O
	2	13	15
	~~3~~	~~4~~	~~5~~
−		7	8

Step 6

345 is now written as 2 hundreds, 13 tens, and 15 ones. Subtract the ones, tens, then hundreds to find the difference.

	H	T	O
	2	13	15
	~~3~~	~~4~~	~~5~~
−		7	8
	2	6	7

Step Up

Estimate the difference. Then use the standard subtraction algorithm to calculate the exact difference.

a. Estimate

	H	T	O
	7	9	3
−		7	1

b. Estimate

	H	T	O
	6	7	8
−	4	7	3

c. Estimate

	H	T	O
	3	7	1
−	1	0	8

d. Estimate

	H	T	O
	5	2	8
−		8	1

e. Estimate

	4	0	7
−	1	8	2

f. Estimate

	5	6	2
−		9	8

g. Estimate

	2	3	8
−		5	7

h. Estimate

	8	3	7
−	4	5	9

Step Ahead

Paul used the standard subtraction algorithm to calculate 525 − 89. He regrouped 525 to carry out the steps.

	H	T	O
	4	11	15
	~~5~~	~~2~~	~~5~~
−		8	9
	4	3	6

Write in words how you can prove that 4 hundreds, 11 tens, and 15 ones have the same total value as 5 hundreds, 2 tens, and 5 ones.

Step In — Using the Standard Subtraction Algorithm (Large Numbers)

What does this table show?

How many more people visited the national park in January than in March?

National Park Visitors	
January	17,475
February	9,305
March	5,950

It must be about 11,000 because that's the difference between 17,000 and 6,000.

Jadyn used the standard subtraction algorithm to calculate the exact difference.

Look at the letters above the algorithm. What do the letters **TTh** and **Th** mean?

What steps did Jadyn follow?

Why did he cross out 4 then write 14?

What does the 14 represent?

	TTh	Th	H	T	O
		6	14		
	1	~~7~~	~~4~~	7	5
−		5	9	5	0
	1	1	5	2	5

Step Up

1. Estimate the difference. Then use the standard subtraction algorithm to calculate the exact difference.

a. Estimate ______

	Th	H	T	O
	3	7	1	6
−		6	1	3

b. Estimate ______

	Th	H	T	O
	4	8	3	9
−		6	5	4

c. Estimate ______

	TTh	Th	H	T	O
	2	3	7	7	5
−		5	3	1	6

Use the information in this table to answer the questions on this page.

National Park Visitors			
	September	October	November
Pine Canyon	7,495	9,030	13,081
Cedar Valley	8,935	13,062	10,306

2. Compare the number of people who visited these national parks. Use the standard subtraction algorithm to calculate the exact difference each month.

September	October	November

3. Use the standard subtraction algorithm to calculate the answers to these.

a. How many more people visited Pine Canyon in November than in October?

b. How many fewer people visited Cedar Valley in September than in November?

Step Ahead

Use the standard subtraction algorithm to calculate the answer to this problem.

Emily's mom wants to buy a new house.
She found one she liked for $327,095.
She then saw a similar house for only $315,500.

How much money would she save if she bought the less expensive house?

$ ________________

Step In Analyzing Decomposition Across Places Involving Zero (Large Numbers)

What does this table show?

About how many more people visited the Helpful Hints website than the Gaming Zone website?

Popular Websites	
Site	Visits (monthly)
Helpful Hints	16,035
Toy Shack	8,595
Gaming Zone	12,470

Do you think the difference is more than or less than 4,000?

How could you figure out the exact difference?

Ricardo decided to use the standard subtraction algorithm to calculate the exact difference.

What steps should he follow to complete the calculation?

How can he subtract in the tens place when there are no hundreds to regroup?

Complete his calculation to show the difference.

	TTh	Th	H	T	O
	1	6	0	3	5
−	1	2	4	7	0
					5

Step Up

1. Estimate the difference. Then use the standard subtraction algorithm to calculate the exact difference.

a. Estimate ______

	Th	H	T	O
	6	7	0	2
−		5	1	4

b. Estimate ______

	TTh	Th	H	T	O
	5	0	3	2	5
−		7	4	1	5

c. Estimate ______

	TTh	Th	H	T	O
	3	4	0	6	6
−	1	2	9	9	4

Use the information in this table to answer the questions on this page.

Number of Website Visits	March	April	May
Doggy Day Care	11,039	9,503	12,041
Pooch's Paradise	10,257	8,377	14,035

2. Compare the number of website visits each month. Estimate the difference in your head. Then use the standard subtraction algorithm to calculate the exact difference.

March	April	May

3. Use the standard subtraction algorithm to calculate the answers to these.

a. How many fewer people visited the Doggy Day Care website in April than in May?

b. How many more people visited the Pooch's Paradise website in May than in March?

Step Ahead

The Doggy Day Care site had a total of 201,049 website visits this year. In the previous year it had 145,325 visits. How many more website visits were recorded this year?

______ visits

Step In Solving Word Problems Involving Addition and Subtraction

This display shows the prices of some rare baseball cards.

How could you estimate the total cost of the three cards on each shelf?

Choose one card from the top shelf and one card from the middle shelf.

What is the total cost of the two cards?
How did you figure it out?

Choose two cards from the bottom shelf.

What is the difference in cost between these two cards?
How did you figure it out?

Step Up

1. Solve these word problems. Show your thinking.

a. Loop one card from each shelf. Write the total cost.

$ ______

b. Imagine you have $5,000. Choose one card and figure out the amount you will have left after the purchase.

$ ______

2. Solve these word problems. Show your thinking.

a. A club store reported sales of \$12,550 for shirts, \$6,805 for sweaters, and \$2,090 for caps. What were the total sales for shirts and caps?

\$ ______

b. A club has 14,225 members who are male and 10,965 members who are female. 5,427 members are over 65 years of age. What is the total number of members?

______ members

c. A stadium seats 110,000 people. 65,045 tickets were sold on Monday. 27,307 tickets were sold on Tuesday. How many tickets are still available?

______ tickets

d. A club reported \$145,390 in membership sales. This was \$27,500 more than the previous year. What were the total sales for the previous year?

\$ ______

Step Ahead

Beatrice and Helen put all their cards in a stack. They have a total of 150 cards. Beatrice owns 28 more cards than Helen. How many cards does Helen own?

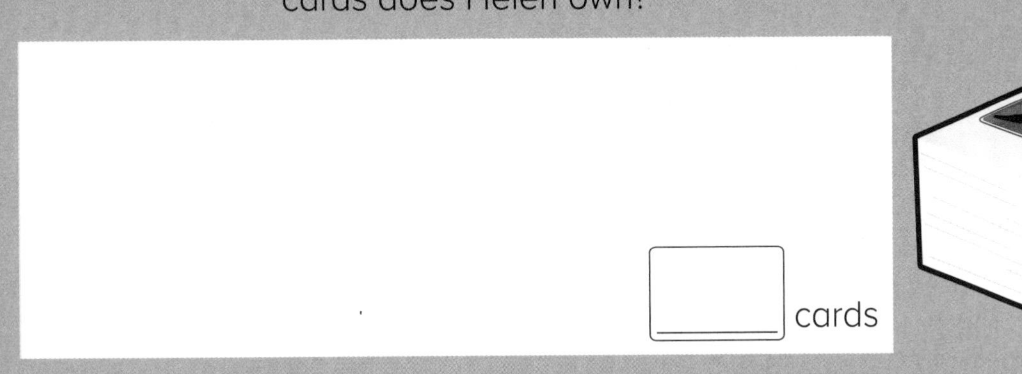

______ cards

Step In Reviewing Time Measurement

Read the time on this clock.

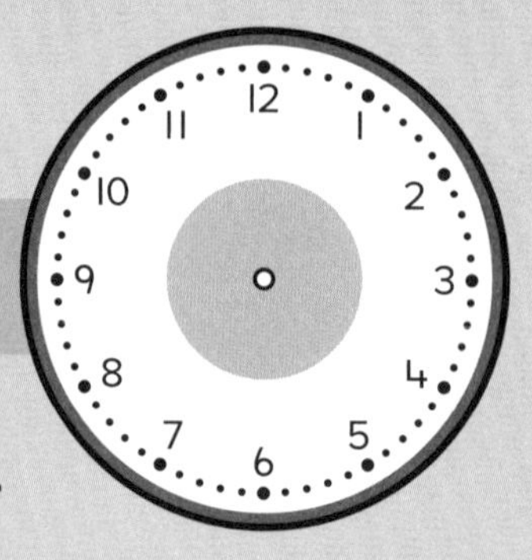

What do you do at about this time?

What other information do you need to know?

Draw hands on this clock to show the same time.

What are all the different ways you could say this time?
How can you figure out the number of minutes **to the hour** when you know the number of minutes **past the hour**?

I know the time is 45 minutes past the hour.
I can figure out the number of minutes to the hour by thinking 45 + ? = 60.

Read the time on this clock.

How many minutes to 10 o'clock? How do you know?

Write a number sentence to show your thinking.

____

Step Up

1. A train leaves Central Station at 3 o'clock. Look at each watch below. How many minutes does each person need to wait for the train?

a.

_______ minutes

b.
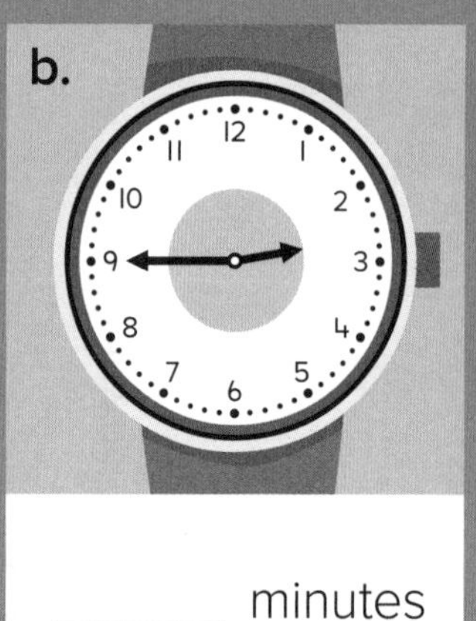

_______ minutes

c.

_______ minutes

d.

_______ minutes

2. Write these times using **minutes to**.

a.

_______ minutes to _____

b.

_______ minutes to _____

c.

_______ minutes to _____

d.

_______ minutes to _____

3. Show the time on the analog and digital clocks.

a. 15 minutes to 3

b. 20 minutes to 5

c. 17 minutes to 6

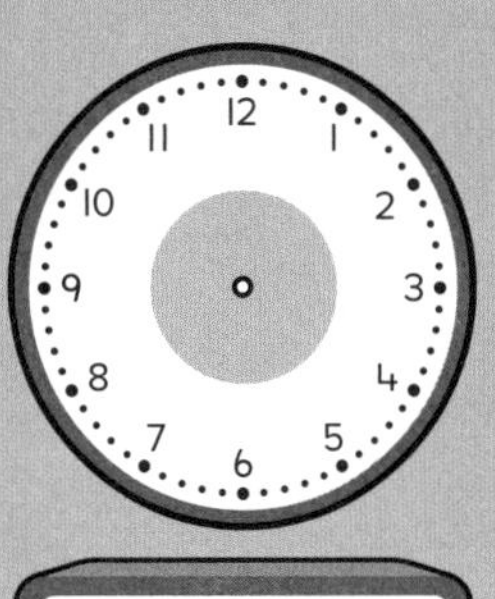

d. 7 minutes to 9

Step Ahead Write the answers.

a. Patricia plays soccer at 4:30 on Wednesday afternoons. She plays for 45 minutes. What time does she finish?

b. Aston caught a train at 7:55. The trip is expected to take 35 minutes. What time will he arrive?

c. Gracia left home at 6:45 and arrived at work at 7:32. How many minutes did it take her to travel to work? _______ minutes

d. It takes Samuru 20 minutes to travel to school. If he gets to school at 8:18, what time did he leave home?

e. Anya reads for half an hour before bed. If she goes to bed at 8:12 p.m., what time does she start reading?

Step In Converting between Units of Time

This table shows the length of time that activities took in one school day.

Activity	Time
Math	1 hour
Reading	55 minutes
Writing	30 minutes
Library	30 minutes
Science	30 minutes
Art	25 minutes
Sport	45 minutes
Music	25 minutes
Social Studies	30 minutes

What is the total length of time for math and science? How could you figure out the total in minutes?

What is another way you could write the total?

1 hour + 30 minutes
is the same as

minutes

What are some other times in the table that total more than one hour?

Step Up

1. Figure out the total number of minutes. Then write the total another way.

a.

Rode to store	28 minutes
Shopped for DVDs	1 hour

____ hour _______ minutes

_______ minutes

b.

Watched TV	2 hours
Read book	58 minutes

____ hours _______ minutes

___________ minutes

c.

Ate breakfast	9 minutes
Swam in pool	3 hours
Ate lunch	35 minutes

____ hours _______ minutes

___________ minutes

d.

Mowed lawn	1 hour
Trimmed hedges	12 minutes
Raked leaves	9 minutes

____ hour _______ minutes

_______ minutes

2. Read each story. Then write the total time in two different ways.

a. In a triathlon, Kevin swam for 27 minutes, cycled for 35 minutes, and ran for 23 minutes. How long did it take him to finish the course?

_______ minutes

____ hour _______ minutes

b. Abigail watched two shows. The first went for 1 hour. The second went for 33 minutes. What is the total time for the shows?

____ hour _______ minutes

_______ minutes

c. Joe is cooking dinner. It takes 12 minutes to prepare the food, 35 minutes to cook the food, and 15 minutes to serve the food. What is the total amount of time taken?

_______ minutes

____ hour _______ minutes

d. Ethan is going on vacation. It takes 15 minutes to pack, 1 hour to drive to the beach, and another 20 minutes to unpack. What is the total amount of time it takes?

____ hour _______ minutes

_______ minutes

Step Ahead Figure out the total time for each trip.

a.

		Total time
Fly San Jose to Los Angeles	40 min	
Stopover in Los Angeles	35 min	
Fly Los Angeles to Denver	1 hr 50 min	_____ hours _______ minutes

b.

		Total time
Fly Houston to Atlanta	2 hr 10 min	
Stopover in Atlanta	50 min	
Fly Atlanta to Richmond	1 hr 40 min	_____ hours _______ minutes

Step In Solving Problems Involving Intervals of Time

What do you notice about this clock?

What does the red hand represent?

Where have you seen or heard the word **seconds** used before?

What numbers will you say as the second hand moves around the clock?

What happens to the minute hand when the second hand passes 12?

How would you read the time on this clock?
Do you say the number of seconds?

Most people just want to know the number of minutes that have passed the hour or the number of minutes to the next hour.

There are 60 seconds in one minute. A short way to write second is s.

How could you figure out the total number of seconds in three minutes?

How could you figure out the total number of seconds in one and a half minutes?

Step Up

1. These start and finish times are in the morning on the same day. Write the number of seconds that have passed.

a.

_______ seconds

b.

_______ seconds

2. These start and finish times are in the afternoon on the same day. Write the number of seconds that have passed.

a.

start

finish

_______ seconds

b.

start

finish

_______ seconds

3. Read each story. Then write your answer in seconds.

a. The microwave instructions say to heat on high for $1\frac{1}{2}$ minutes. How many seconds would you enter on the microwave?

_______ s

b. The first TV commercial went for 20 seconds. The next went for 5 seconds more than the first. What is the total time of the two commercials?

_______ s

c. At the start of the year it took Sarah 52 seconds to answer all her multiplication facts. Now it takes her 35 seconds. By how many seconds has she improved?

_______ s

d. It took Benjamin 1 minute and 5 seconds to finish the race. His time was 10 seconds slower than the winner's time. How long did it take the winner to finish?

_______ s

Step Ahead

Blake used one cup of sand to make this timer. The timer went for only 20 seconds. It needs to run for exactly one minute so he decides to add more sand.

How many more cups of sand should he add?

_______ cups

3.1

Step In Exploring Multiplication Patterns

What is the same about these quantities? What is different?

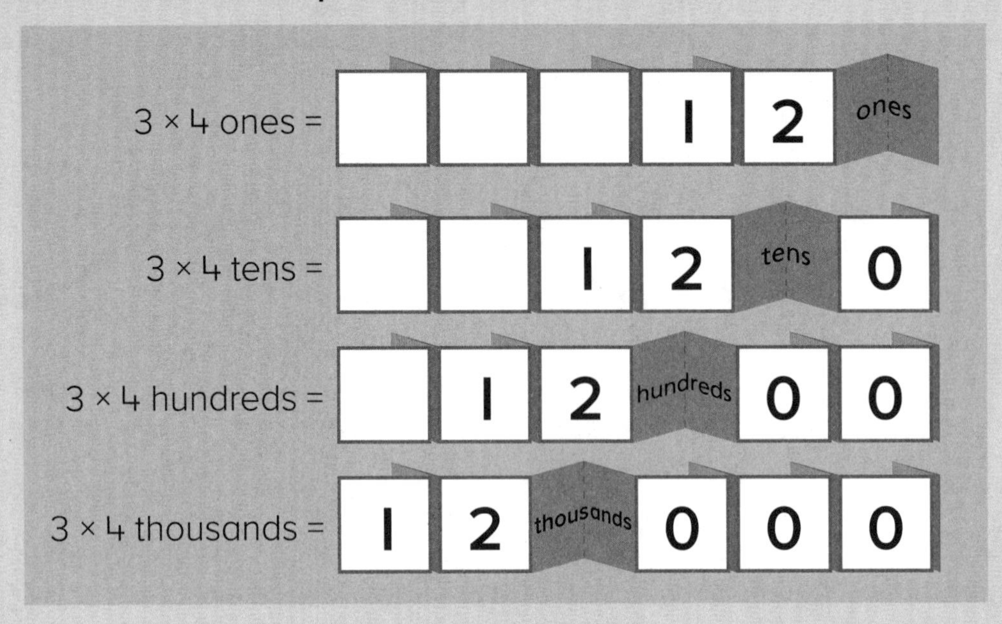

What is another way to say the last three products?

What are the different ways you could say the products of these?

4 × 6 tens = ______

4 × 6 hundreds = ______

4 × 6 thousands = ______

Step Up

1. Use a pattern to help you write the products.

6 × 2 ones = 12 ones	so	6 × 2 = 12
6 × 2 tens = ______ tens	so	6 × 20 = ______
6 × 2 hundreds = ______ hundreds	so	6 × 200 = ______
6 × 2 thousands = ______ thousands	so	6 × 2,000 = ______

2. Use a pattern to help you complete these equations.

a.

9 × 4 = ______

9 × 40 = ______

9 × 400 = ______

9 × 4,000 = ______

b.

8 × 9 = ______

8 × 90 = ______

8 × 900 = ______

8 × 9,000 = ______

c.

7 × 6 = ______

70 × 6 = ______

700 × 6 = ______

7,000 × 6 = ______

d.

3 × 7 = ______

30 × 7 = ______

300 × 7 = ______

3,000 × 7 = ______

3. Loop all the expressions that have the middle number as the product.

a. 240

12 × 20

60 × 4

3 × 80

400 × 6

b. 3,600

4 × 9,000

600 × 6

180 × 2

3 × 1,200

Step Ahead Write some multiplication expressions to match these products.

a.

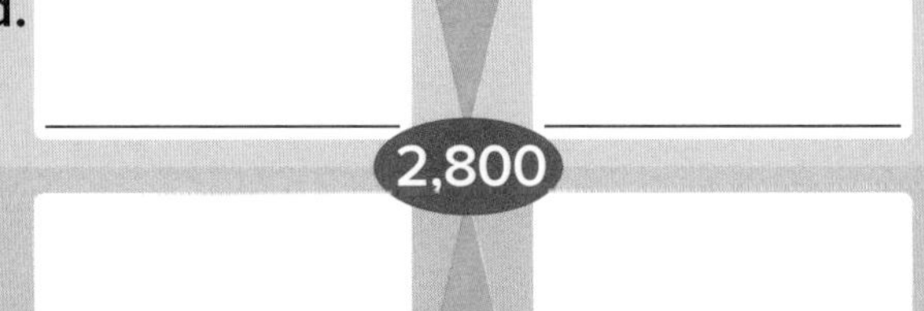

2,800

b.

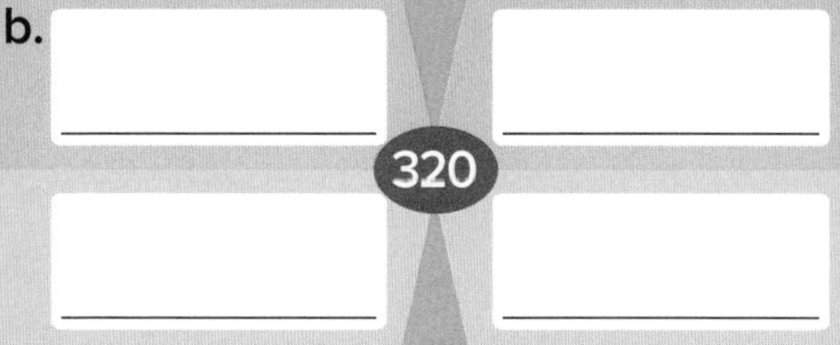

320

Step In Using the Partial-Products Strategy to Multiply Three- and Four-Digit Numbers

Compare these dimensions of two paper strips.

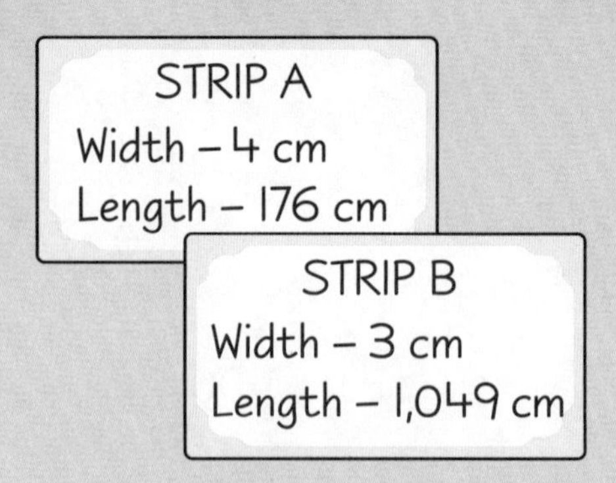

Which strip has the greater area?
How do you know?

How could you figure out the exact area of each strip?

Look at this diagram.

How has the rectangle been split?

What does each of the red numbers represent?

How could you use the diagram to figure out the total area of Strip A?

You can split a rectangle into parts to find the **partial products**.

How could you figure out the exact area of Strip B?

Step Up

1. Figure out each partial product. Then add to figure out the total.

6 × 354

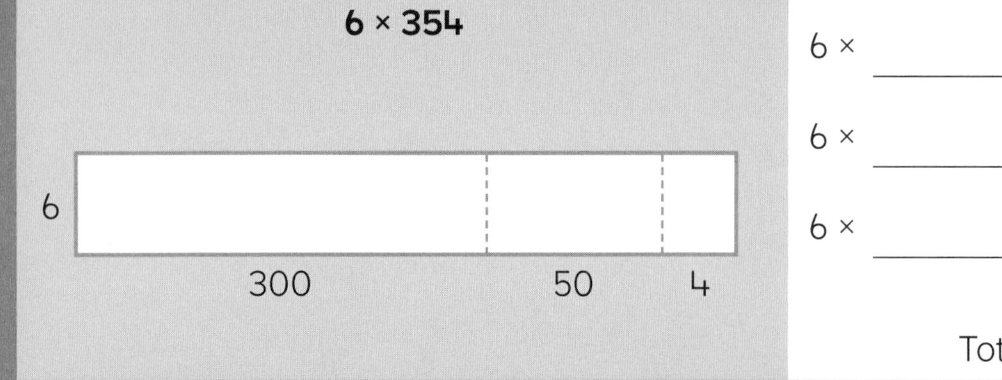

6 × ______ = ______

6 × ______ = ______

6 × ______ = ______

Total ______

2. Write the dimensions around the rectangle. Figure out each partial product. Then add to figure out the total.

a. 4 × 289

___ × ___ = ___
___ × ___ = ___
___ × ___ = ___

Total ___

b. 4 × 1,795

___ × ___ = ___
___ × ___ = ___
___ × ___ = ___
___ × ___ = ___

Total ___

c. 2 × 3,208

___ × ___ = ___
___ × ___ = ___
___ × ___ = ___

Total ___

Step Ahead

Color yellow the part of the rectangle that shows 8 × 20.
Color blue the part of the rectangle that shows 8 × 500.
Color red the part of the rectangle that shows 8 × 3,000.

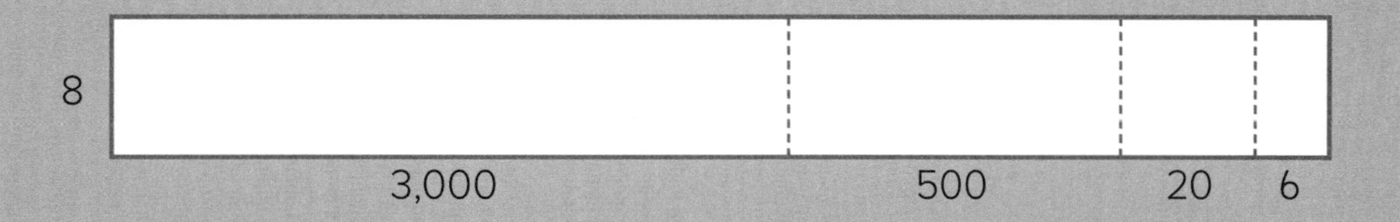

Step In Using the Standard Algorithm to Multiply Three-Digit Numbers

A room at the Sunshine Hotel costs $142 for one night.

About how much is the total cost for 3 nights?

How would you figure out the exact cost?

Gerardo multiplied the parts to figure out the total cost.

What steps did he follow?

What is the total cost? How do you know?

Write the total cost in the empty boxes.

	1	4	2
×			3
			6
	1	2	0
	3	0	0

Isaac used the standard algorithm for multiplication to calculate the total cost.
He followed these steps.

Step 1

	H	T	O
	1	4	2
×			3
			6

Step 2

	H	T	O
	1 (regrouped 1)	4	2
×			3
		2	6

Step 3

	H	T	O
	1 (regrouped 1)	4	2
×			3
	4	2	6

What numbers did he multiply in each step?

What happens when he multiplies the tens? How does he record the product?

Compare the two methods above. How are they the same? How are they different?

Step Up

1. Estimate each product. Then use the standard multiplication algorithm to calculate the exact answer.

a. Estimate ______

	H	T	O
	3	1	2
×			3

b. Estimate ______

	H	T	O
	4	2	4
×			2

c. Estimate ______

	H	T	O
	2	1	2
×			4

d. Estimate ______

	H	T	O
	1	3	1
×			3

2. Complete each of these.

a. Estimate

	H	T	O
	1	0	3
×			3

b. Estimate

	H	T	O
	3	4	7
×			2

c. Estimate

	H	T	O
	1	2	3
×			4

d. Estimate

	H	T	O
	2	1	0
×			4

e. Estimate

	2	8	2
×			3

f. Estimate

	4	4	1
×			2

g. Estimate

	1	6	1
×			5

h. Estimate

	2	7	3
×			3

i. Estimate

	Th	H	T	O
		6	2	3
×				3

j. Estimate

	Th	H	T	O
		3	0	2
×				4

k. Estimate

	Th	H	T	O
		4	7	6
×				2

l. Estimate

	Th	H	T	O
		5	3	7
×				4

Step Ahead Write **M** on the card below that shows partial products that match this multiplication algorithm.

$$\begin{array}{r} 2313 \\ \times \quad 3 \\ \hline 6939 \end{array}$$

3 × 3 = 9	3 × 3 = 9	3 × 3 = 9
1 × 3 = 3	10 × 3 = 30	10 × 3 = 30
3 × 3 = 9	300 × 3 = 900	30 × 3 = 90
2 × 3 = 6	2,000 × 3 = 6,000	200 × 3 = 600

Step In — Using the Standard Algorithm to Multiply Four-Digit Numbers

Camella needs 4 new laptops for her workplace.
She has $4,500 in her account.
Does she have enough money to buy the laptops?

What numbers will you multiply to help you decide?

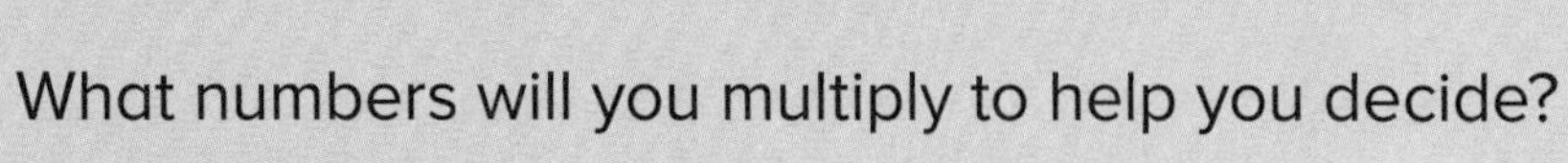

Camella figures out the exact cost like this.

What steps did she follow?

Write the total cost in the algorithm.

1	0	4	5
×			4
		2	0
	1	6	0
4	0	0	0

Liam used the standard algorithm for multiplication to calculate the exact cost.

Step 1

Th	H	T	O
		2	
1	0	4	5
×			4
			0

Step 2

Th	H	T	O
	1	2	
1	0	4	5
×			4
		8	0

Step 3

Th	H	T	O
	1	2	
1	0	4	5
×			4
	1	8	0

Step 4

Th	H	T	O
	1	2	
1	0	4	5
×			4
4	1	8	0

Describe each of the steps he followed.

How could you combine Step 2 and Step 3?

Step Up

1. Estimate the total cost. Write the numbers that you chose to multiply.

a. Buy 5 

Estimate $ ____________

b. Buy 3 

Estimate $ ____________

c. Buy 7 

Estimate $ ____________

2. Write your estimate. Then use the standard multiplication algorithm to calculate the exact product.

a. Estimate

	Th	H	T	O
	1	3	1	2
×				2

b. Estimate

	Th	H	T	O
	1	0	1	2
×				4

c. Estimate

	Th	H	T	O
	3	0	3	1
×				3

d. Estimate

	2	0	1	6
×				4

e. Estimate

	1	6	1	2
×				4

f. Estimate

	2	5	4	0
×				3

g. Estimate

	3	4	2	5
×				3

h. Estimate

	5	7	9	1
×				6

i. Estimate

	4	0	3	9
×				6

Step Ahead Write the correct answer. Then describe the mistake in words.

		4	5	
		6	0	7
×				8
	5	2	0	6

Step In — Using the Distributive Property to Multiply Two-Digit Numbers (Partial Products)

New turf is being laid in a playground.
This diagram shows the dimensions of the playground.

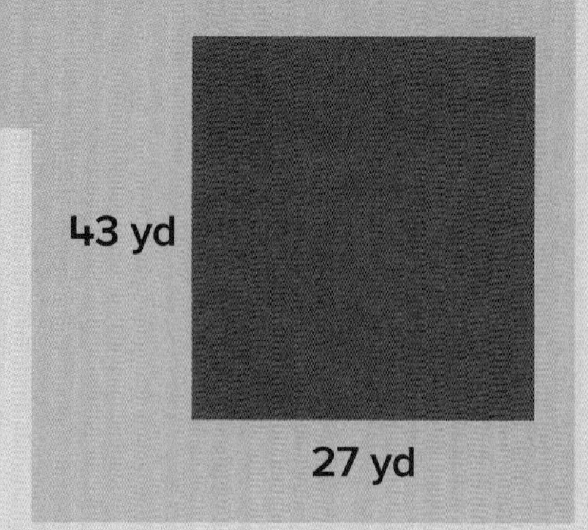

Estimate the amount of turf needed.

I know 40 x 3 is 120.
40 x 30 is ten times more,
so about 1,200 sq yards of
turf will be needed.

How could you figure out the exact amount of turf to order?

Juliana drew this diagram.
What does her diagram show?

How did she split the rectangle?

What does each red number represent?

What is the unknown value? How do you know?

How could you figure out the total area of the playground?

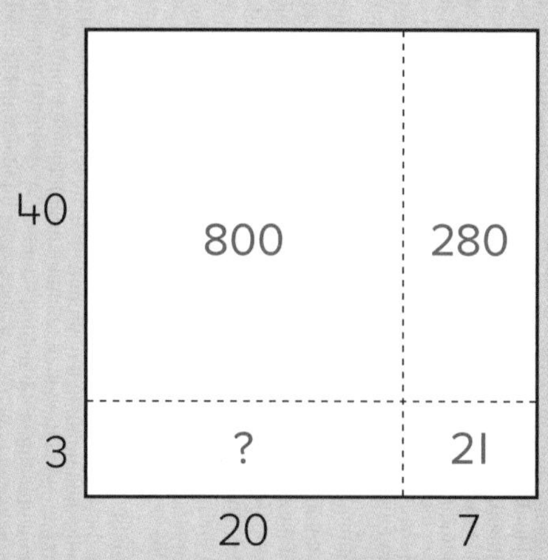

Step Up

1. Figure out each partial product.
Then write the total of the four products.

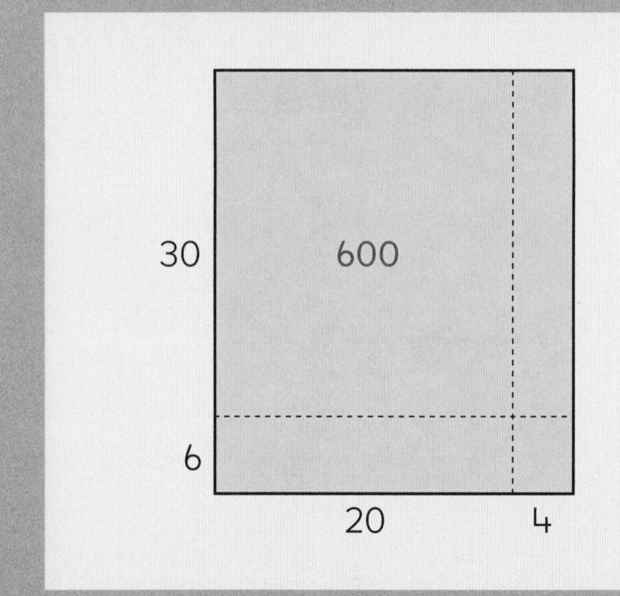

36 × 24

30 × 20 = 600

30 × 4 = ______

6 × 20 = ______

6 × 4 = ______

Total ______

2. Write a multiplication sentence to show each part.
Then write the total of the four partial products.

a.

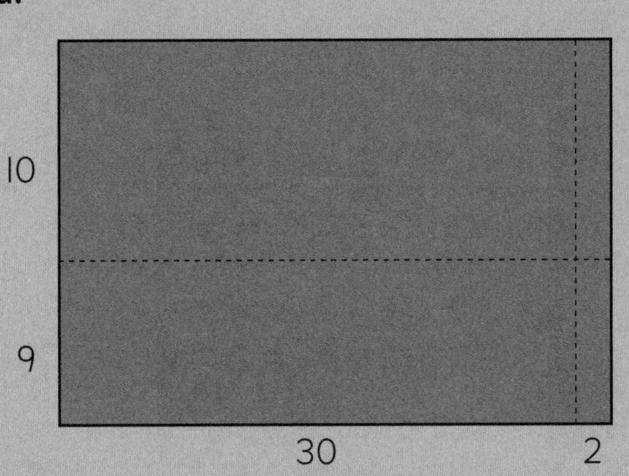

19 × 32				
____	×	____	=	____
____	×	____	=	____
____	×	____	=	____
____	×	____	=	____
			Total	____

b.

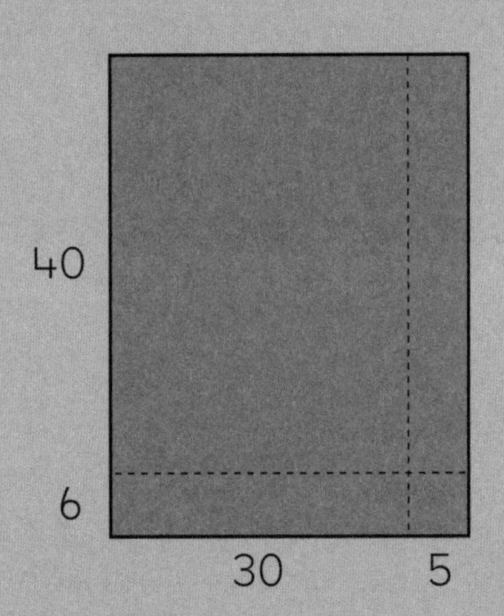

46 × 35				
____	×	____	=	____
____	×	____	=	____
____	×	____	=	____
____	×	____	=	____
			Total	____

Step Ahead

Write the dimensions around the rectangle.
Write a multiplication sentence to show each part. Then add the partial products to figure out the total.

28 × 42				
____	×	____	=	____
____	×	____	=	____
____	×	____	=	____
____	×	____	–	____
			Total	____

Step In — Using the Standard Algorithm to Multiply Two-Digit Numbers

A school hall has a rectangular floor. The dimensions are 24 yd × 32 yd.

How would you estimate the area of the floor?

How could you figure out the exact area?

Cary drew this diagram. How will it help him figure out the area of the floor?

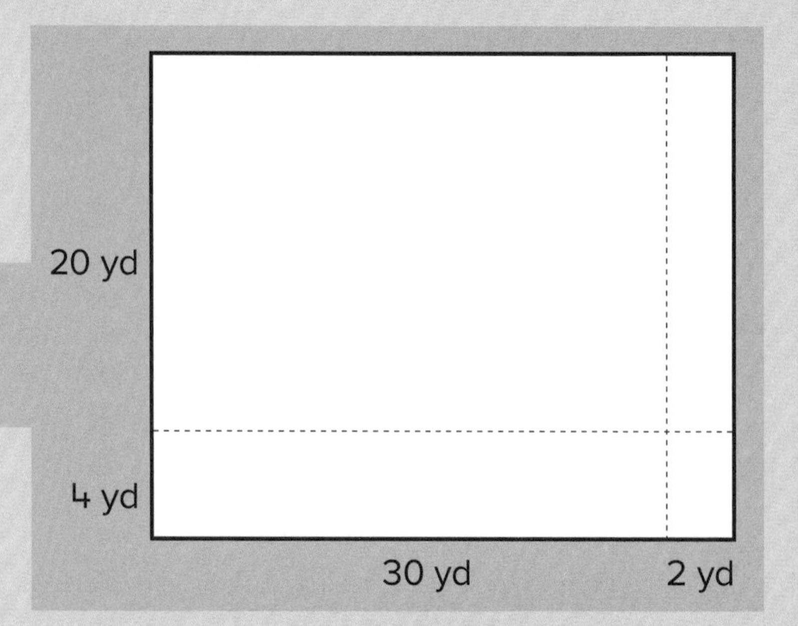

Write the partial product inside each part of the diagram.

What is the area? How do you know?

Hailey used the standard multiplication algorithm to calculate the exact area.

Step 1

	H	T	O
		2	4
×		3	2
			8

Step 2

	H	T	O
		2	4
×		3	2
		4	8

Step 3

	H	T	O
		1	
		2	4
×		3	2
		4	8
		2	0

Step 4

	H	T	O
		1	
		2	4
×		3	2
		4	8
	7	2	0

Step 5

	H	T	O
		1	
		2	4
×		3	2
		4	8
	7	2	0
	7	6	8

Does it matter which factor is written in the top row? How do you know?
What numbers did she multiply in each step?

Compare the partial-products method and the standard algorithm. How are they similar?

Look carefully at the numbers being multiplied in each step of the algorithm.
Where are the matching partial products in Cary's diagram?

What is another way you could figure out the area?

I would break the rectangle into two parts. That's 24 x 3 tens plus 24 x 2.

Step Up A builder made some quick calculations. Make an estimate, then check each calculation and shade the ⬭ to show if it is correct or not. If it is not correct, write the correct calculation to the side.

a.
```
   39
×  41
   39
  156
  195
```
⬭ correct
⬭ not correct

b.
```
   29
×  31
   29
  870
  899
```
⬭ correct
⬭ not correct

c.
```
   26
×  35
  130
  780
  910
```
⬭ correct
⬭ not correct

d.
```
    70
×   61
    70
  3600
  3670
```
⬭ correct
⬭ not correct

e.
```
    53
×   27
   371
  1060
  1431
```
⬭ correct
⬭ not correct

f.
```
   39
×  62
   78
  234
  302
```
⬭ correct
⬭ not correct

Step Ahead Look at the algorithm that Hailey used on page 66. Explain why she wrote a zero in the ones place in Step 3.

Step In Solving Word Problems Involving Multiplication

This table shows the number of accessories that are made at a clothing factory each day.

The manager receives an order for 3,000 handbags.

About how many days will it take to complete the order?

Which numbers did you multiply to form your estimate?

Discount Clothing

Item	Quantity
Handbags	798
Belts	1,425
Wallets	1,035

How many belts are made in 7 days?

Pedro used the standard algorithm for multiplication to figure out this answer.

Write the missing number.

$$\begin{array}{r} 1\ 4\ 2\ 5 \\ \times\ \ \ \ \ \ \ 7 \\ \hline 9\ 9\ \square\ 5 \end{array}$$

How would you figure out the difference between the number of belts and the number of wallets that can be made in 5 days?

Step Up

1. Solve each problem. Show your thinking.

a. There are 6 large containers. 405 hats are packed into each container. How many hats have been packed in total?

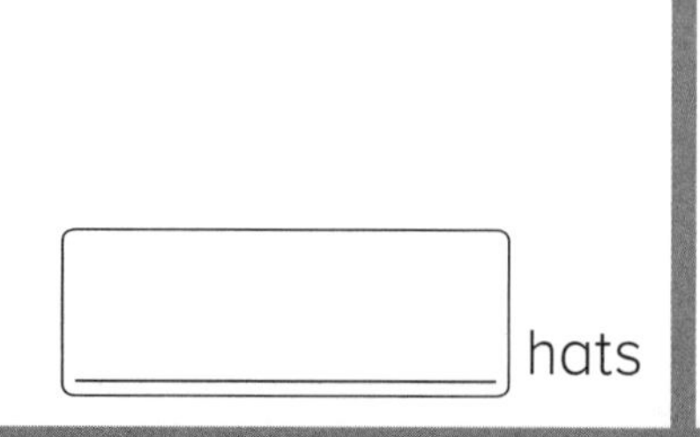

hats

b. 965 pairs of shoes are made each day. How many days will it take to complete an order for 5,000 pairs of shoes?

days

2. Solve each problem. Show your thinking.

a. 274 pairs of blue jeans and 195 pairs of black jeans are made each day. How many pairs are made in 5 days?

_______ pairs of jeans

b. It costs $4 in material to make a pair of shorts. It costs $3 more to make a sweater. What is the total cost of making 650 sweaters?

$ _______

c. Jude sells 10 skirts on Monday and 19 skirts on Tuesday. The skirts cost $26 each. What is the total amount paid for these skirts?

$ _______

d. It costs $15 to buy a shirt. Each shirt costs $9 to make. How much profit is made if 1,450 shirts are sold?

$ _______

Step Ahead

Aki works 27 hours each week. He earns $18 an hour. Charlotte works 19 hours a week. She earns $24 an hour. What is the difference between the amounts that they earn each week?

$ _______

Step In Reviewing Fraction Concepts

The large rectangle is one whole.
Into how many equal parts has it been divided?

What fraction describes each part?

Shade parts of the rectangle to show four-sixths.

Is four-sixths closer to one whole, one-half, or zero?

Write four-sixths using numerals. 

Which numeral is the denominator? What does it tell you?
Which numeral is the numerator? What does it tell you?

A fraction presented in the form $\frac{a}{b}$ is a **common fraction.**

On this number line, the distance from 0 to 1 is one whole.

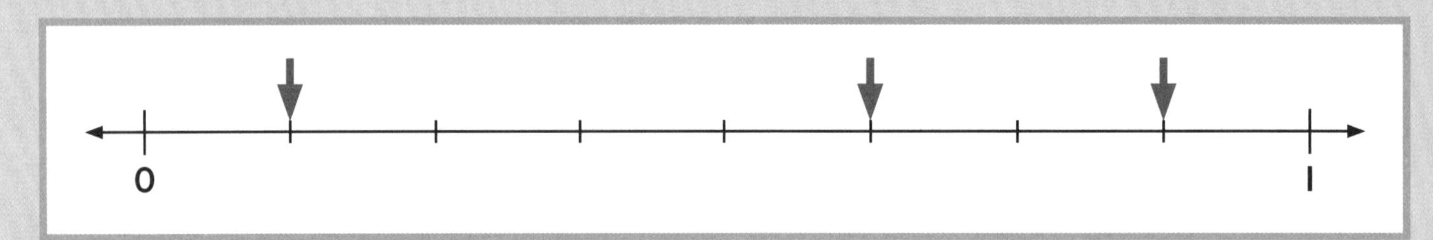

What fractions are the arrows pointing to?
Which is the least fraction? Which is the greatest?

Step Up

1. Each large shape is one whole.
Shade parts to show each fraction.

a. $\frac{1}{4}$ 

b. $\frac{2}{5}$ 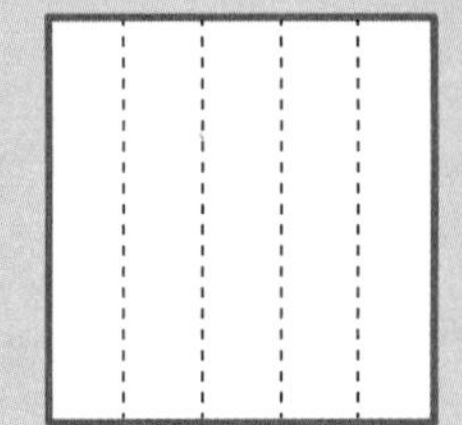

c. $\frac{4}{10}$ 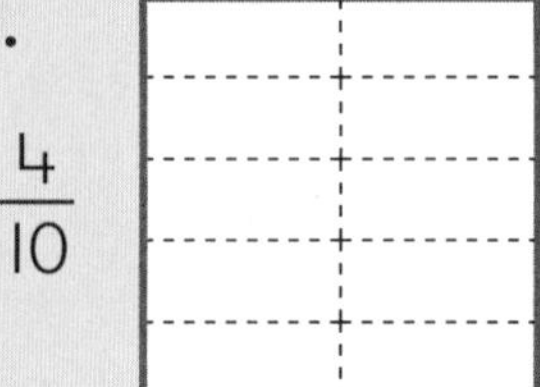

d. $\frac{7}{8}$ 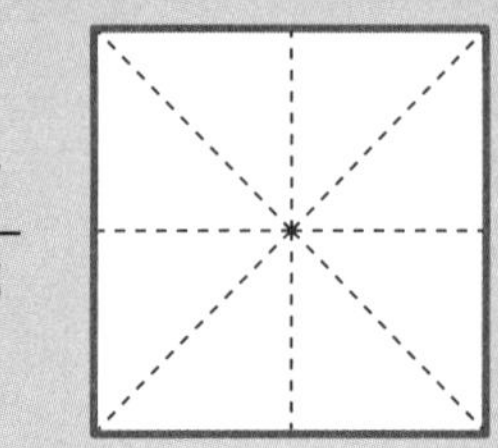

e. $\frac{4}{5}$ 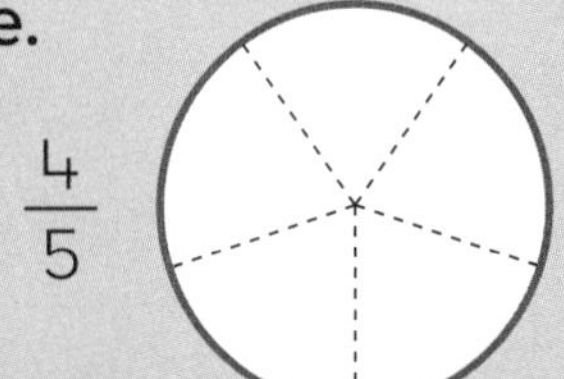

f. $\frac{9}{10}$ 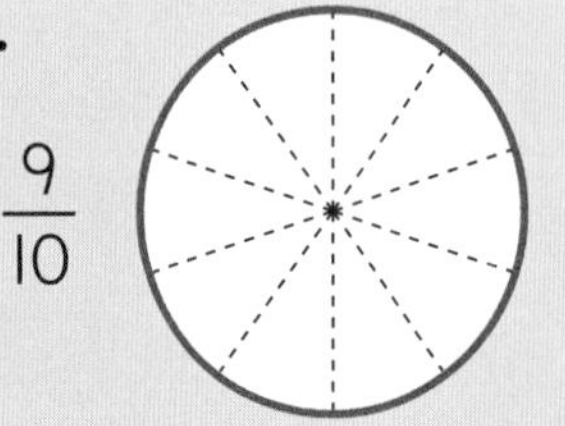

g. $\frac{3}{4}$ 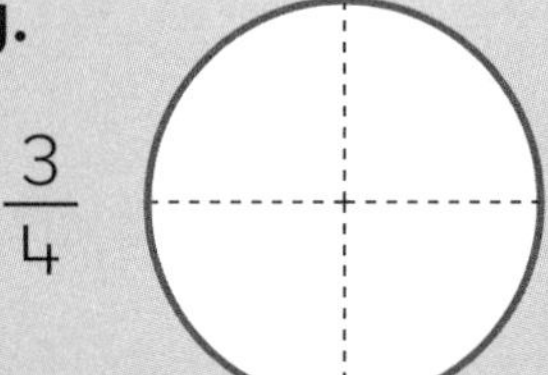

h. $\frac{5}{8}$ 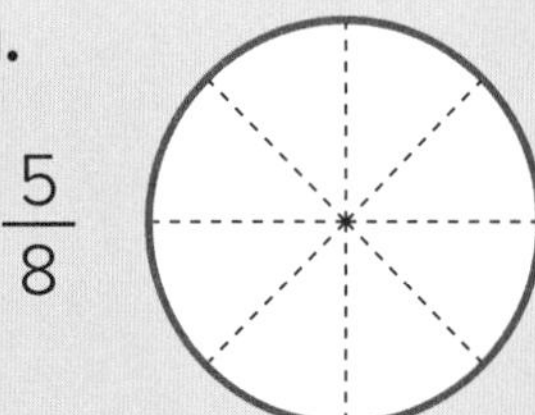

Look at each number line carefully. The distance from 0 to 1 is one whole.
Write the fraction that each arrow is pointing to.

2.

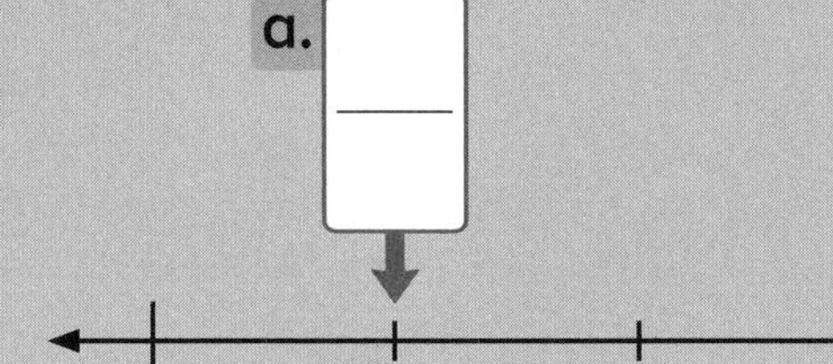 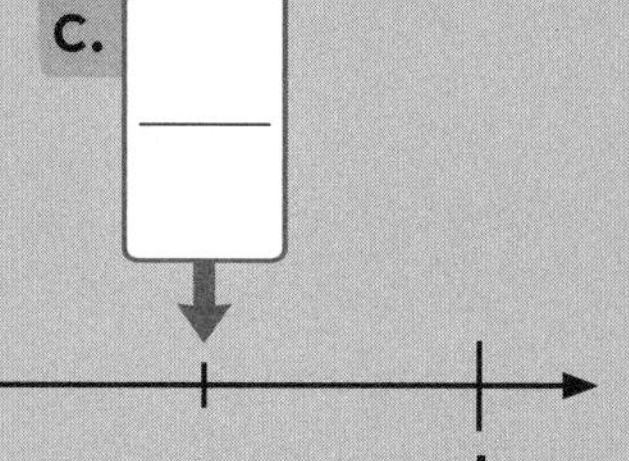

a. ___ b. ___ c. ___

0 1

3.

 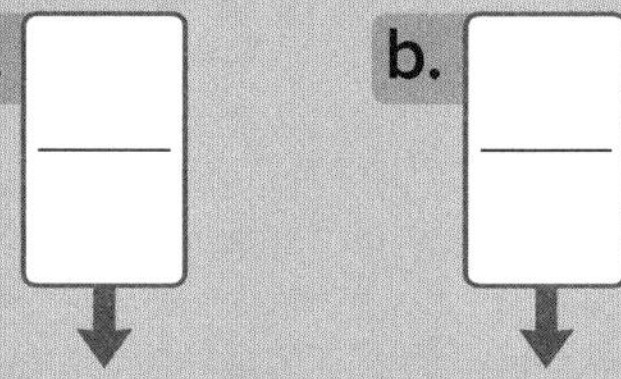 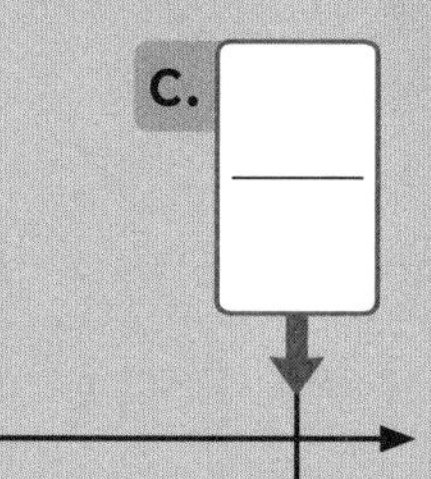

a. ___ b. ___ c. ___

0 1

4.

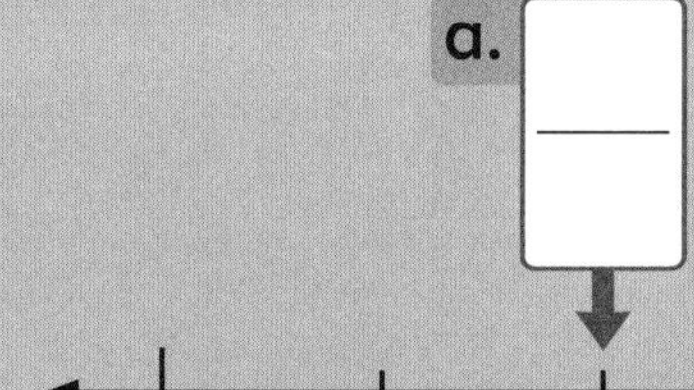 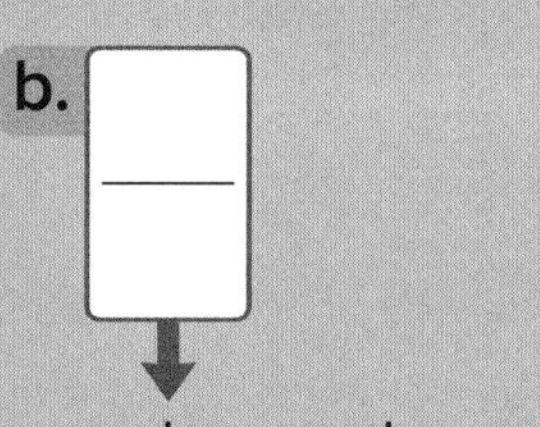 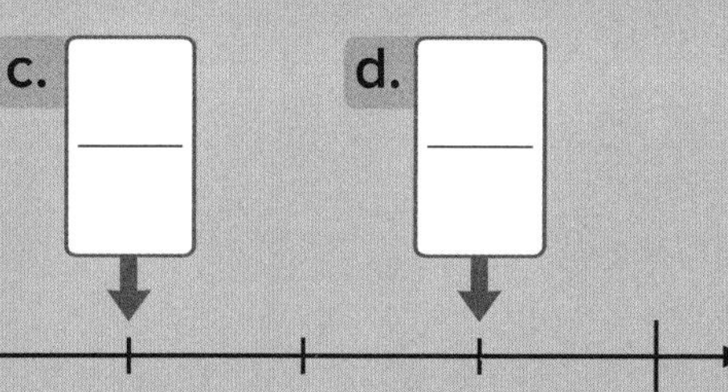

a. ___ b. ___ c. ___ d. ___

0 1

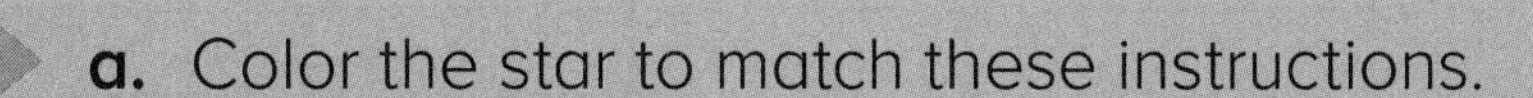

Step Ahead

a. Color the star to match these instructions.

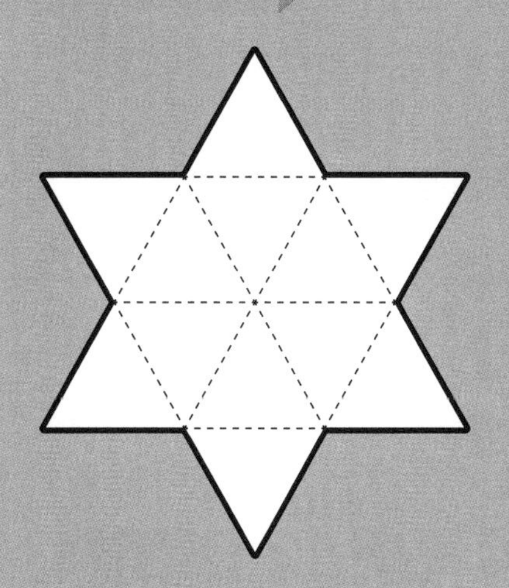

- Color $\frac{1}{3}$ of the star **blue**.
- Color $\frac{1}{4}$ of the star **green**.
- Color the remaining parts **yellow**.

b. What fraction of the star is yellow?

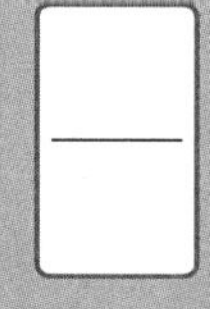

Step In Exploring Improper Fractions (Number Line Model)

One batch of 12 muffins needs $\frac{2}{3}$ cup of mashed banana.
Jennifer wants to make 2 batches but she only has a $\frac{1}{3}$ measuring cup.

What can she do to measure the correct amount of banana for 2 batches of muffins?

Jennifer can use the $\frac{1}{3}$ measuring cup two times for one batch, so she can use it four times for two batches.

An **improper fraction** is a type of common fraction where the numerator is equal to or greater than the denominator.

How could you show your thinking on a number line?

What fraction could you write to show the total amount of banana?

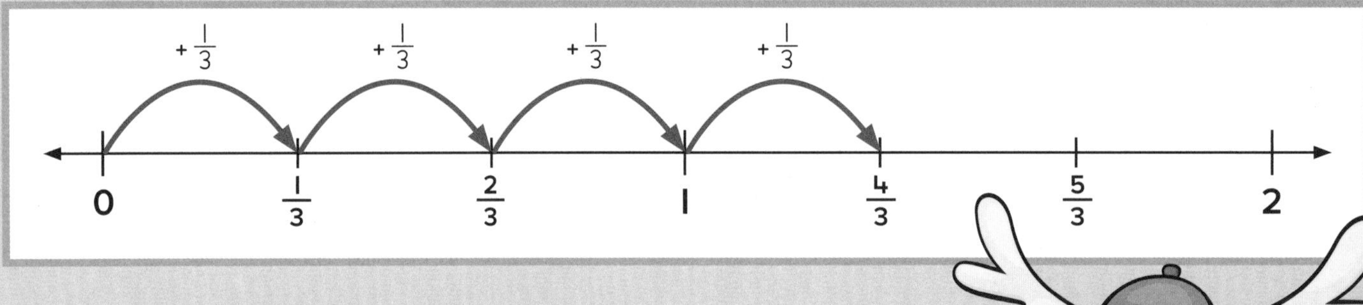

What do you notice about the fraction $\frac{4}{3}$?

The numerator is greater than the denominator.
I can see on the number line that $\frac{4}{3}$ is greater than 1.

Step Up

1. On this number line, the distance from 0 to 1 is one whole. Write the fraction that should be in each box. Draw jumps to help you.

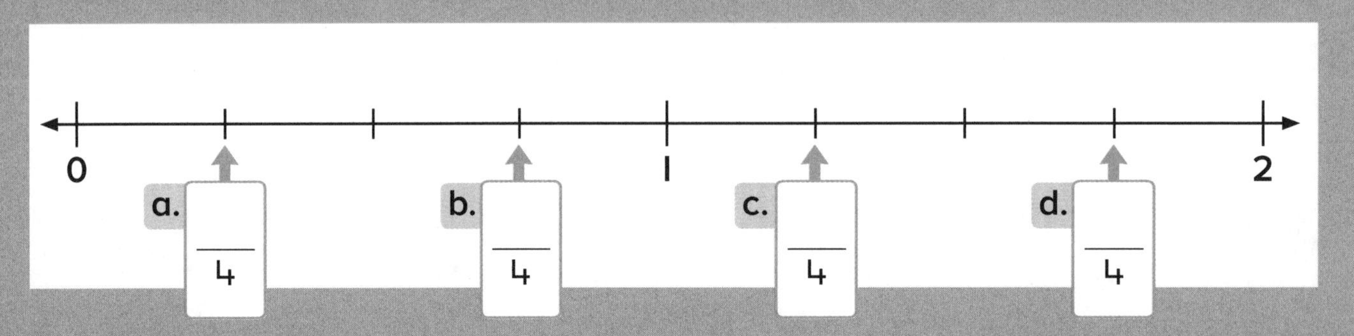

On each number line, the distance from 0 to 1 is one whole.
Write the fraction that should be in each box. Use the number line to help.

2.

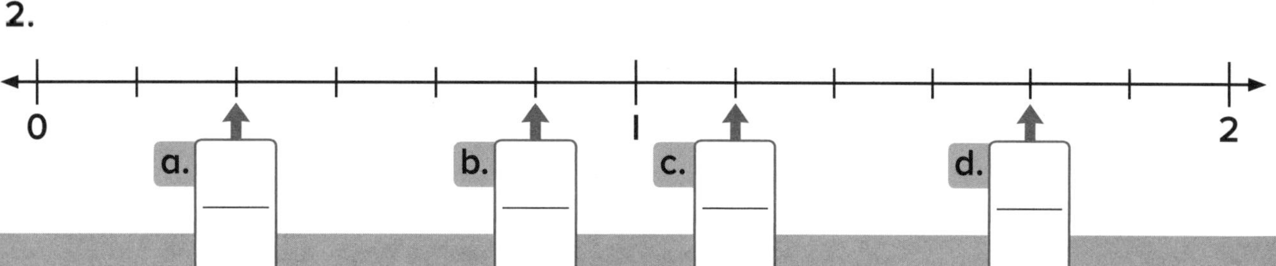

3.

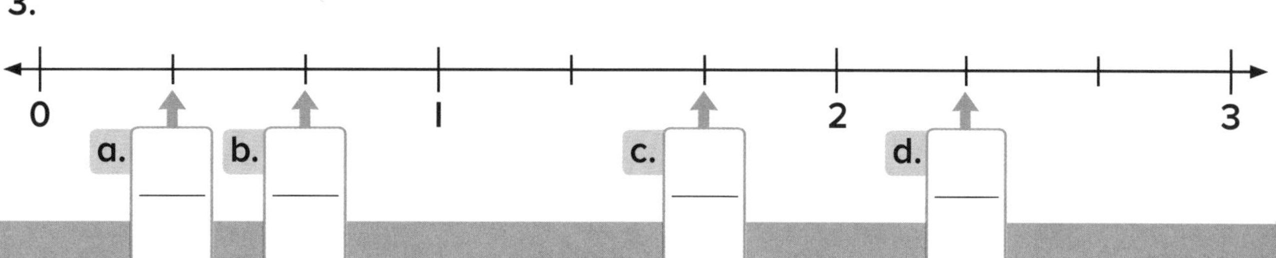

4.

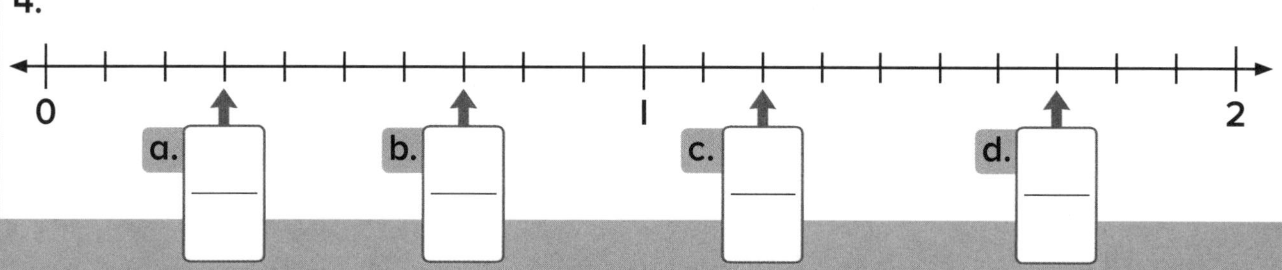

5. Use the fractions you wrote on the number lines above.

a. List the fractions that are less than 1.

b. List the fractions that are greater than 1 but less than 2.

Step Ahead Complete each equation.

a. $\frac{1}{4} + \frac{1}{4} + \frac{1}{4} + \frac{1}{4} + \frac{1}{4} = \frac{\quad}{4}$

b. $\frac{1}{3} + \frac{1}{3} + \frac{1}{3} + \frac{1}{3} = \frac{\quad}{3}$

c. $\frac{1}{6} + \frac{1}{6} + \frac{1}{6} + \frac{1}{6} + \frac{1}{6} + \frac{1}{6} + \frac{1}{6} = \frac{\quad}{6}$

d. $\frac{1}{2} + \frac{1}{2} + \frac{1}{2} + \frac{1}{2} + \frac{1}{2} = \frac{\quad}{2}$

Step In Exploring Improper Fractions (Area Model)

On this number line, the distance from 0 to 1 is one whole.

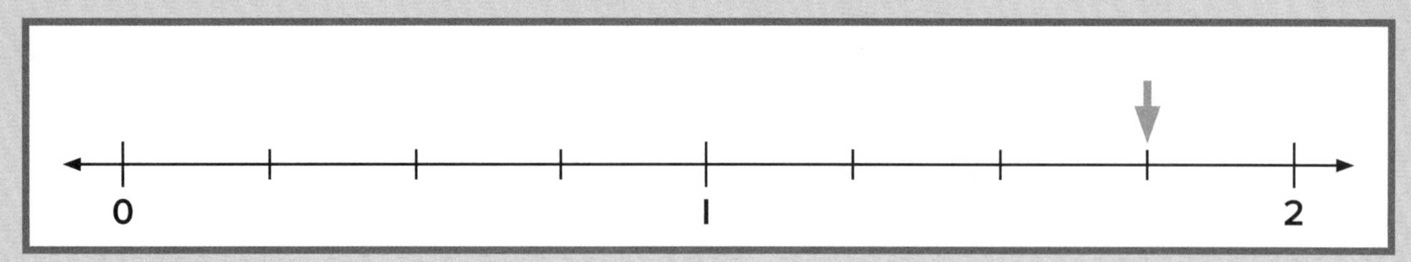

What fraction is the arrow pointing to?

How do you know?

Fractions greater than 1 can also be shown with shapes.

Each large square on the right is one whole.

Each whole is split into four parts of equal size.

How many fourths are shaded in total?

What fraction is shown?

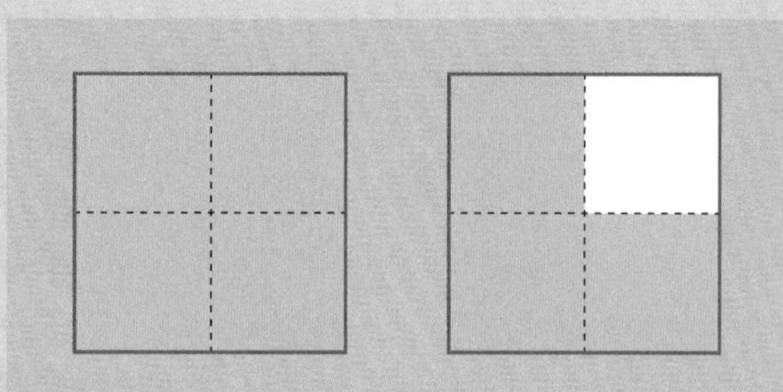

Step Up

1. Each large shape is one whole. Write the fraction that is shaded.

a.

b.

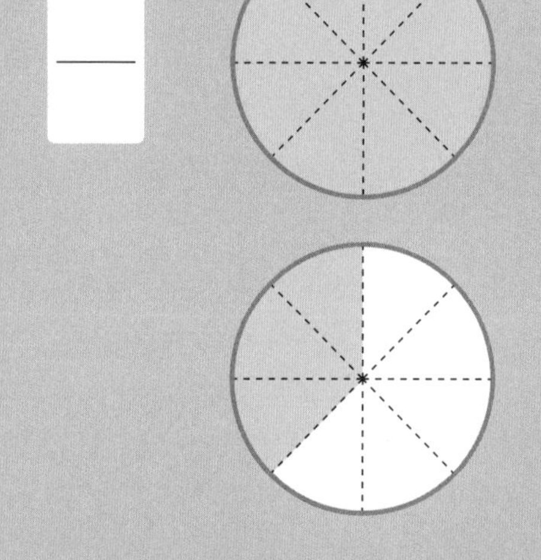

c.

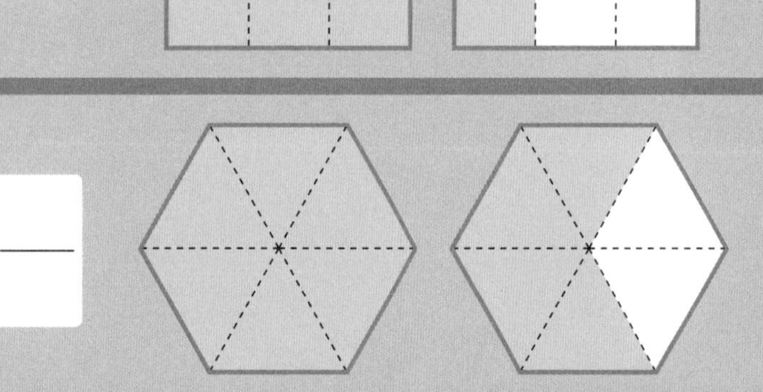

2. Each large shape is one whole. Color the shapes to show each fraction.

a. $\frac{6}{4}$

b. $\frac{5}{2}$

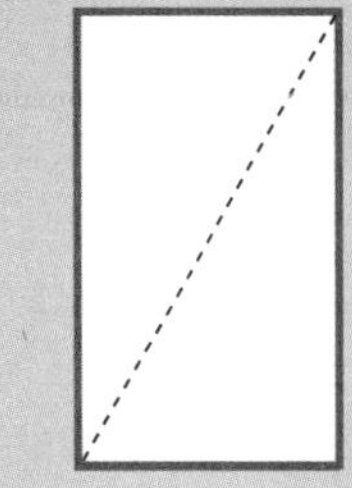
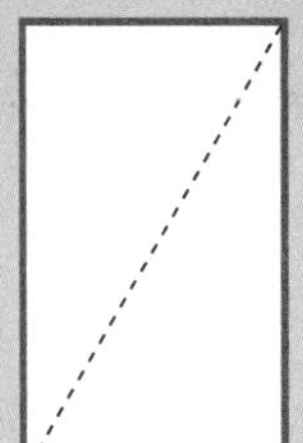
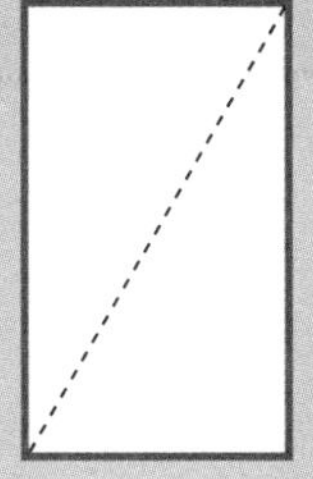

c. $\frac{9}{8}$

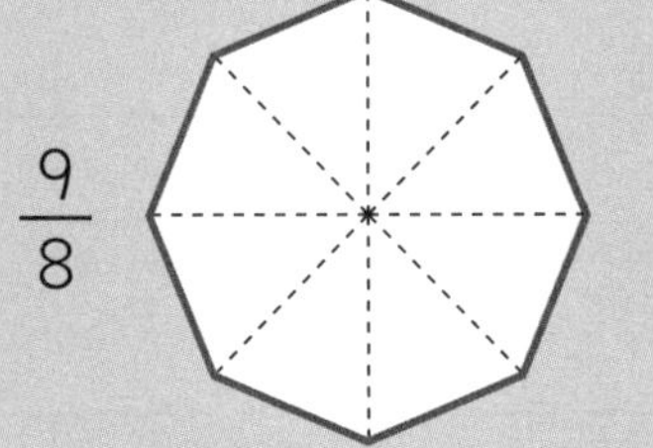

d. $\frac{10}{4}$

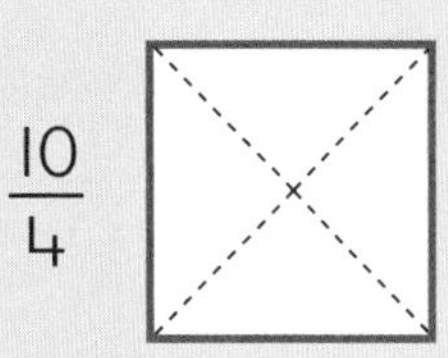
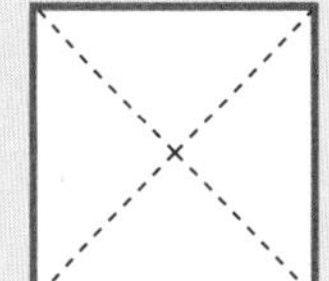
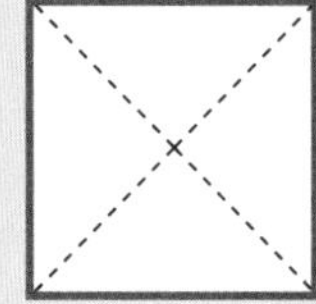

e. $\frac{9}{6}$

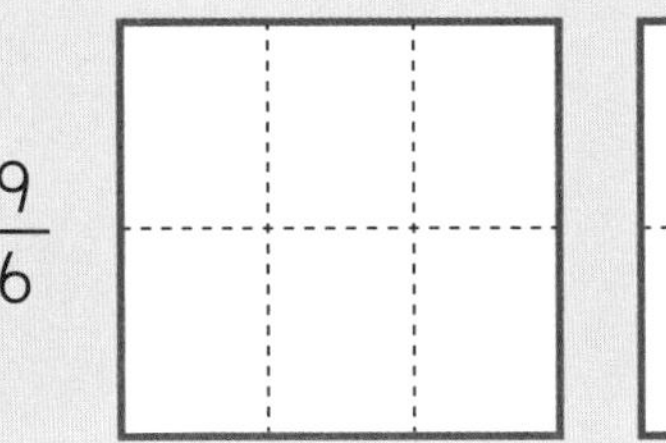

f. $\frac{8}{3}$

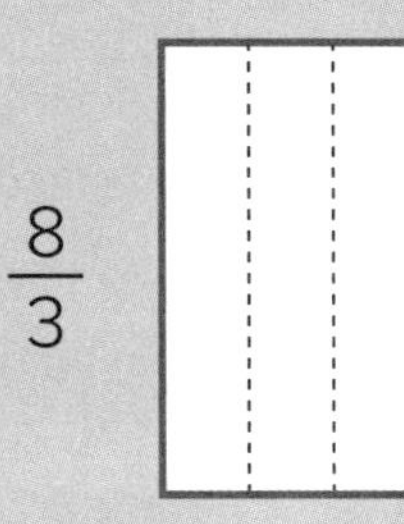
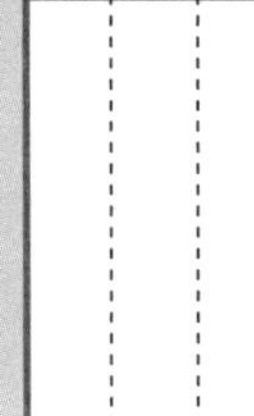
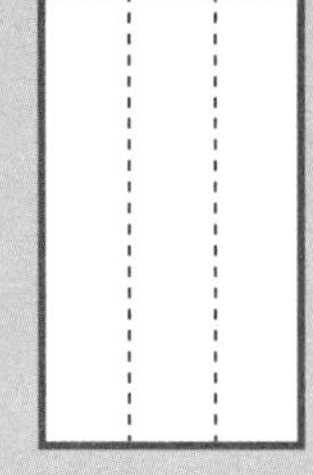

g. $\frac{6}{3}$

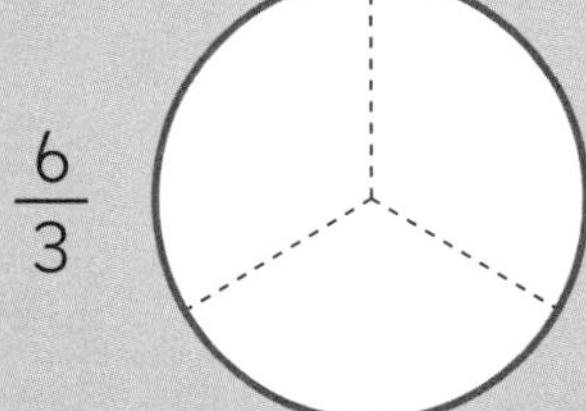

h. $\frac{13}{8}$

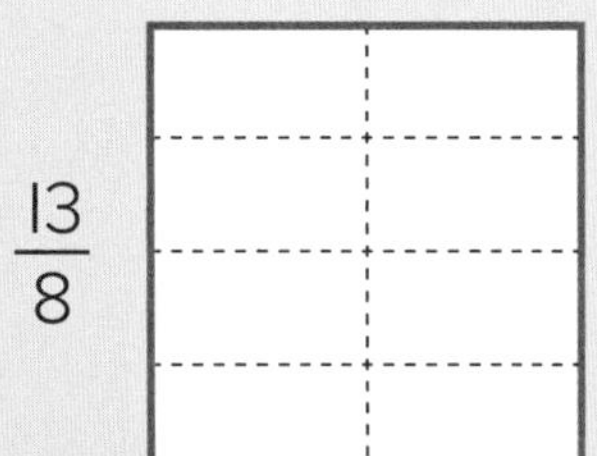
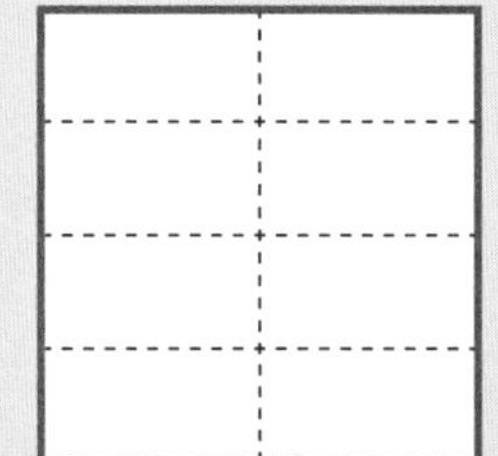

Step Ahead

Each square is one whole. Draw lines to split the squares into parts of equal size. Then color parts to show $\frac{9}{4}$.

Step In Reviewing Equivalent Fractions

Look at this fraction chart. The top strip is one whole.

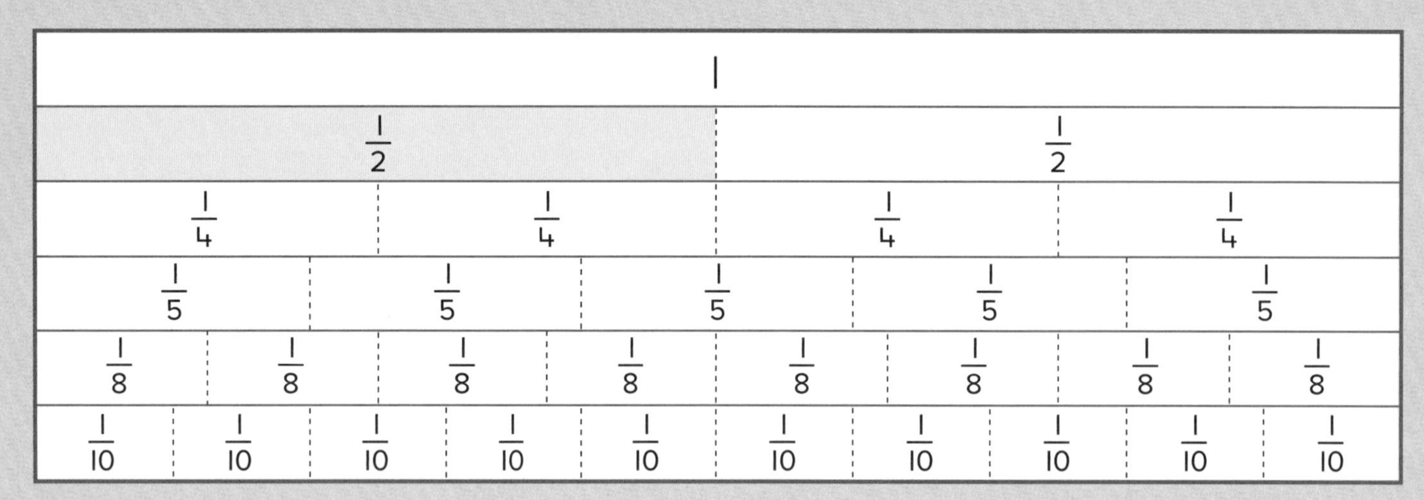

Point to the strip that is divided into two parts. What fraction of that strip is shaded?

What parts of other strips can you shade to show the same fraction? How do you know?

Write the fractions to complete this sentence.

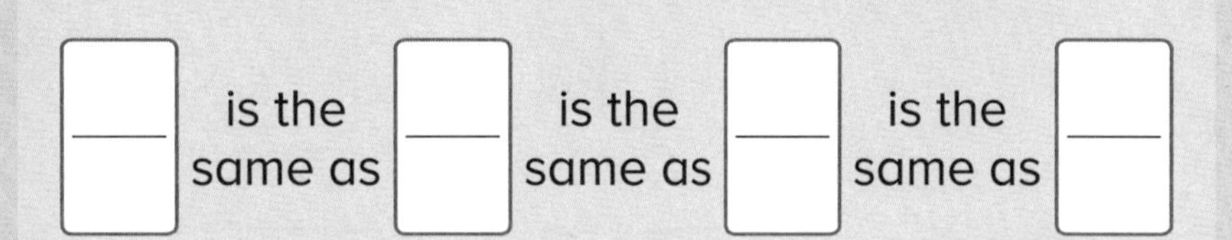

What do you notice about fractions such as $\frac{4}{4}$, $\frac{10}{10}$, and $\frac{8}{8}$?

What fractions do you think are equivalent to 3?

Whole numbers (like 1, 2, and 3) can be written as fractions in many ways. One way is with a denominator of 1.

$1 = \frac{1}{1}$ $2 = \frac{2}{1}$ $3 = \frac{3}{1}$

Step Up

1. Use the fraction chart above to help you write equivalent fractions.

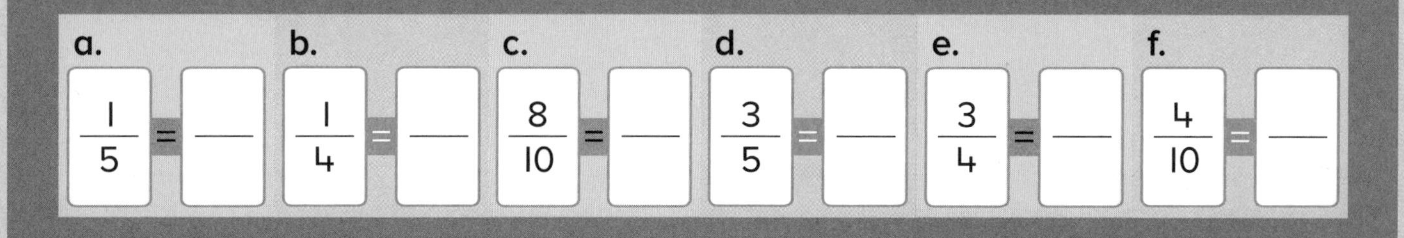

On each number line below, the distance from 0 to 1 is one whole.

2. Write the fractions that the arrows are pointing to.

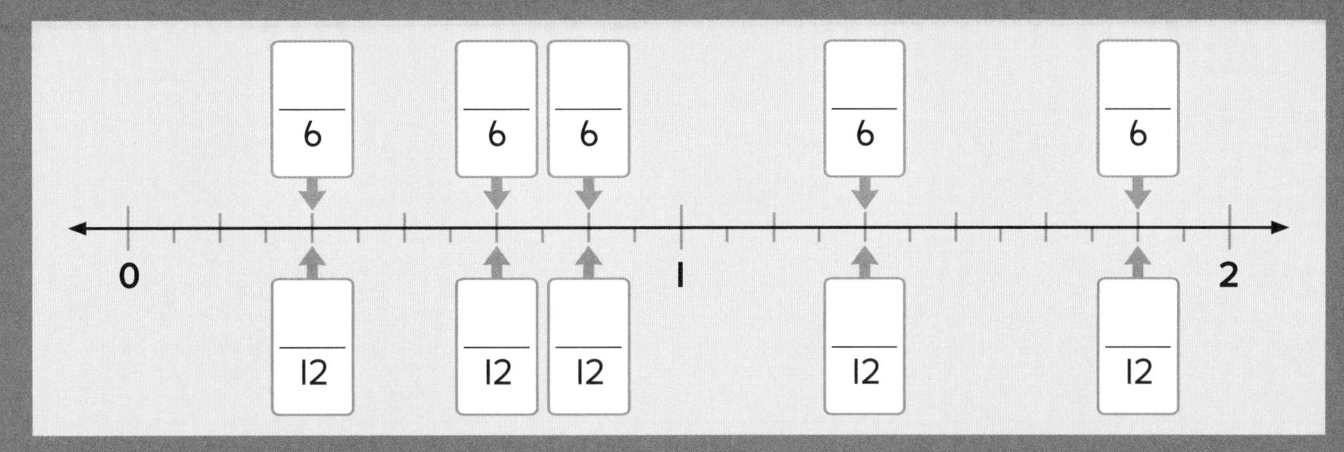

3. Use this number line to help you write equivalent fractions.

a. $\frac{1}{4} = \frac{\quad}{8}$

b. 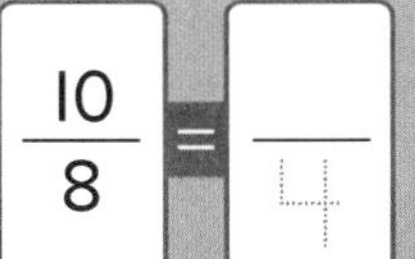

c. 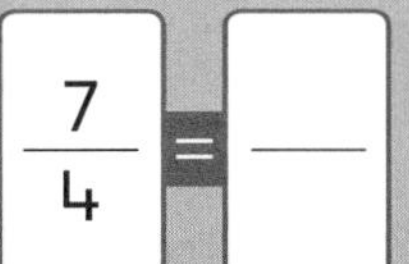

d. $\frac{22}{8} = $ ___

e. $\frac{1}{1} = $ ___

f. 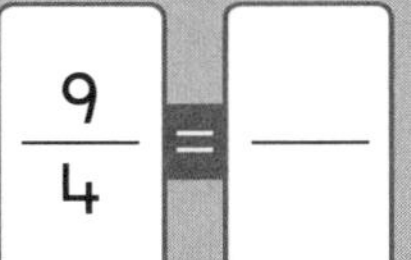

g. 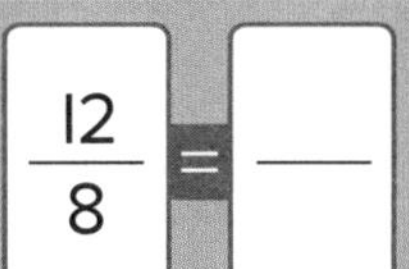

h. 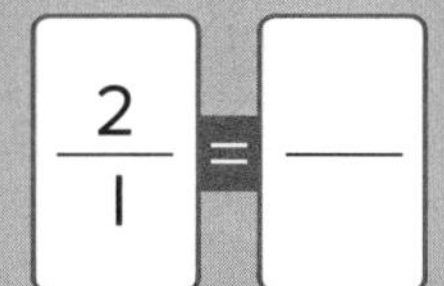

Step Ahead Draw lines to divide the last strip into **sixteenths**. Then complete two different equivalence statements involving sixteenths.

$\frac{1}{2}$				$\frac{1}{2}$			
$\frac{1}{4}$		$\frac{1}{4}$		$\frac{1}{4}$		$\frac{1}{4}$	
$\frac{1}{8}$	$\frac{1}{8}$	$\frac{1}{8}$	$\frac{1}{8}$	$\frac{1}{8}$	$\frac{1}{8}$	$\frac{1}{8}$	$\frac{1}{8}$

a. 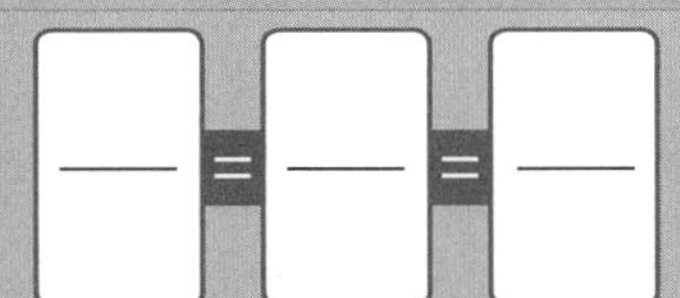

b. 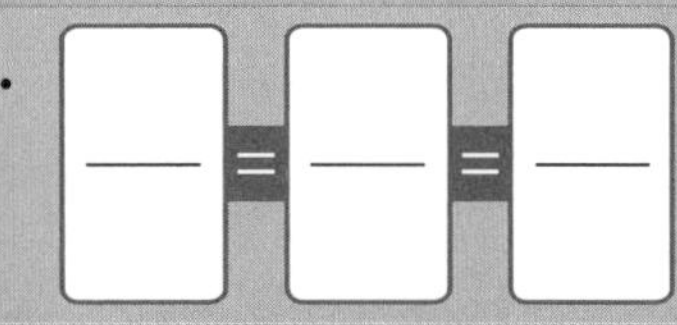

Step In Comparing Common Fractions (Length Model)

The top strip is one whole.

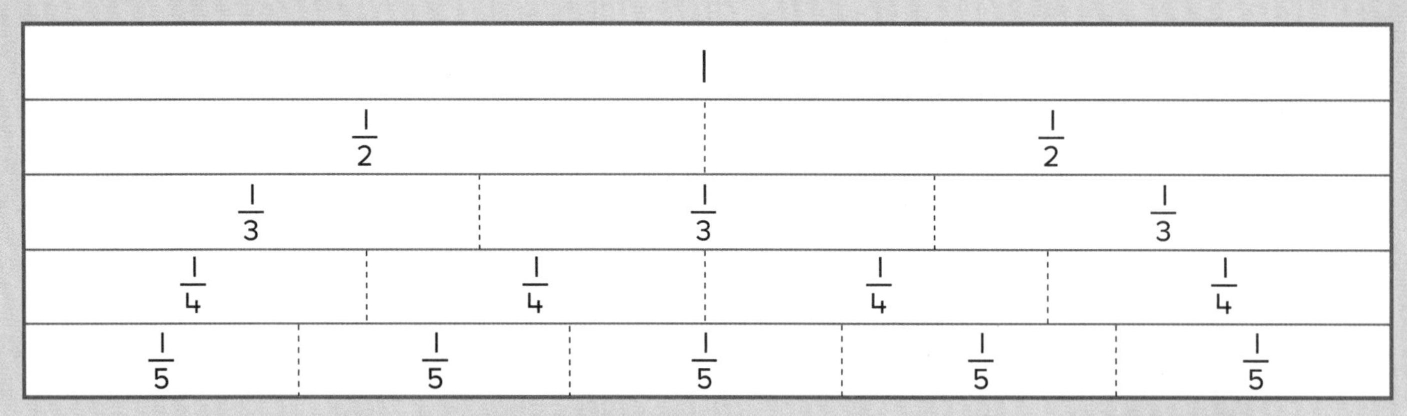

What do you notice about the number of parts in each strip?
What do you notice about the size of the parts in each strip?

Which fraction is greater?
How did you decide?

$\frac{1}{2}$ or $\frac{1}{5}$

Which fraction is greater?
What helps you figure it out?

$\frac{1}{8}$ or $\frac{1}{10}$

I think $\frac{1}{8}$ is greater than $\frac{1}{10}$. If you split a shape into 8 equal parts, each part would be bigger than if you split the shape into 10 equal parts.

Which fraction is greater?

$\frac{1}{2}$ or $\frac{2}{5}$

How could you use the fraction chart above to help you?
What is another way you could figure it out?

Step Up

1. Loop the fraction that is **greater** in each pair.
Use the fraction chart to help you.

a. $\frac{1}{5}$ or $\frac{1}{12}$

b. $\frac{3}{8}$ or $\frac{1}{2}$

c. $\frac{3}{5}$ or $\frac{9}{12}$

d. $\frac{4}{5}$ or $\frac{7}{8}$

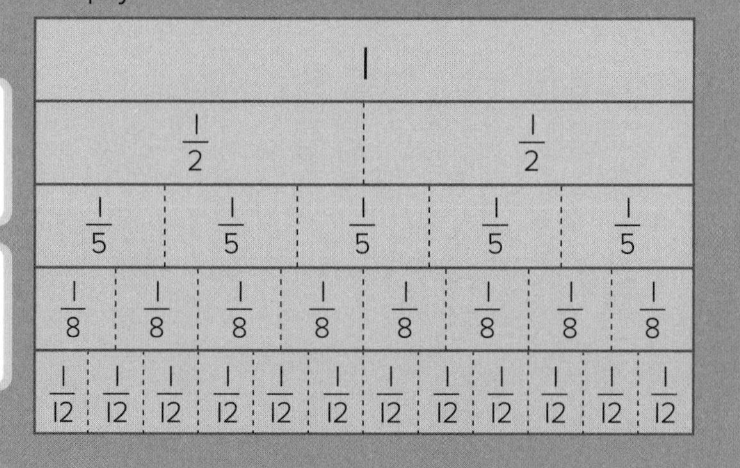

The top strip in this fraction chart shows two wholes.

<table>
<tr><td colspan="12">1</td><td colspan="12">1</td></tr>
<tr><td colspan="6">$\frac{1}{2}$</td><td colspan="6">$\frac{1}{2}$</td><td colspan="6">$\frac{1}{2}$</td><td colspan="6">$\frac{1}{2}$</td></tr>
<tr><td colspan="4">$\frac{1}{3}$</td><td colspan="4">$\frac{1}{3}$</td><td colspan="4">$\frac{1}{3}$</td><td colspan="4">$\frac{1}{3}$</td><td colspan="4">$\frac{1}{3}$</td><td colspan="4">$\frac{1}{3}$</td></tr>
<tr><td colspan="3">$\frac{1}{4}$</td><td colspan="3">$\frac{1}{4}$</td><td colspan="3">$\frac{1}{4}$</td><td colspan="3">$\frac{1}{4}$</td><td colspan="3">$\frac{1}{4}$</td><td colspan="3">$\frac{1}{4}$</td><td colspan="3">$\frac{1}{4}$</td><td colspan="3">$\frac{1}{4}$</td></tr>
<tr><td colspan="2">$\frac{1}{6}$</td><td colspan="2">$\frac{1}{6}$</td><td colspan="2">$\frac{1}{6}$</td><td colspan="2">$\frac{1}{6}$</td><td colspan="2">$\frac{1}{6}$</td><td colspan="2">$\frac{1}{6}$</td><td colspan="2">$\frac{1}{6}$</td><td colspan="2">$\frac{1}{6}$</td><td colspan="2">$\frac{1}{6}$</td><td colspan="2">$\frac{1}{6}$</td><td colspan="2">$\frac{1}{6}$</td><td colspan="2">$\frac{1}{6}$</td></tr>
<tr><td>$\frac{1}{12}$</td><td>$\frac{1}{12}$</td><td>$\frac{1}{12}$</td><td>$\frac{1}{12}$</td><td>$\frac{1}{12}$</td><td>$\frac{1}{12}$</td><td>$\frac{1}{12}$</td><td>$\frac{1}{12}$</td><td>$\frac{1}{12}$</td><td>$\frac{1}{12}$</td><td>$\frac{1}{12}$</td><td>$\frac{1}{12}$</td><td>$\frac{1}{12}$</td><td>$\frac{1}{12}$</td><td>$\frac{1}{12}$</td><td>$\frac{1}{12}$</td><td>$\frac{1}{12}$</td><td>$\frac{1}{12}$</td><td>$\frac{1}{12}$</td><td>$\frac{1}{12}$</td><td>$\frac{1}{12}$</td><td>$\frac{1}{12}$</td><td>$\frac{1}{12}$</td><td>$\frac{1}{12}$</td></tr>
</table>

2. Write **=**, **<**, or **>** to make each sentence true. Use the fraction chart to help you.

a. $\frac{3}{12}$  $\frac{1}{3}$

b. 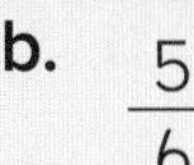 $\frac{5}{6}$  $\frac{1}{3}$

c. 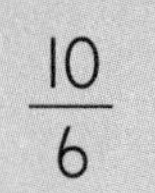 $\frac{10}{6}$ ◯ $\frac{10}{12}$

d. $\frac{4}{3}$  $\frac{8}{6}$

e. $\frac{6}{12}$  $\frac{12}{6}$

f. $\frac{3}{2}$ ◯ 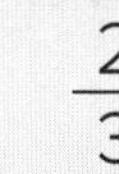 $\frac{2}{3}$

3. a. Write three fractions that are greater than $\frac{3}{4}$ but less than $\frac{14}{12}$. Use a variety of denominators.

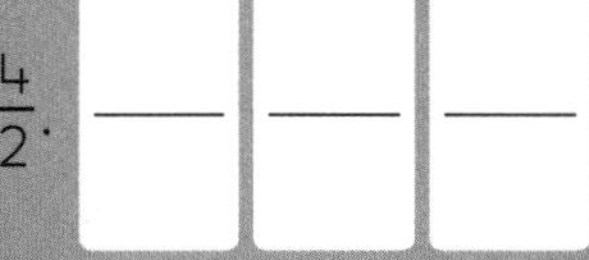

b. Write three fractions that are greater than 1 but less than $\frac{7}{4}$. Use a variety of denominators.

Step Ahead Choose fractions from below to complete the equations on the right. Use each fraction only once. Use the fraction chart above to help you.

 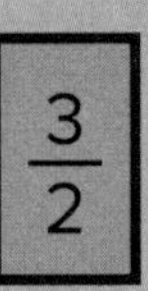 

$\frac{3}{4}$ $\frac{8}{5}$ $\frac{3}{2}$ $\frac{9}{10}$

$\frac{7}{5}$ $\frac{13}{10}$ $\frac{1}{2}$ $\frac{2}{8}$

a. ___ > ___

b. ___ > ___ 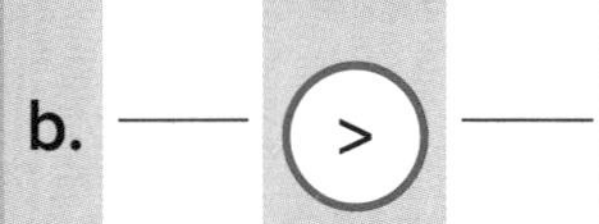

c. ___ > ___ 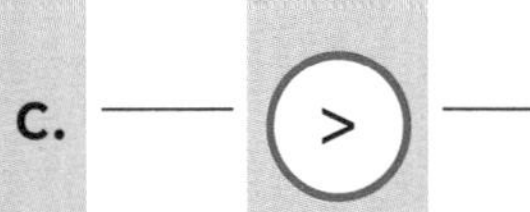

d. ___ > ___ 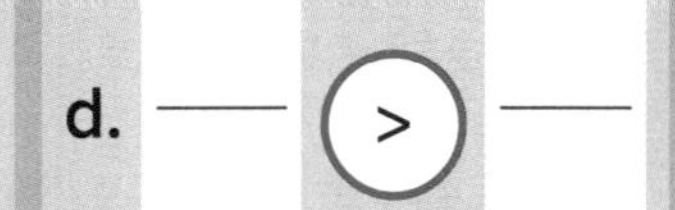

Step In Building a Picture of One Million

Imagine you start at 1,000 and skip count by 1,000.

What number will you say after 999,000?

Have you heard the word **millions** being used before?
How much is one million?

Look carefully at the place-value chart below.

What place names belong in the three spaces below **Millions**?

What abbreviations would you write?

Millions			Thousands			Ones		
			H	T	O	H	T	O

Write numbers in the chart to show one million.

How could you represent one million using different base-10 blocks?

How many ones blocks would you need? How many tens blocks?
How many hundreds blocks? What pattern would you see?

Step Up

1. Imagine you had base-10 blocks of each size. Write the missing numbers. Then write the matching equations.

A **millions** block could be traded for

_____ hundred thousands _____ × _____ = _____

_____ ten thousands _____ × _____ = _____

_____ thousands _____ × _____ = _____

_____ hundreds _____ × _____ = _____

_____ tens _____ × _____ = _____

_____ ones _____ × _____ = _____

2. Color ⬭ to show the answer that makes sense.

a. A large sports stadium seats about ...

⬭ 1,000,000 people ⬭ 100,000 people ⬭ 1,000 people

b. The population of Dallas is about ...

⬭ 1,000,000 people ⬭ 10,000 people ⬭ 1,000 people

c. The height of a skyscraper is about ...

⬭ 1,000,000 feet ⬭ 100,000 feet ⬭ 1,000 feet

3. Write **10**, **100**, or **1,000** to make each statement true.

a. 100,000 is ________ times more than 10,000.

b. 10,000 is ________ times more than 100.

c. 1,000,000 is ________ times more than 100,000.

d. 1,000,000 is ________ times more than 1,000.

e. 100,000 is ________ times more than 1,000.

Step Ahead Write the number of bills that you could trade for $1,000,000.

a. ________

b. ________

c. ________

d. ________

e. ________

f. ________

Step In Reading and Writing Seven-Digit Numbers

What place-value names are said when you say a seven-digit number?

How would you say the number on this expander?

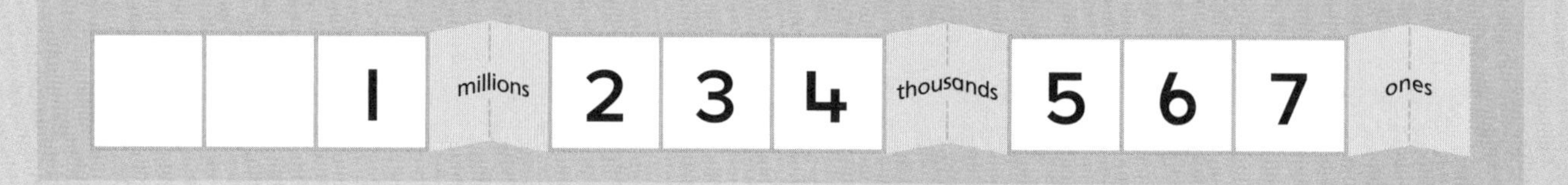

Read this number.

five million four hundred twenty thousand two hundred eighteen

Write it on this expander.

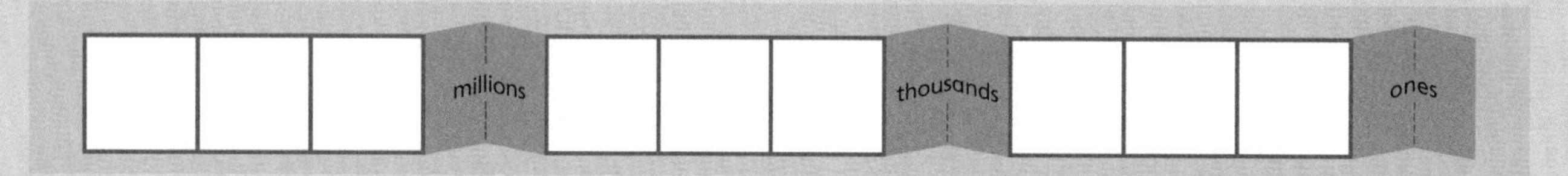

How did you know where to write each digit?

How did you know where to write the zeros?

Zeros are written when there is no value in a place.

Step Up

1. Read the number name. Then write the matching number on each expander.

a. one million seven hundred fifteen thousand twenty-nine

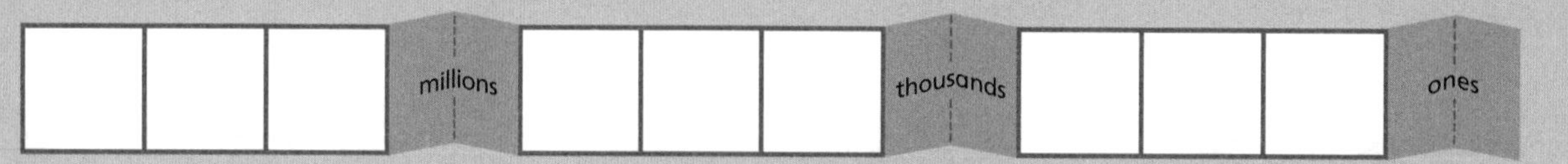

b. four million three hundred eighty thousand two hundred one

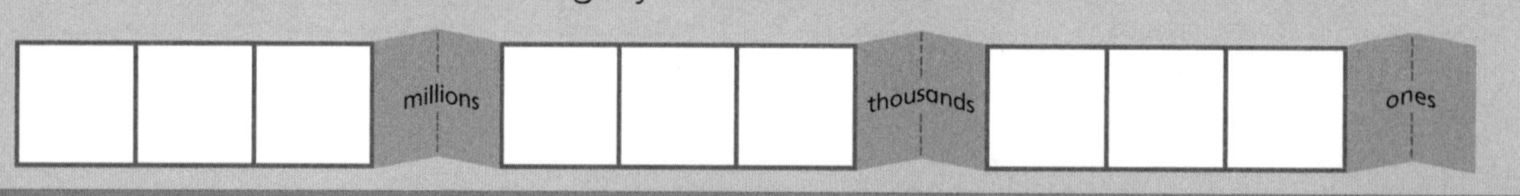

2. Write the matching number on each expander.

a. seven million fifty-six thousand nine hundred thirty

			millions				thousands				ones

b. five million one hundred eight thousand five

			millions				thousands				ones

c. six million six thousand four hundred eighty-eight

			millions				thousands				ones

3. Read the number. Then write the matching numeral.

a. two million eight hundred three thousand ______________

b. five million eight hundred thirty-three thousand four hundred two ______________

c. one million eighteen thousand three hundred forty-two ______________

d. nine million eighty-three thousand four hundred twenty ______________

Step Ahead

Read the number on the expander.
Then write in words the number that is **10 thousand greater**.

		5	millions	2	0	8	thousands	6	1	5	ones

____

____

____

Step In Writing Seven-Digit Numbers Using Expanded Notation

Read the number on the expander.

		7	millions	0	5	4	thousands	3	0	2	ones

How would you describe the value of each digit?

Write the missing numbers to show the number using expanded notation.

(____ × 1,000,000) + (____ × 10,000) + (____ × 1,000) + (____ × 100) + (____ × 1)

Betty wrote a different number with expanded notation as shown below.

6(1,000,000) + 7(100,000) + 1(1,000) + 4(100) + 7(1)

What number did she expand?

I figured out the value of each part:
6,000,000 + 700,000 + 1,000 + 400 + 7.

Write the number in standard form. ____________

Step Up

1. Write the missing numbers to show each seven-digit number using expanded notation.

a. 4,502,045

(____ × 1,000,000) + (____ × 100,000) + (____ × 1,000) + (____ × 10) + (____ × 1)

b. 9,008,710

____ (1,000,000) + ____ (1,000) + ____ (100) + ____ (10)

2. Write each number using expanded notation.

a. 7,301,095

b. 2,090,153

c. 1,808,350

d. 6,425,008

3. Write the number that has been expanded.

a. $(2 \times 1{,}000{,}000) + (4 \times 10{,}000) + (7 \times 1{,}000) + (2 \times 100) + (5 \times 10) + (8 \times 1)$

b. $9(1{,}000{,}000) + 4(100{,}000) + 9(100) + 1(10) + 2(1)$

Step Ahead Read this number name. Write the matching number using expanded notation.

eight million seventy thousand four hundred three

Step In Locating Seven-Digit Numbers on a Number Line

This poster was used to show the total funds raised to help build a new wing at a hospital.

What amount was raised?

What does each mark on the poster represent?

What amount is each month showing?
How do you know?

How can you figure out the increase in the amount raised from one arrow to the next on the poster?

Where do you think September might be located?
How did you decide?

How could you use the marks to help you locate each of these amounts?

$1,290,000	**$1,920,000**	**$920,000**
$810,000	**$180,000**	**$1,180,000**

$1,290,000 is just a little less than the third mark above $1,000,000.

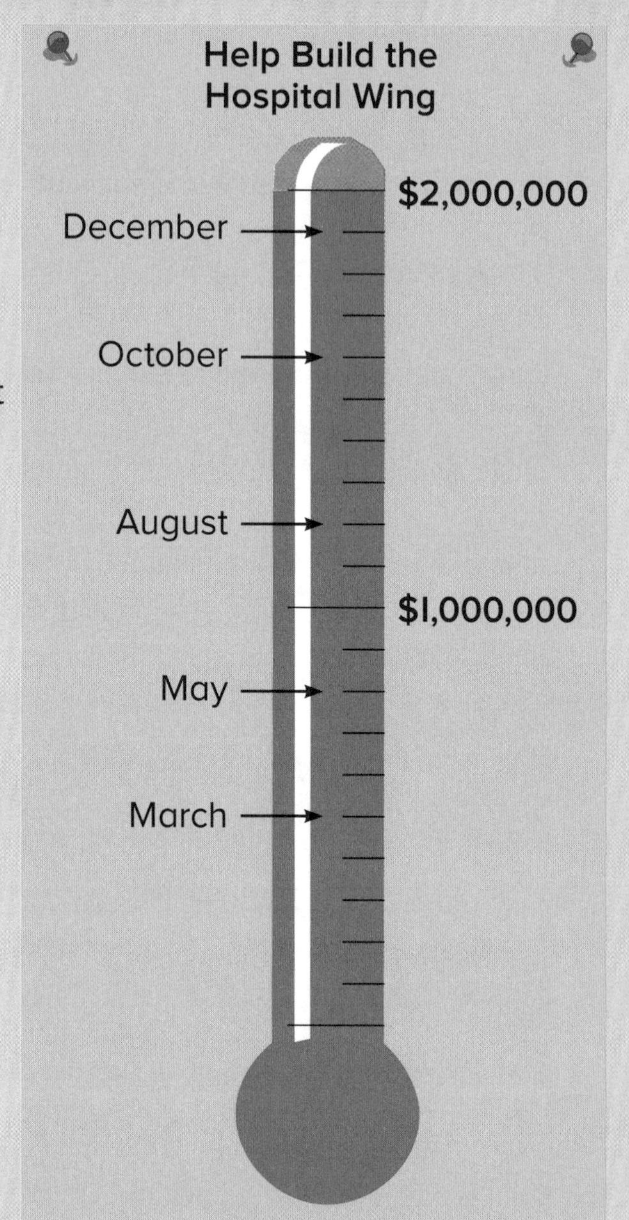

Step Up

For Questions 1 to 4, write the number shown by each arrow.

1.

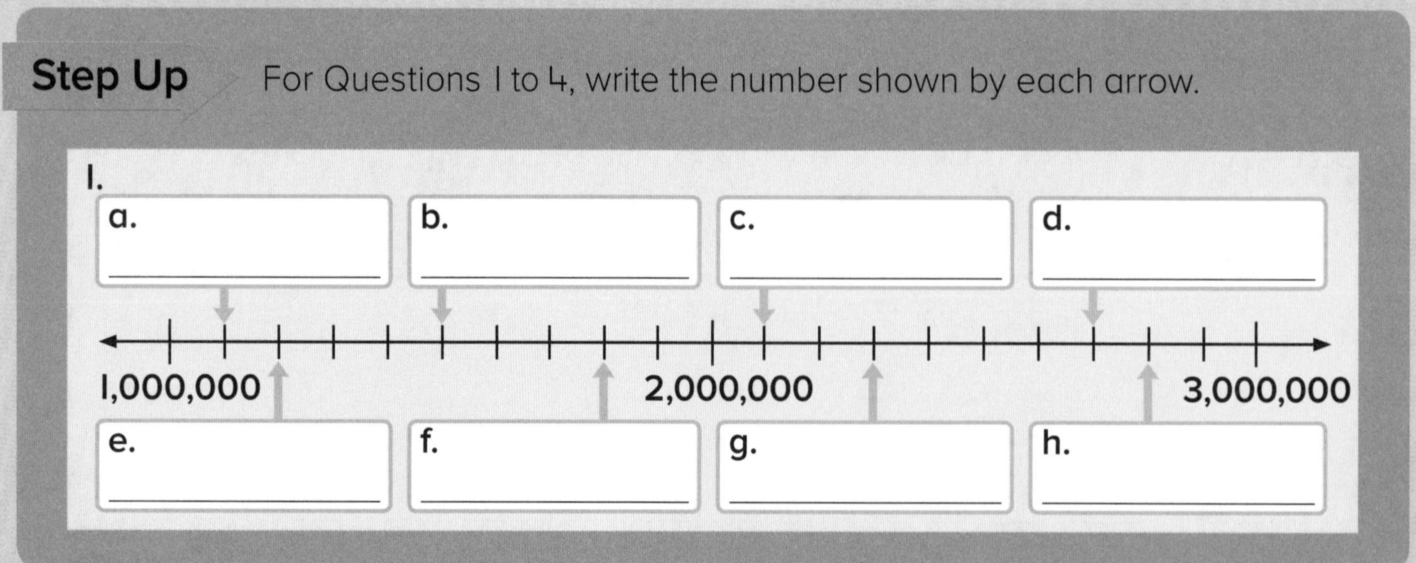

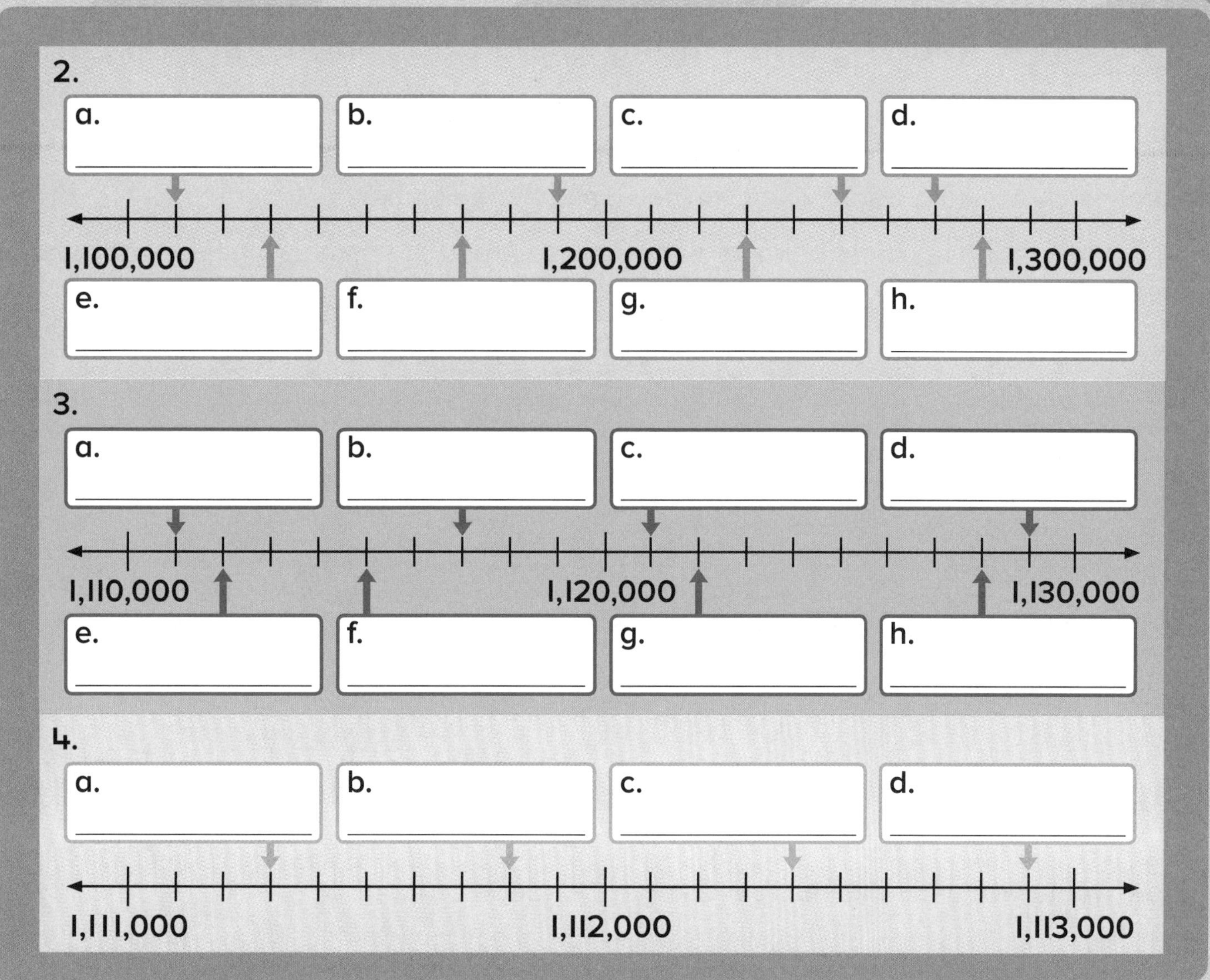

Step Ahead

a. Add **twenty thousand** to this number then write the new number in words.

8	millions	0	5	6	thousands	0	0	9

____

b. Add **four hundred thousand** to this number then write the new number on the expander.

2	millions	8	9	0	thousands	3	0	0

	millions				thousands			

Step In Reading and Writing Eight- and Nine-Digit Numbers

Where have you seen eight- or nine-digit numbers recorded?

What place values are said when you say a nine-digit number?

Write the missing numbers below to show how you read the number on this expander.

Read this number. two hundred forty-six million seven hundred five thousand ninety

Write it on this expander.

How would you write this number using expanded notation?

Step Up

1. Read the number name. Then write the matching number on the expander.

a. seventy-three million five hundred thirty thousand six hundred three

millions | thousands | ones

b. four hundred eighty million five thousand three hundred fifty-eight

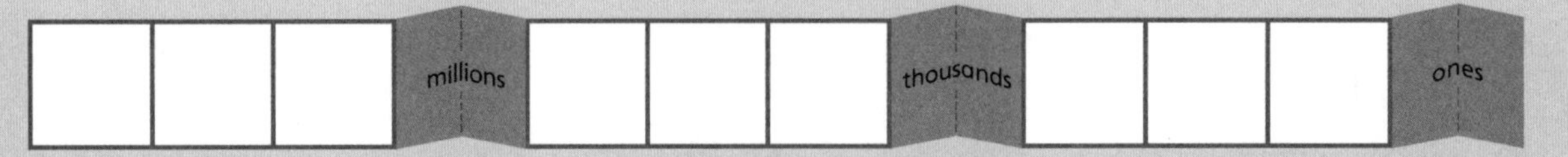

c. seven hundred three million three thousand forty

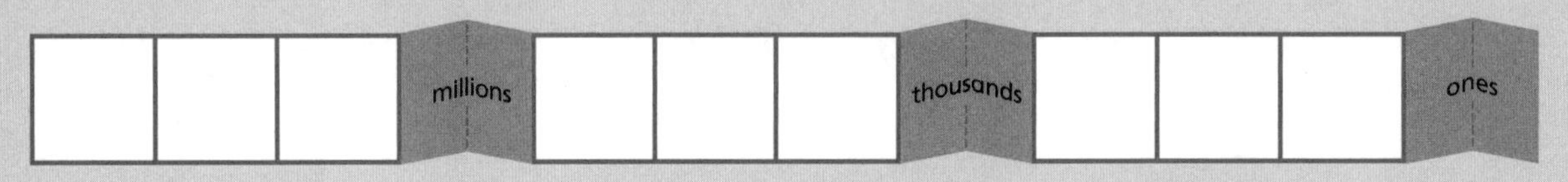

2. Write the matching number in words.

a.

	3	5	millions	5	9	2	thousands	8	0	5	ones

b.

3	0	9	millions	0	4	7	thousands	5	0	0	ones

3. Write the matching number or number name.

a. 70,293,430

b. one hundred eight million four thousand two hundred seventy-five

c. 418,720,912

Step Ahead Read this number name. Then write the number that is **10 million less.**

fourteen million three thousand twenty-three

Step In — Using Place Value to Compare and Order Eight- and Nine-Digit Numbers

Look at these digit cards. Imagine you use each digit once to form a number.

Is it possible to form this number? **410,275,316**
How do you know?

I crossed out the digits as I read the number.

What number(s) could you form to match these descriptions?

- The greatest number that ends in zero
- The least number that ends in zero
- Numbers between 300,000,000 and 400,000,000
- Numbers between 250,000,000 and 300,000,000
- The number that is as close to 450,000,000 as possible

Step Up

1. Look at these digit cards.

0	8	1	4	9	5	6	3	2

Use each digit once to make these.

a. the **greatest** and **least** numbers

greatest	least

b. the greatest and least **even** and **odd** numbers.

greatest even	least even

greatest odd	least odd

c. any three numbers that are between 350,000,000 and 351,000,000

2. Choose nine digit cards. Write the numbers that you chose on these cards.

Use each digit once to make these.

	greatest	least
a. the **greatest** and **least** numbers		

b. the greatest **odd** number

c. the greatest **even** number

d. a number that is as close to 500,000,000 as possible

e. a number that is as close to 250,000,000 as possible

3. Write < or > to make each sentence true.

a. 532,460,008 ◯ 802,793,428

b. 617,095,350 ◯ 609,818,377

c. 98,703,586 ◯ 103,092,210

d. 215,964,090 ◯ 210,899,715

Step Ahead

These are the top seven scores from a popular online game.

SCORES	
Nina	145,685,125
Rodrigo	139,264,305
Yuma	127,816,919
Ruth	145,099,012
Jose	136,810,055
Fiona	145,609,301
Lewis	99,475,218

a. Write the top three scores in order from **greatest** to **least**.

1st

2nd

3rd

b. Write the scores for the players that came 7th, 6th, and 5th.

7th

6th

5th

c. Whose score was closest to 130,000,000?

Step In Rounding Eight- and Nine-Digit Numbers

This table shows the number of motor vehicles that were produced by different countries around the world.

Country/Region	2010	2011	2012	2013
China	18,264,667	18,418,876	19,271,808	22,116,825
European Union	17,107,350	17,707,126	16,240,476	16,183,846
United States	7,761,443	8,653,560	10,328,884	11,045,902
Japan	9,625,940	8,398,654	9,942,711	9,630,070

How many motor vehicles were produced by the United States in each year shown?
Where did the production of motor vehicles decrease in the years shown?

Which country produced closest to 8,000,000 motor vehicles in 2011?
How can you figure it out? What digit did you look at to help you decide?

Draw an arrow on this number line to show the approximate location of the number of motor vehicles produced in Japan in 2013.

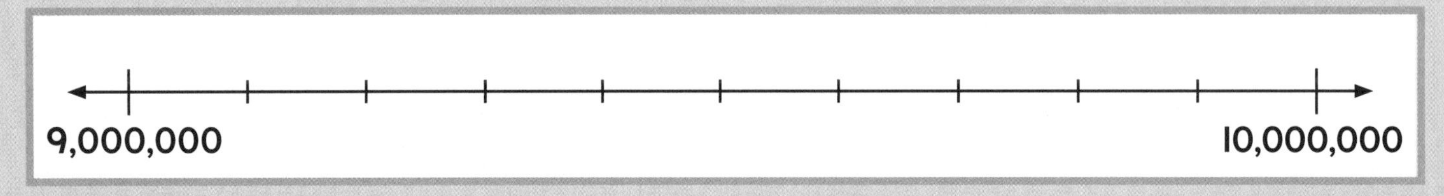

If you had to round the number of vehicles that were produced in Japan to the nearest **hundred thousand**, what number would you write? Why?

Step Up

1. Use the table above to complete these.

a. Round the motor vehicles produced to the nearest **million**.

China (2010) ____________ United States (2013) ____________

b. Round the motor vehicles produced to the nearest **hundred thousand**.

European Union (2012) ____________ Japan (2011) ____________

This table shows the number of registered vehicles in different countries.

Country	Registered Vehicles
Brazil	64,817,974
China	207,061,286
Indonesia	72,692,951
India	114,952,000
United States	258,957,503

2. Write the countries that have more than 150,000,000 registered vehicles.

____

____

____

3. Round the number of registered vehicles to the nearest **ten**.

China _______________ Indonesia _______________

4. Round the number of registered vehicles to the nearest **hundred**.

Indonesia _______________ United States _______________

5. Round the number of registered vehicles to the nearest **thousand.**

United States _______________ Brazil _______________

6. Round the number of registered vehicles to the nearest **ten thousand**.

Brazil _______________ India _______________

Step Ahead

A car company sold 6,475,394 motor vehicles in a year. Their marketing department decides to round this number **up** for a television commercial. What number should they round it to? Color the ⬭ to show your answer. Then explain your thinking.

⬭ 6,470,000 ⬭ 6,500,000 ⬭ 7,000,000

____

____

____

Step In — Reviewing the Relationship between Multiplication and Division

What do you know about this array?

How could you figure out the number of dots in each row?

What number sentences could you write to show your thinking?

What do you know about this array?

How could you figure out the number of rows?

What number sentences could you write to show your thinking?

35 dots
in total

Write the matching fact family.

___ × ___ = ___ ___ ÷ ___ = ___

___ × ___ = ___ ___ ÷ ___ = ___

How did you figure out the facts?

Step Up

1. Write the multiplication fact you would use to figure out the number of rows or the number of dots in each row. Then complete the related division fact.

a.

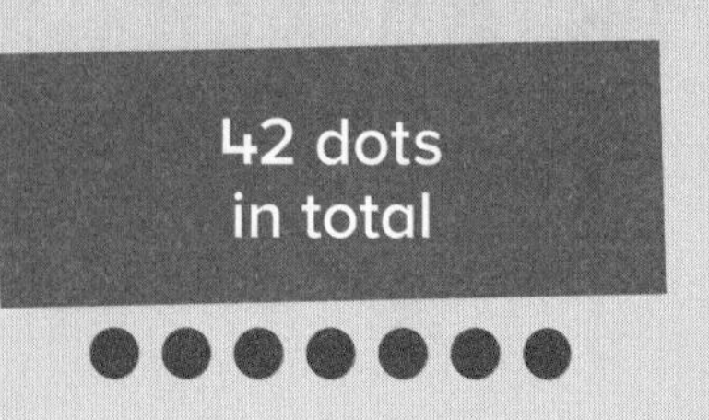

___ × 7 = 42 42 ÷ 7 = ___

b.

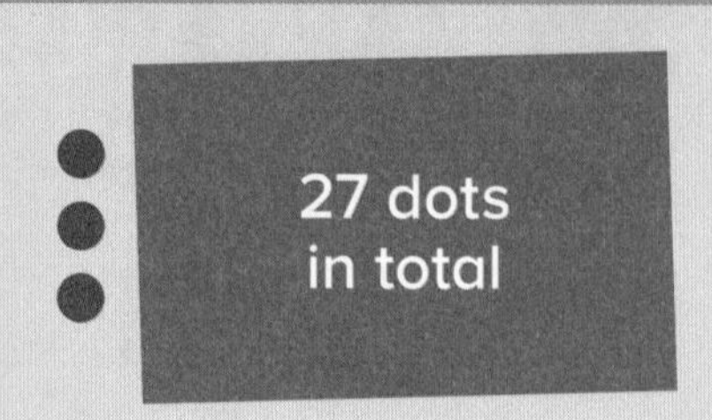

3 × ___ = 27 27 ÷ 3 = ___

2. Write the multiplication fact you would use to figure out the division fact. Then complete the division fact.

a. 18 ÷ 6 = ____

____ × ____ = ____

b. 72 ÷ 9 = ____

____ × ____ = ____

c. 54 ÷ 9 = ____

____ × ____ = ____

d. 45 ÷ 5 = ____

____ × ____ = ____

e. 30 ÷ 6 = ____

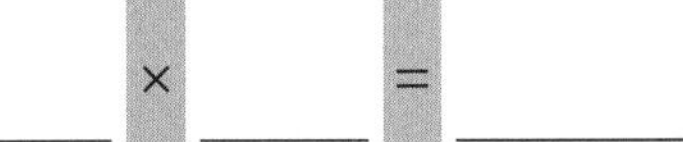

____ × ____ = ____

f. 63 ÷ 7 = ____

____ × ____ = ____

3. Read the division problem. Write a multiplication fact you would use to help you figure out the answer. Then write the answer.

a. Four families evenly shared the cost of a pizza meal. The meal cost $32. How much did each family pay?

____ × ____ = ____ $____ each

b. Muffins are baked in trays of 24. There are 6 muffins in each row. How many rows are there?

____ × ____ = ____

____ rows

c. Burgers cost $3 each. How many can you buy for $21?

____ × ____ = ____ ____ burgers

d. Each car on a roller coaster carries 6 people. How many cars are needed to carry 48 people?

____ × ____ = ____ ____ cars

Step Ahead

Frida has been asked to arrange 48 chairs into equal rows. Write multiplication or division facts to show the possible arrangements. You can draw a picture to help your thinking.

Step In Finding Whole-Number Quotients and Remainders

Look at these jars of marbles.

Imagine you want to share the jar of 34 marbles equally among 4 friends.

How many marbles will be in each share?

How many marbles will be left over?

What thinking did you use to figure out the number of marbles in each share?

> The amount left over in a division problem is also called the **remainder** (R).

I shared 34 cubes into 4 equal groups. There are 2 left over.

I thought of a fours fact that has a product near 34. 8 x 4 = 32. I then have 2 more.

Kyle shares the jar of 22 marbles into bags of 6. How many bags does he use?

How many marbles are left over? How do you know?

Step Up

1. Share each jar of marbles into bags of 5. Write the multiplication fact that helped you figure out the number of bags. Then write the number of marbles left over.

a.

___ × ___ = ___

___ bags with ___ marbles left over

b.

34

___ × ___ = ___

___ bags with ___ marbles left over

2. Share these marbles. Write the multiplication fact that helped you figure out the number in each share. Then write the number left over.

a. 62 marbles shared by 8 people

___ × ___ = ___

___ each remainder ___

b. 50 marbles shared by 7 people

___ × ___ = ___

___ each remainder ___

c. 37 marbles shared by 5 people

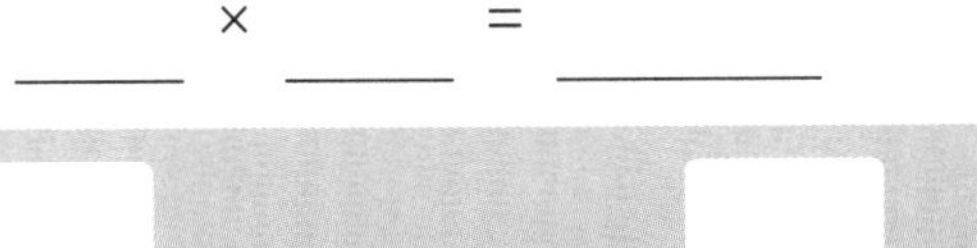

___ × ___ = ___

___ each remainder ___

d. 75 marbles shared by 9 people

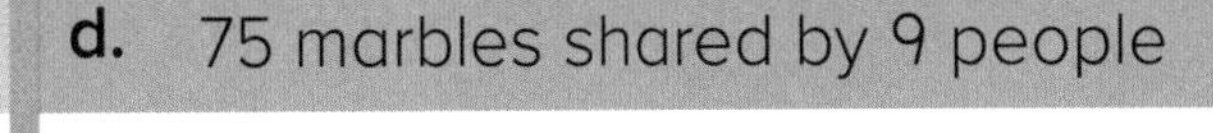

___ × ___ = ___

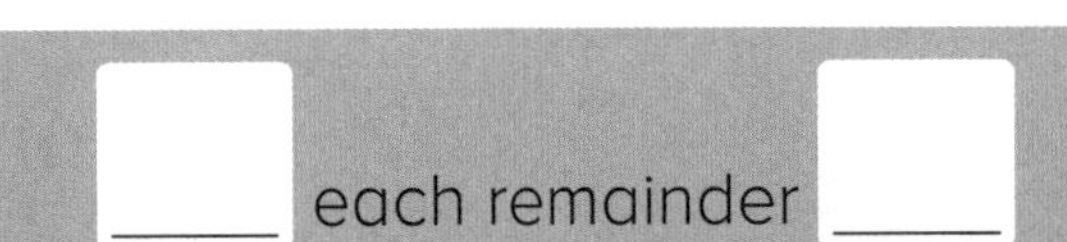

___ each remainder ___

3. Think of a multiplication fact to help you solve each division problem. Then write the answer.

a. 17 ÷ 5 = ___ R ___

b. 32 ÷ 7 = ___ R ___

c. 22 ÷ 3 = ___ R ___

d. 39 ÷ 4 = ___ R ___

e. 49 ÷ 6 = ___ R ___

f. 51 ÷ 9 = ___ R ___

Step Ahead

Brian shares his collection of marbles equally among five friends. He then keeps the four marbles left over. Figure out how many marbles might have been in Brian's collection.

___ marbles

Step In Using Partitioning and Multiplication to Divide

Four people equally share the cost of this gift.

How could you figure out the amount that they each have to pay?

How could you use multiplication to find the amount that each person pays?

Terri follows these steps.

Step 1	Step 2	Step 3
Look for a useful multiple of 10. Each person pays \$10 because 4 × 10 = 40. That leaves \$24 remaining.	**Share the amount remaining.** \$24 shared among 4 people is \$6 each.	**Add the shared amounts together.** \$10 + \$6 = \$16. Each person pays \$16.

Describe each step that Terri follows.

How would you use this strategy to figure out \$75 ÷ 5?

Step Up

1. Six people equally share the cost of this gift. Follow the steps to figure out how much each person pays.

Step 1	Step 2	Step 3
Look for a useful multiple of 10.	**Share the amount remaining.**	**Add the shared amounts together.**
6 × \$_____ = \$_____.	\$_____ shared among	\$_____ + \$_____ = \$_____
\$_____ is remaining.	_____ people is \$_____.	The total that each
Each person pays \$_____.	Each person pays \$_____.	person pays is \$_____.

2. Use the strategy from Question 1 to figure out each answer. Show your thinking.

a. $45 \div 3 =$ ____

b. $78 \div 6 =$ ____

c. $84 \div 7 =$ ____

d. $96 \div 3 =$ ____

e. $80 \div 5 =$ ____

f. $52 \div 4 =$ ____

Step Ahead

Cruz is using blocks to figure out $126 \div 3$. Color tens and ones blocks to show each group. Use a different color for each group.

Step In — Using the Partitioning Strategy to Divide with Remainders

There are 5 balloons in each bunch.

There are 72 balloons.

How many bunches can be made?

There are 50 balloons in 10 bunches. 5 x 10 = 50.
22 balloons are left over, so another 4 bunches can be made.

How many balloons are left over?

Complete this equation. 72 ÷ 5 = ____ R ____

Do you need to know the remainder to solve this problem?

Step Up

1. Write each answer. Show your thinking.

a. 58 ÷ 3 = ____ R ____

b. 70 ÷ 6 = ____ R ____

c. 94 ÷ 5 = ____ R ____

d. 99 ÷ 7 = ____ R ____

2. Solve each word problem. Show your thinking.

a. Kinu buys 90 yards of string. He cuts the string into lengths of 8 yards. How many lengths can he cut?

_____ lengths

b. There are 80 cans to pack. 6 cans fit in each box. How many boxes are needed to pack all the cans?

_____ boxes

3. Solve each word problem. Think about how you could share the remainder. Show your thinking. You may wish to draw pictures.

a. 50 cookies are shared equally onto 4 plates. How many cookies are on each plate?

cookies

b. Reece walks 74 miles in 4 days. He walks the same distance each day. How far does he walk each day?

miles

Step Ahead Write a word problem that leaves a remainder. Then exchange problems with another student and figure out the solution.

_____

_____

_____

Step In Solving Division Word Problems with Remainders

Read each of these problems.

A necklace costs $75. Fatima makes 6 equal monthly repayments to pay for it. How much does she pay each month?

6 eggs are packed into each carton. There are 75 eggs. How many egg cartons are filled?

75 students go on a camping trip. 6 students sleep in each tent. How many tents are needed?

What is the same about each problem? What is different?

The remainders mean different things in each problem. How do the remainders help you answer each problem?

Step Up

1. Solve each of these word problems. Show your thinking.

a. Sakeem is walking 100 miles for charity. He walks 7 miles each day. How many days will it take to complete the walk?

☐ days

b. 40 tennis balls are packed into cans. There are 3 balls in each can. How many tennis balls are left out?

☐ ball

2. Solve each word problem. Show your thinking.

a. 4 friends equally share the cost of a gift that costs $50. What amount should each friend pay?

$________

b. A roll of plastic wrap is 120 meters long. Roberta cuts the plastic wrap into lengths of 9 meters. How many of these lengths can she cut?

________ lengths

c. Two couples equally share the cost of a meal. The food costs $50. The drinks cost $37. What amount should each couple pay?

$________

d. A roller coaster has 6 cars. Each seats 8 people. 50 people are waiting. How many will have to wait for the next roller coaster?

________ people

Step Ahead Read the word problem. Then write the number of balls in each bag.

A soccer team has 62 training balls and 5 ball bags. The coach wants about the same number of balls in each bag. How many balls should be in each bag?

Step In Making Equivalent Fractions (Area Model)

**Four families are at a picnic.
They cut a cake to share it equally among the families.**

Lisa's family has the part with red icing.
What fraction of the cake do they have?

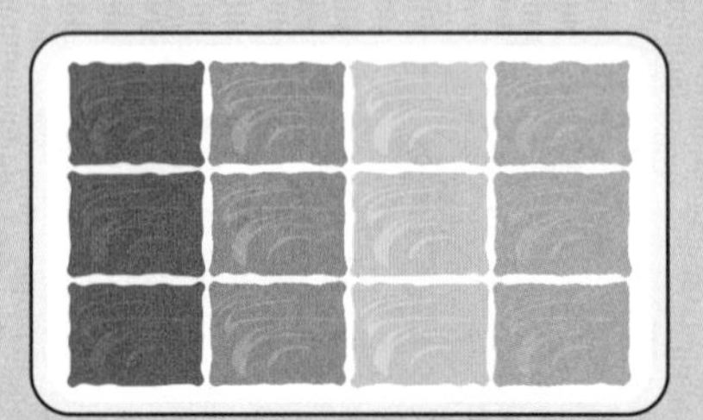

Each family has three people so their piece of cake is then cut into thirds to share it equally in each family.

What fraction of the cake does Lisa's family have now?

Think about the amount of cake that Lisa's family has each time the cake is cut.

Does the amount of cake change? Why?

They always have the same amount.
I can see that $\frac{1}{4}$ is the same as $\frac{3}{12}$.
The fractions are **equivalent**.

Step Up

1. Each large rectangle is one whole. Write how much is shaded in each rectangle. Then draw extra lines to figure out an equivalent fraction. The first one has been partly done for you.

a.

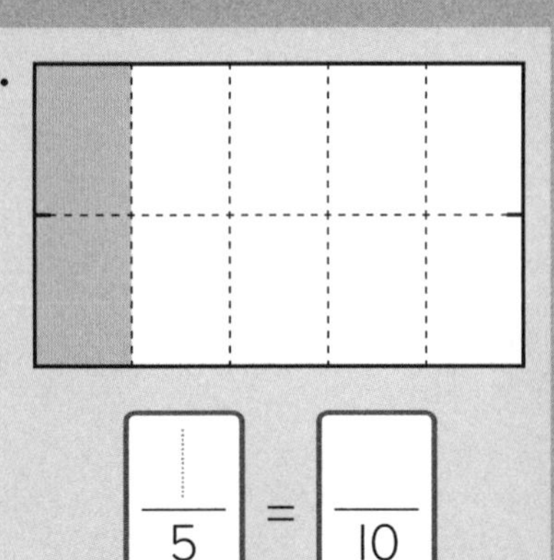

$\frac{}{5} = \frac{}{10}$

b.

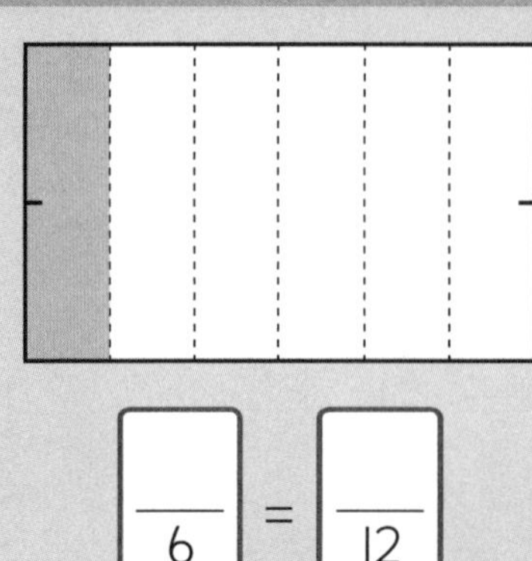

$\frac{}{6} = \frac{}{12}$

c.

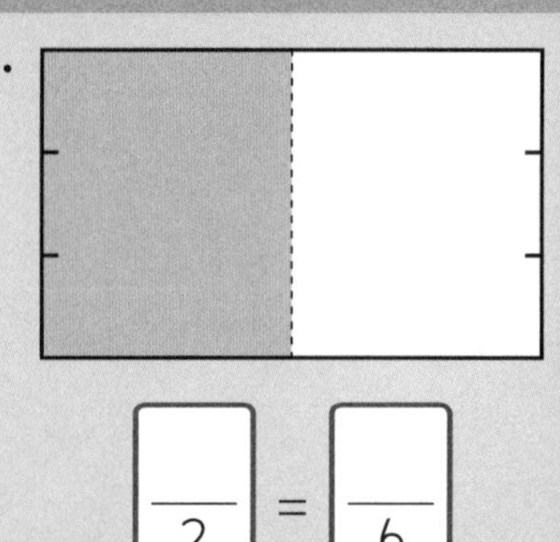

$\frac{}{2} = \frac{}{6}$

2. Each large rectangle is one whole. Write how much is shaded in each rectangle. Then draw extra lines to figure out an equivalent fraction.

a.

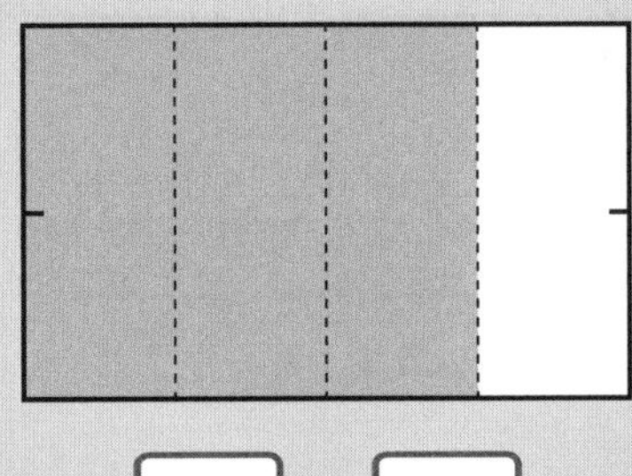

$\frac{\square}{4} = \frac{\square}{8}$

b.

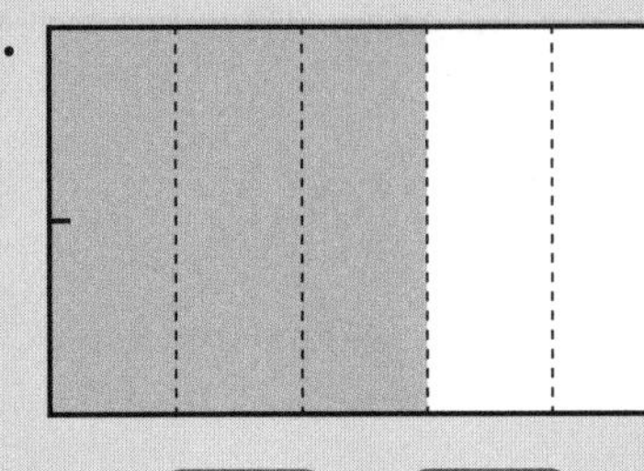

$\frac{\square}{5} = \frac{\square}{10}$

c.

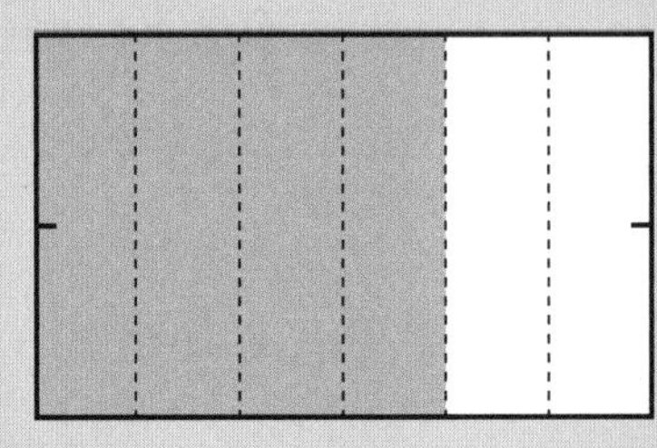

$\frac{\square}{6} = \frac{\square}{12}$

d.

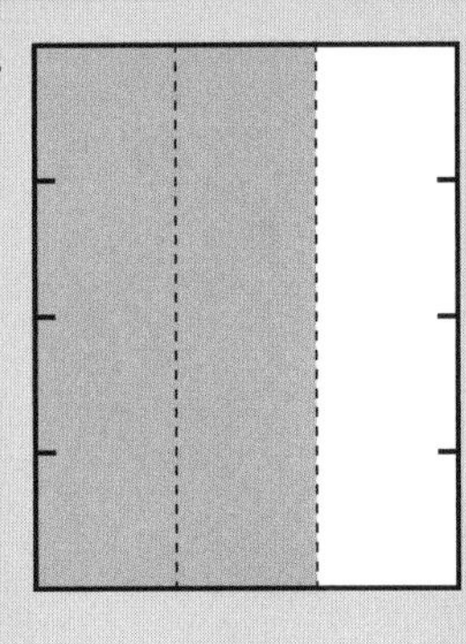

$\frac{\square}{3} = \frac{\square}{\square}$

e.

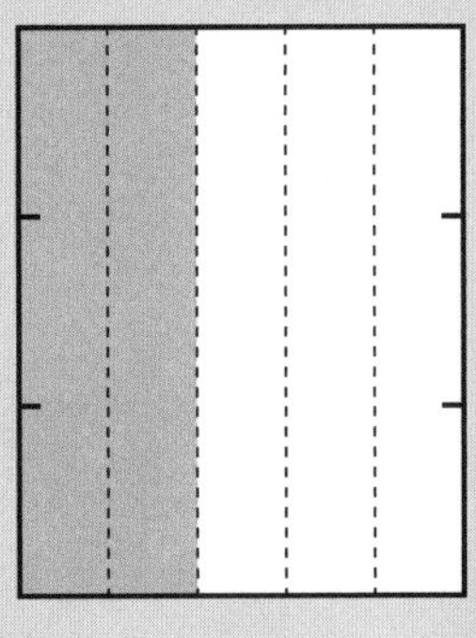

$\frac{\square}{5} = \frac{\square}{\square}$

f.

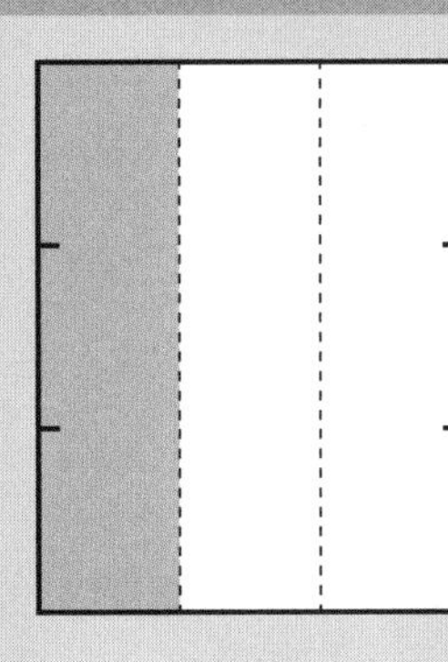

$\frac{\square}{3} = \frac{\square}{\square}$

g.

$\frac{\square}{1} = \frac{\square}{\square}$

Step Ahead Solve these problems. You can draw diagrams to help you.

a. A loaf of garlic bread was cut into tenths and Angelo ate two-fifths of the loaf. How much did he eat?

$\frac{\square}{10}$

b. A large pie was cut into 12 pieces. Two-sixths of the pie was eaten. How much is left over?

$\frac{\square}{12}$

Step In Calculating Equivalent Fractions

Julie wanted to figure out an equivalent fraction for $\frac{5}{6}$.

She drew this picture to help.

Julie realized that if she drew another line horizontally, she would find an equivalent fraction.

She noticed that splitting the shape that way would double the value of the denominator.

What would happen to the numerator? Why?

Complete this diagram to show Julie's thinking.

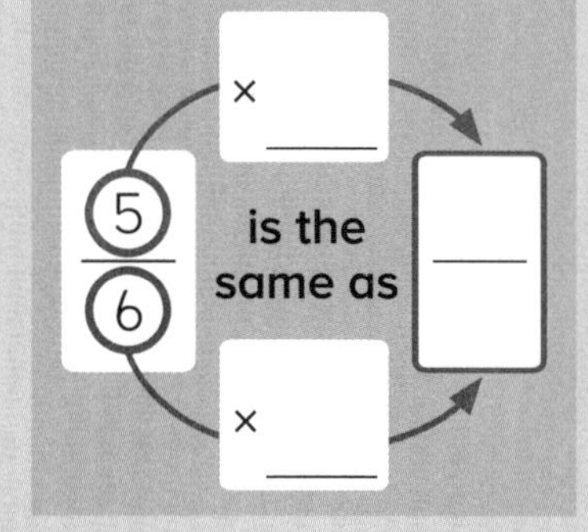

How did the total number of parts change?

How did the number of yellow parts change?

Did the total amount that was shaded change?

What do you notice about the denominators?

I see that 12 is a multiple of 6.

Step Up

1. In each shape, color a part to show the first fraction. Then draw more lines and complete the diagram to show an equivalent fraction.

a. $\frac{1}{4}$ is the same as $\frac{}{12}$ (× ___ , × ___)

b. $\frac{1}{3}$ is the same as $\frac{}{12}$ (× ___ , × ___)

c. $\frac{1}{2}$ is the same as $\frac{}{12}$ (× ___ , × ___)

d. $\frac{1}{2}$ is the same as $\frac{}{6}$ (× ___ , × ___)

2. Complete these to show equivalent fractions.

a.

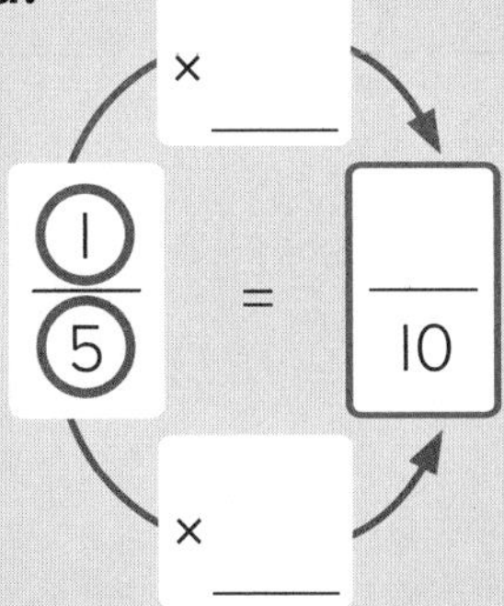

b.

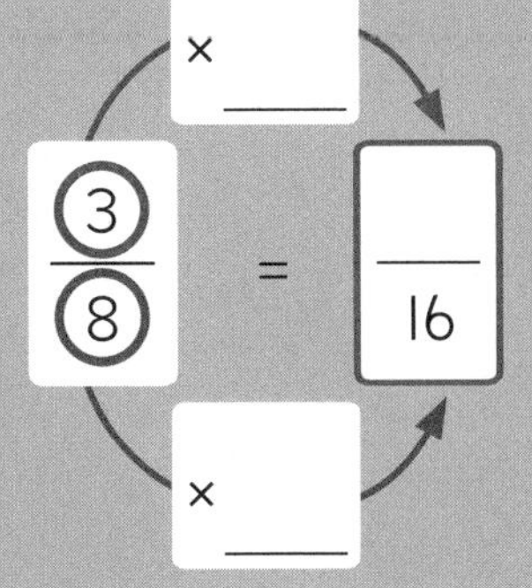

c.

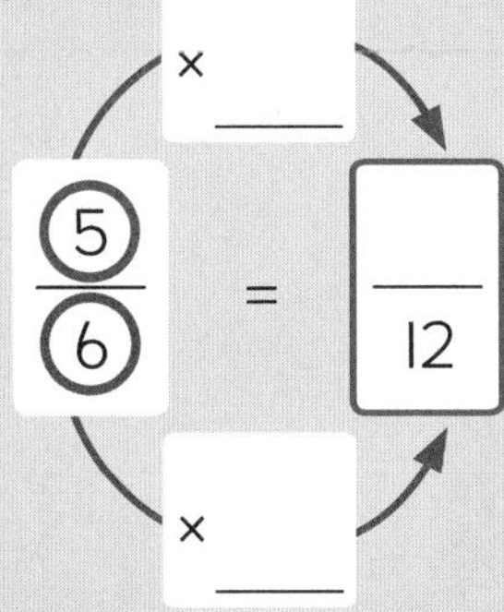

d.

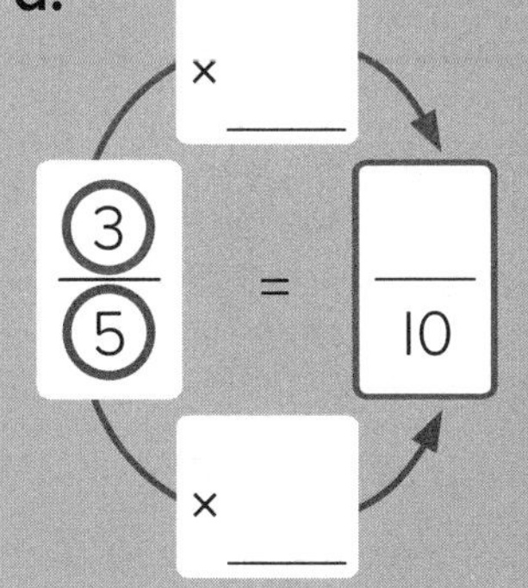

e.

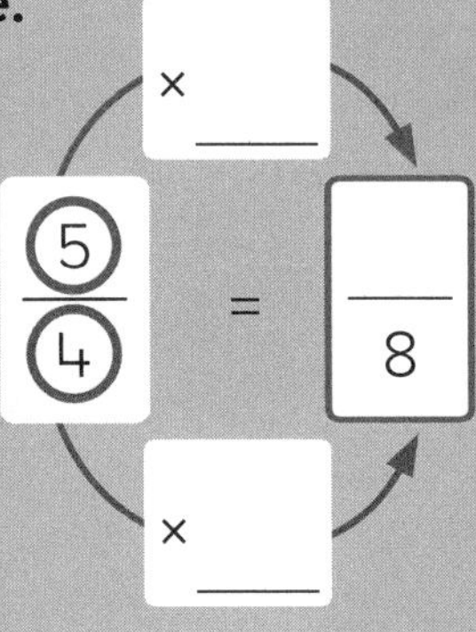

f.

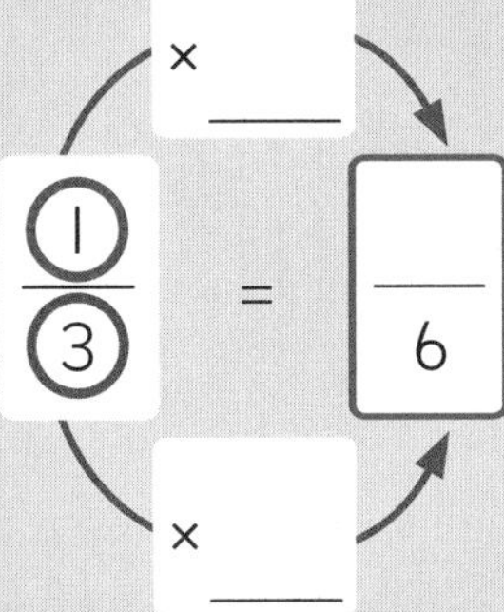

g.

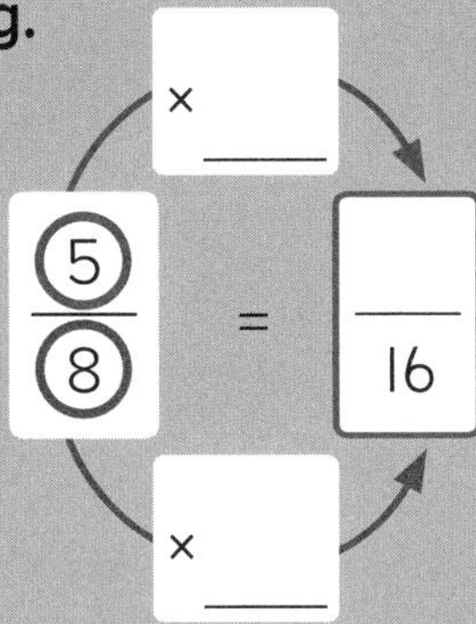

h.

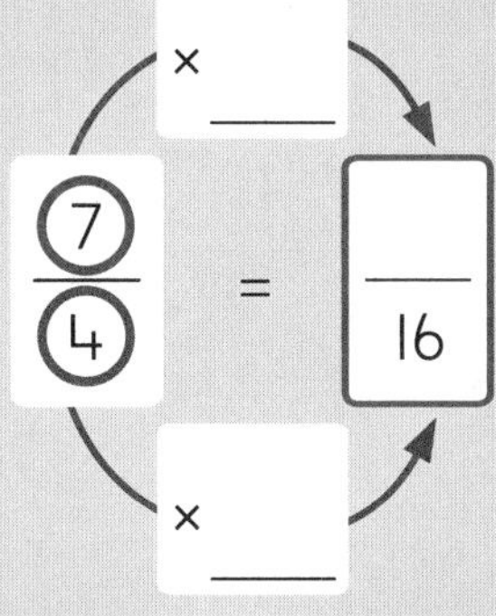

i.

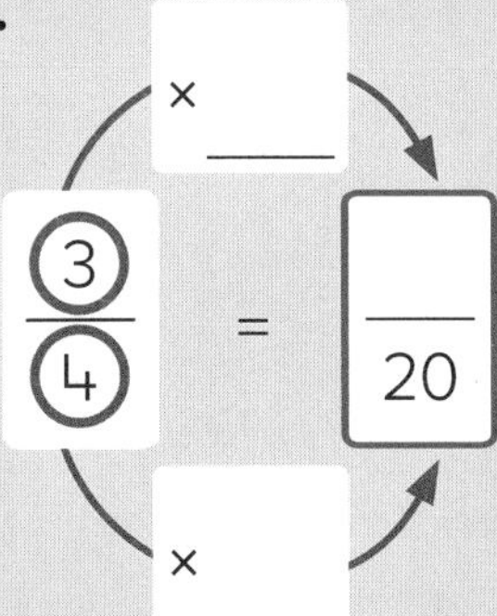

j.

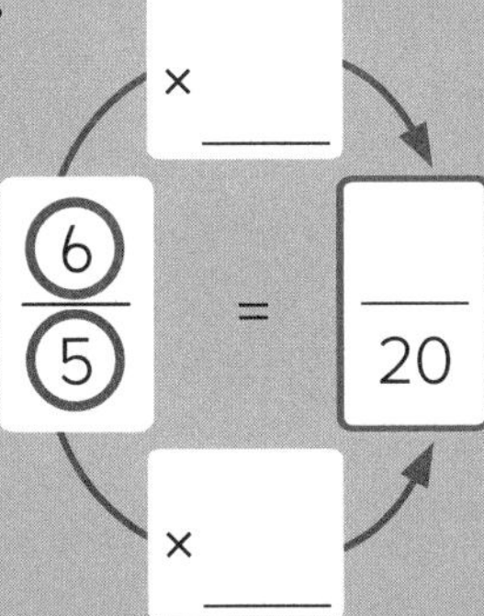

k.

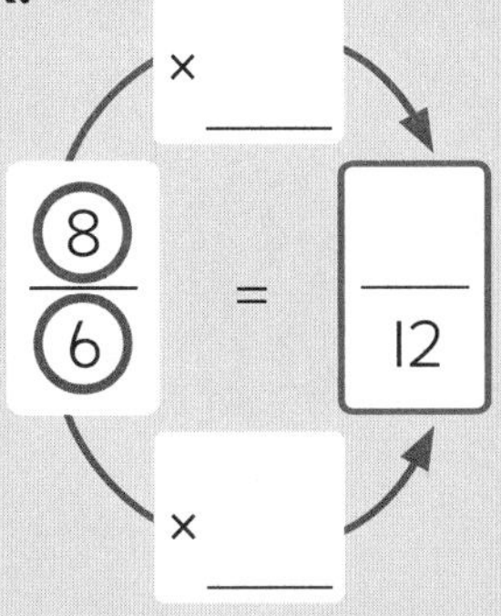

l.

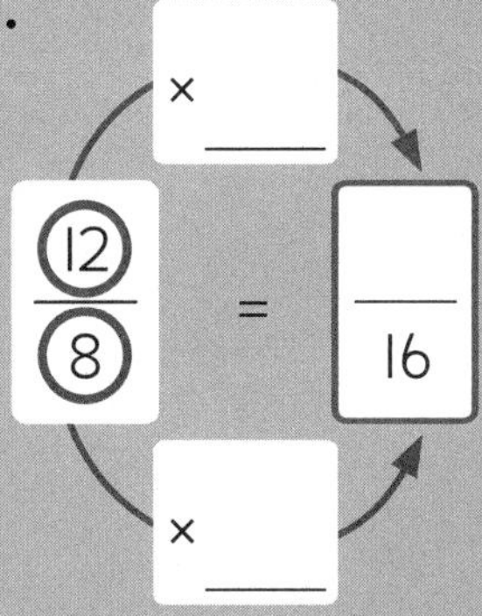

Step Ahead Complete these to show equivalent fractions.

a.

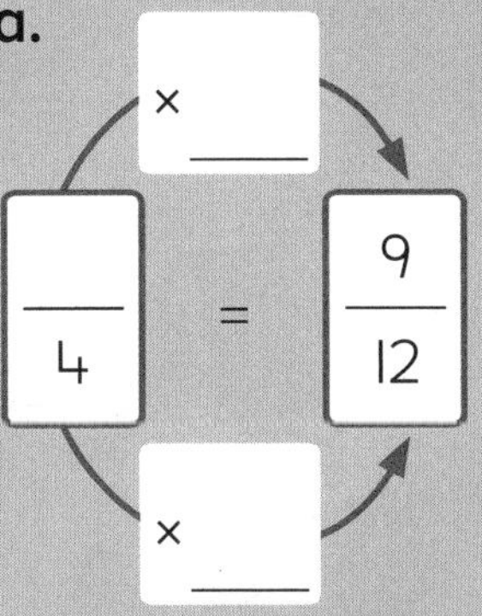

b.

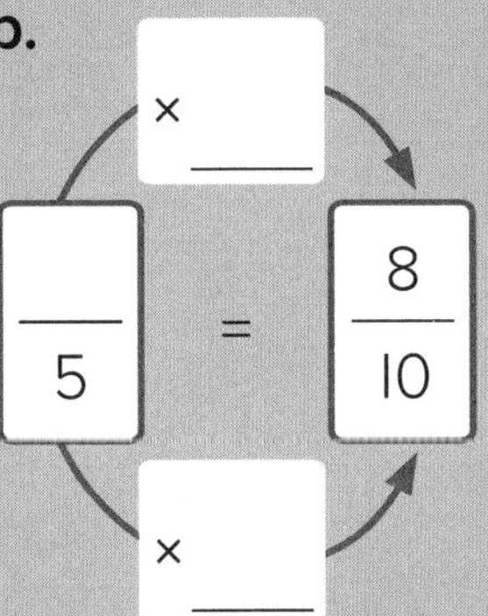

c.

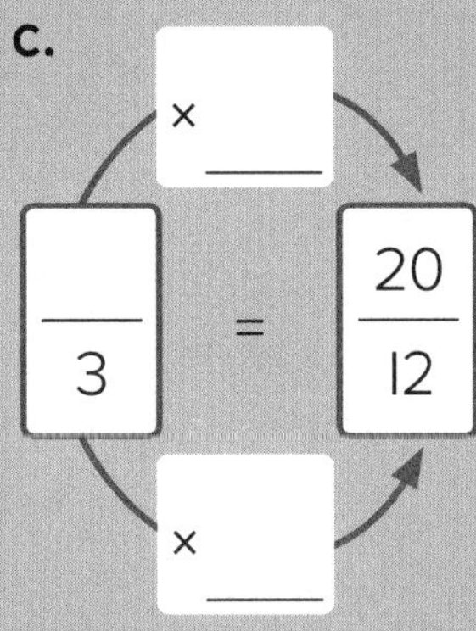

d.

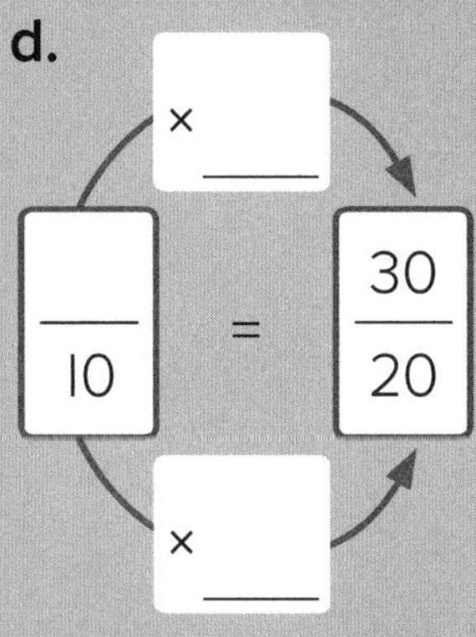

Step In — Comparing Common Fractions (Related Denominators)

Clyde and Carol each bought a blueberry pie on Saturday. On Sunday, they talked about how much pie their families had eaten.

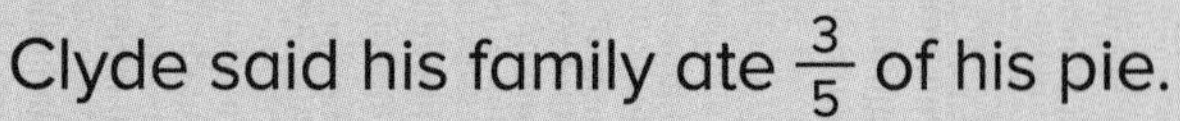

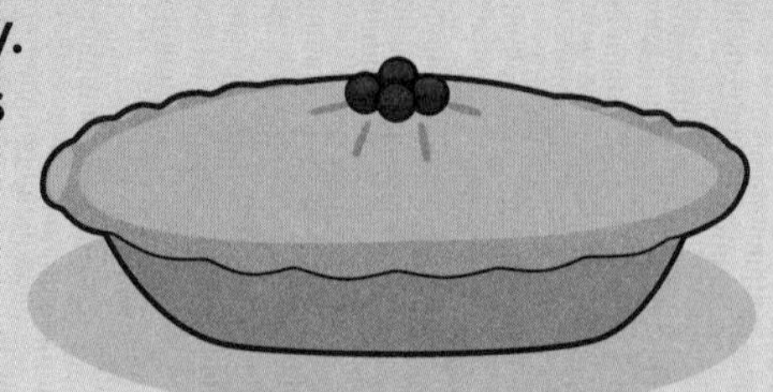

Clyde said his family ate $\frac{3}{5}$ of his pie.

Carol said that her family ate $\frac{8}{10}$ of her pie.

Whose family ate more pie? How could you figure it out?

I know that 10 is a multiple of 5 so I will change $\frac{3}{5}$ into tenths. If I double 5, I get 10. To make sure the fraction is equivalent, I need to double the numerator too.

Then it is easy to compare the fractions.

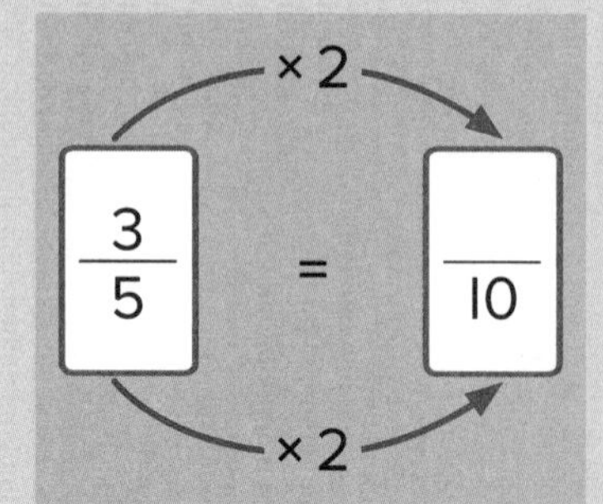

Tina is making muffins. The recipe uses $\frac{3}{4}$ of a stick of butter.

There is $\frac{4}{8}$ of a stick of butter in the refrigerator.

Will Tina have enough butter for the recipe? How could you figure it out?

I know $\frac{4}{8}$ is equal to $\frac{1}{2}$ because 4 is half of 8. I also know that $\frac{3}{4}$ is more than $\frac{1}{2}$ because 2 is half of 4.

8 is a multiple of 4 so I would change $\frac{3}{4}$ into eighths then compare the fractions.

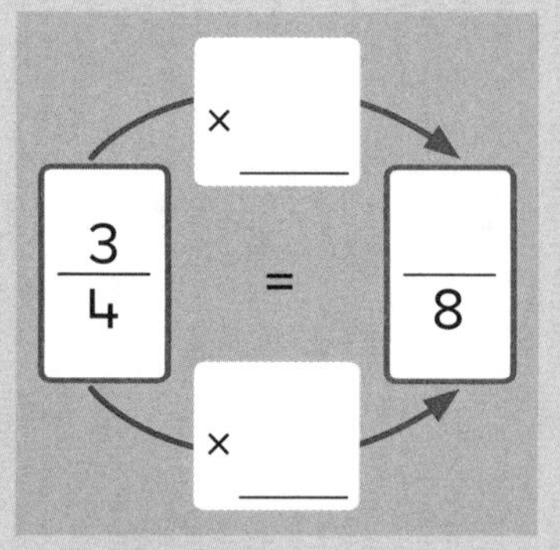

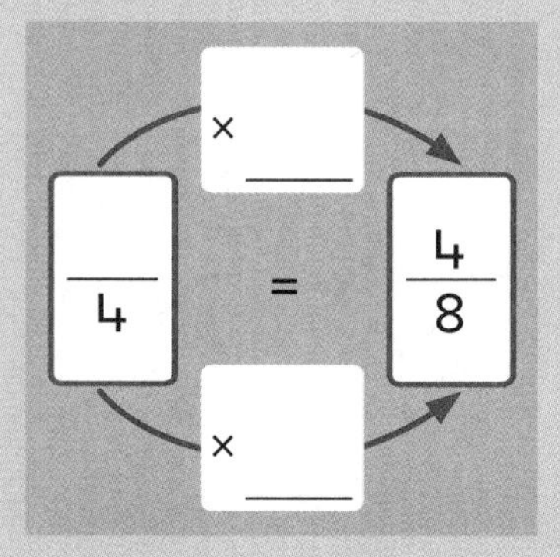

If I can change $\frac{4}{8}$ to 4ths, then I could easily compare $\frac{4}{8}$ and $\frac{3}{4}$. I know that 4 is a factor of 8, so I can change $\frac{4}{8}$ to 4ths. I will divide the numerator of $\frac{4}{8}$ by 2. Then I can compare the fractions.

Step Up

1. Change **one** fraction in each pair so that they have the same denominator. Then rewrite the fractions.

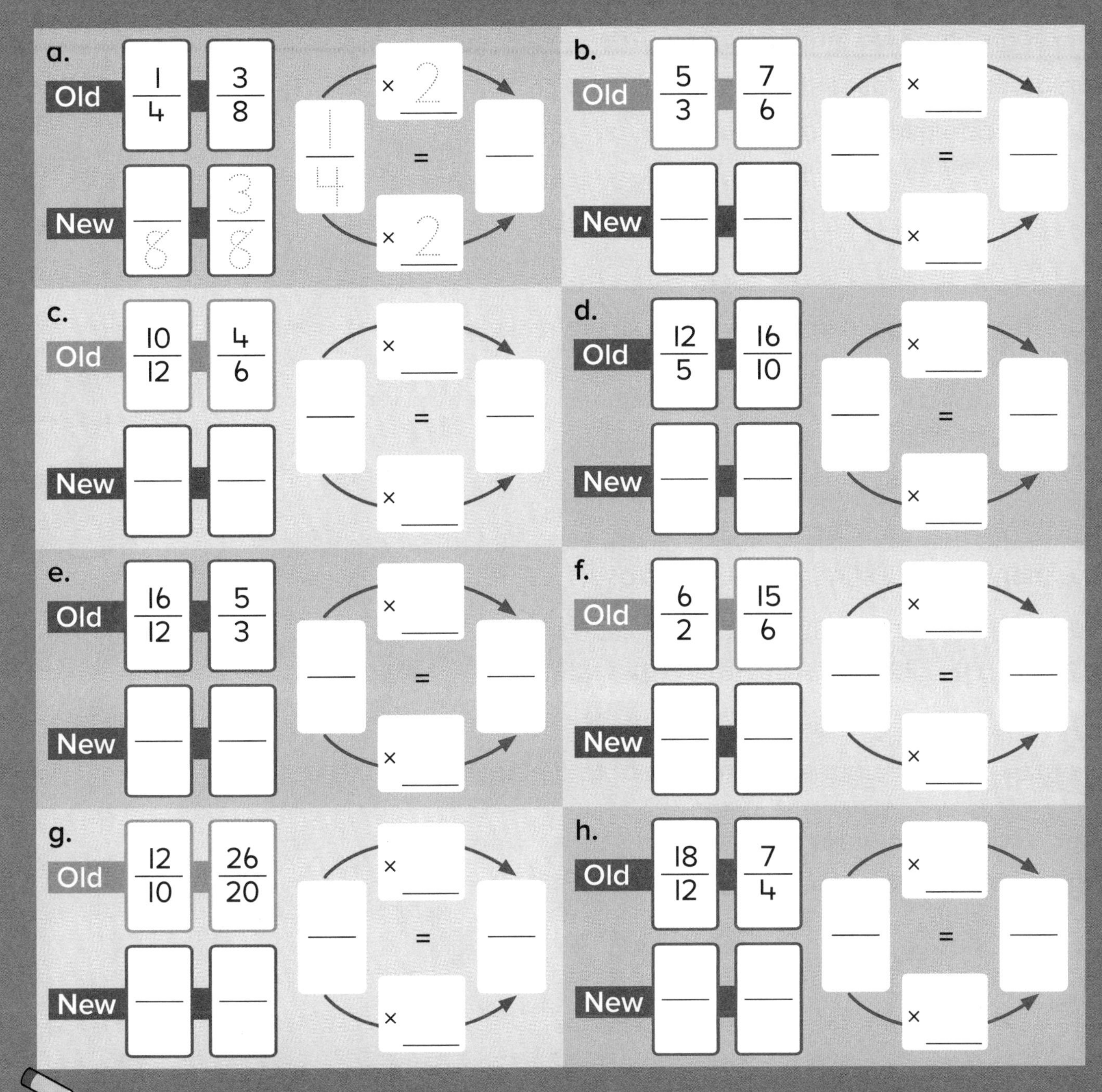

2. Loop the **greater** fraction in each pair of **new** fractions above.

Step Ahead

Will a bolt that is $\frac{7}{16}$ of an inch wide fit into a hole that is $\frac{3}{8}$ of an inch wide? Why?

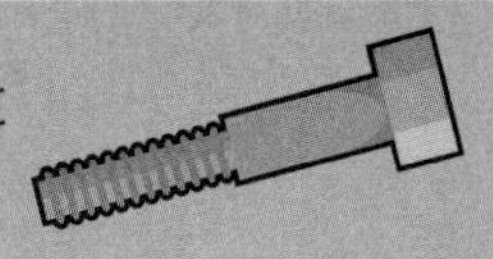

Step In Finding Common Denominators

Hiro compared two muffin recipes. One uses $\frac{2}{3}$ cup of flour. The other recipe uses $\frac{3}{4}$ cup of flour.

Which recipe uses more flour?
How can you figure it out?

What could you do to both denominators to make equivalent fractions?

How could you figure out what multiple they have in common?

Samantha figured it out by listing all the multiples of 3 that she knew. She then started listing the multiples of 4.

3	6	9	12	15	18	21	24	27	30

4	8	12

Loop the multiple that is common to both denominators.

Complete each diagram to show equivalent fractions for $\frac{2}{3}$ and $\frac{3}{4}$.

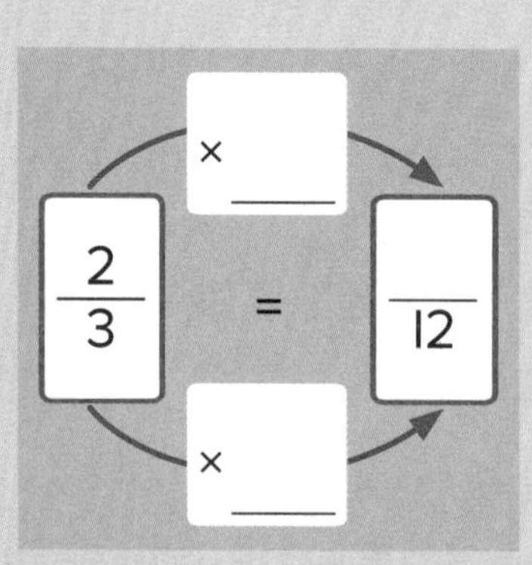

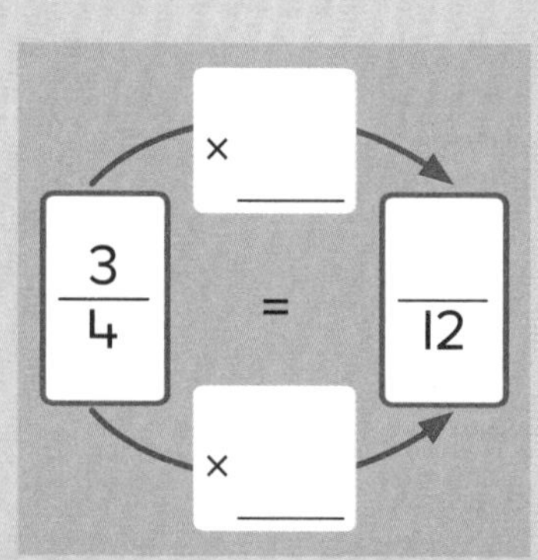

Which fraction is greater?

Step Up

1. Identify whether you have to change **one** denominator or **both** denominators to compare the fractions. Color the ⬭ beside the statement that is correct.

a. $\frac{2}{4}$ $\frac{5}{8}$

⬭ I need to change one.
⬭ I need to change both.

b. $\frac{2}{5}$ $\frac{3}{8}$

⬭ I need to change one.
⬭ I need to change both.

c. $\frac{2}{3}$ $\frac{4}{5}$

⬭ I need to change one.
⬭ I need to change both.

2. Loop the common multiples.

a.

Multiples of 3	3	6	9	12	15	18	21	24	27	30
Multiples of 5	5	10	15	20	25	30	35	40	45	50

b.

Multiples of 4	4	8	12	16	20	24	28	32	36	40
Multiples of 6	6	12	18	24	30	36	42	48	54	60

3. For each pair of fractions, complete the diagram to show equivalent fractions that have a common denominator. Then complete the sentence. Use the common multiples from Question 2 to help you.

a. $\frac{2}{3}$ and $\frac{3}{5}$

A common multiple is ______

so a common denominator is ______.

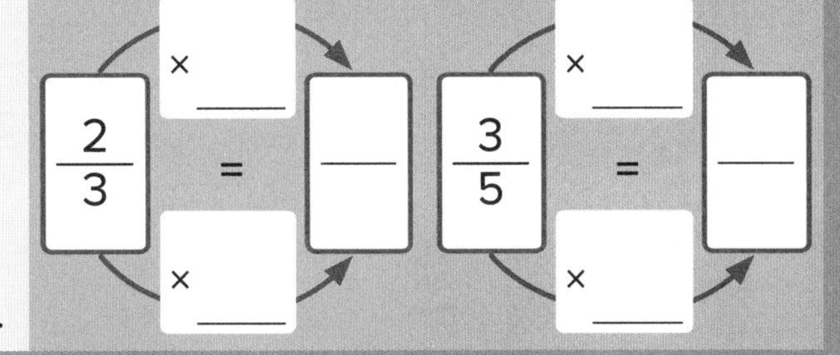

b. $\frac{5}{6}$ and $\frac{3}{4}$

A common multiple is ______

so a common denominator is ______.

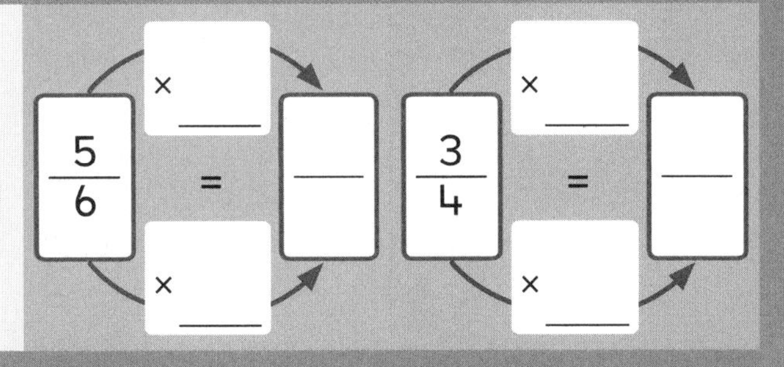

Step Ahead In some problems, a common denominator can be found by using division and looking for common factors.

a. Rewrite $\frac{12}{18}$ and $\frac{10}{12}$ as fractions with a common denominator of 6.

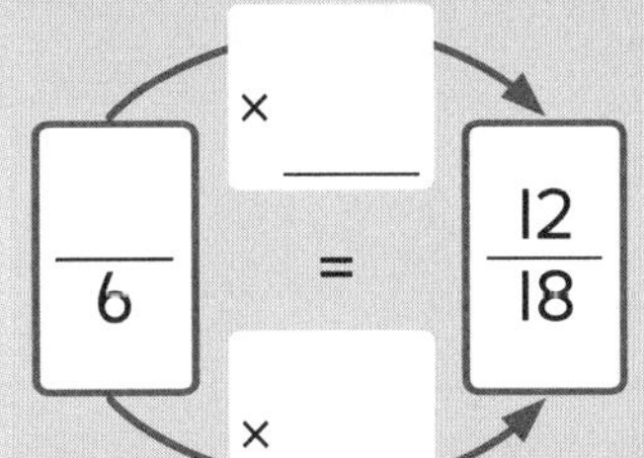

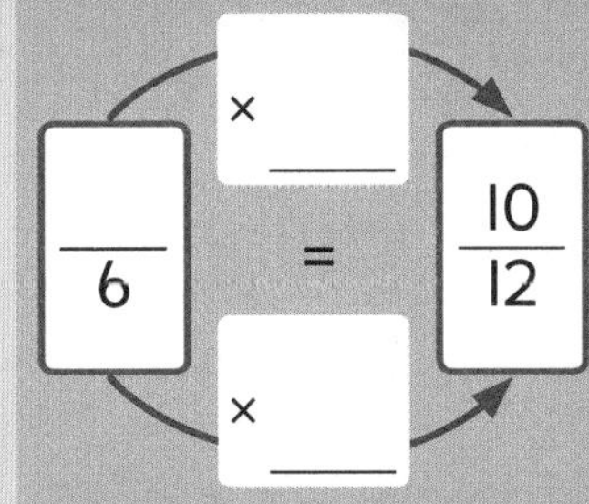

b. Which fraction is greater? ______

Step In — Finding Common Denominators to Compare Common Fractions

Look at these multiples of 5 and 8.

Multiples of 5:	5	10	15	20	25	30	35	40	45	50
Multiples of 8:	8	16	24	32	40	48	56	64	72	80

What is a common multiple of 5 and 8 that is listed above? ______

Now multiply 5 × 8. What do you notice?

Look at these multiples of 3 and 5.

Multiples of 3:	3	6	9	12	15	18	21	24	27	30
Multiples of 5:	5	10	15	20	25	30	35	40	45	50

Which are the common multiples? ______________

Now multiply 3 × 5. What do you notice?

How could you use this to help you write common denominators?

When I multiply the denominators together I get a multiple of each denominator. That's much faster than having to list all the multiples of each denominator.

What is a common multiple of 3 and 8? ______

Use what you know to rewrite $\frac{2}{3}$ and $\frac{6}{8}$ so that they have a common denominator.

$\frac{2}{3} = \frac{\square}{\square}$ (×8 numerator, ×8 denominator)

$\frac{6}{8} = \frac{\square}{\square}$ (×3 numerator, ×3 denominator)

Step Up

1. Write a common multiple of each pair of numbers.

2 and 8	______	10 and 4	______	5 and 2	______	5 and 6	______
6 and 10	______	8 and 3	______	6 and 8	______	5 and 12	______

2. For each pair of fractions, complete the diagram to show equivalent fractions that have a common denominator. Then complete the sentence.

a. $\frac{3}{4}$ and $\frac{5}{6}$

A common multiple is ______

so a common denominator is ______.

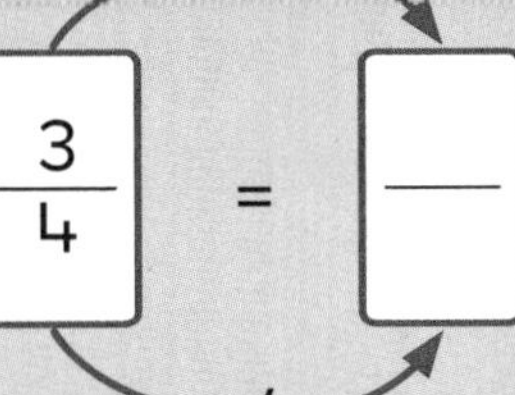
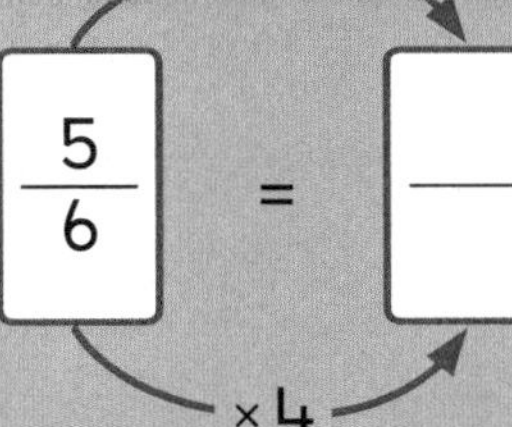
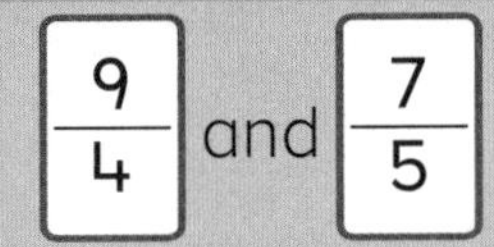

b. $\frac{9}{4}$ and $\frac{7}{5}$

A common multiple is ______

so a common denominator is ______.

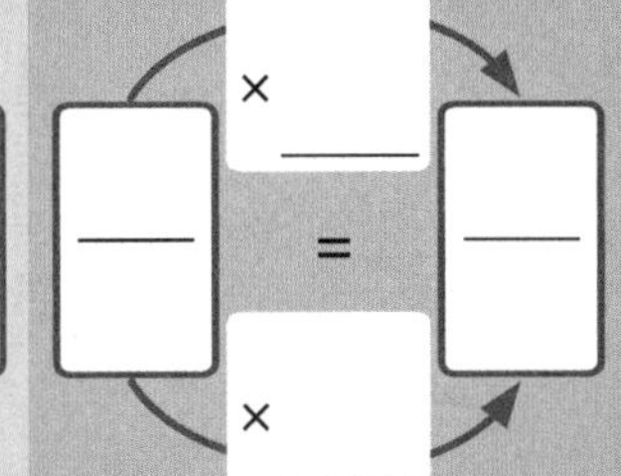
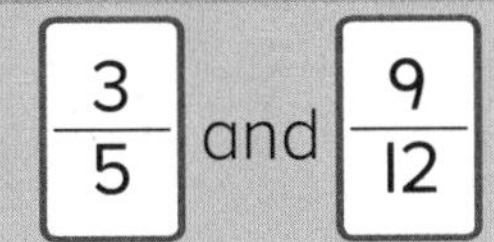

c. $\frac{3}{5}$ and $\frac{9}{12}$

A common multiple is ______

so a common denominator is ______.

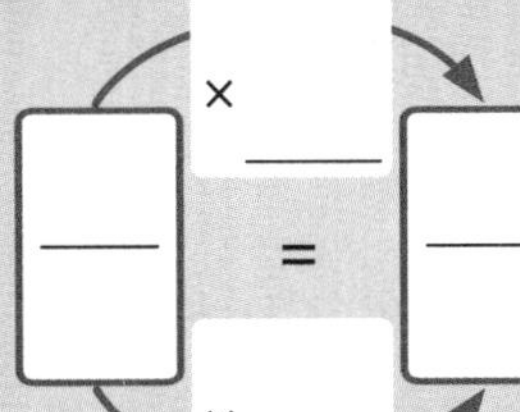
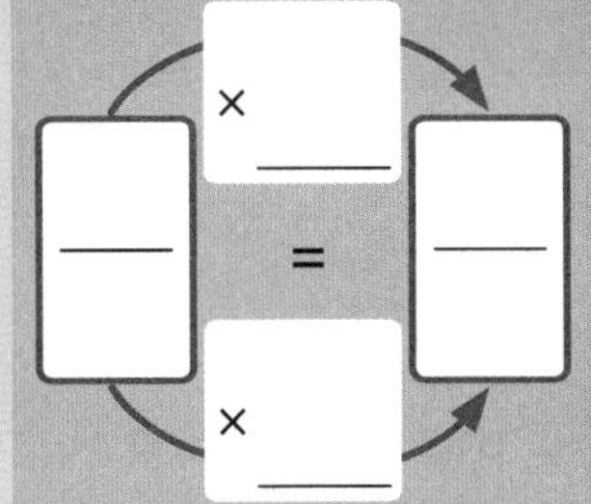

3. Write **<**, **>**, or **=** to make each sentence true. Show your thinking.

a. $\frac{7}{5}$ ◯ $\frac{3}{2}$

b. $\frac{8}{3}$ ◯ $\frac{5}{2}$

c. $\frac{5}{6}$ ◯ $\frac{8}{10}$

d. $\frac{6}{4}$ ◯ $\frac{9}{6}$

Step Ahead

Which fraction is the greatest? Show your thinking.

$\frac{7}{3}$ or $\frac{5}{2}$ or $\frac{12}{5}$

Step In Adding Common Fractions (Area Model)

There was $\frac{7}{8}$ of a pie left over.

In what different ways could two people split the leftover pie?

Complete this equation to match your thinking.

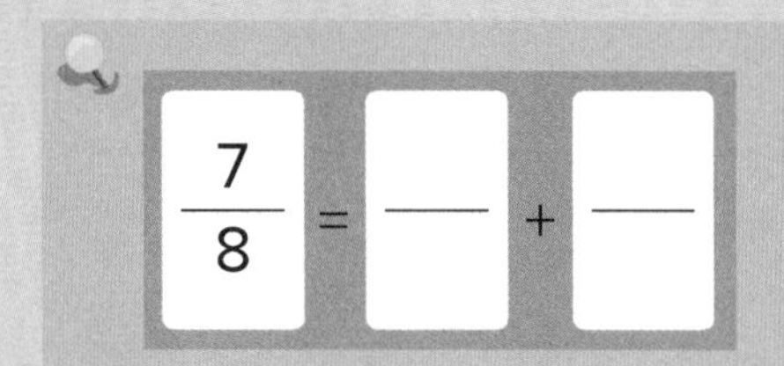

$\frac{7}{8} = \text{\_\_} + \text{\_\_}$

In what ways could three people split the leftover pie?

Complete this equation to match.

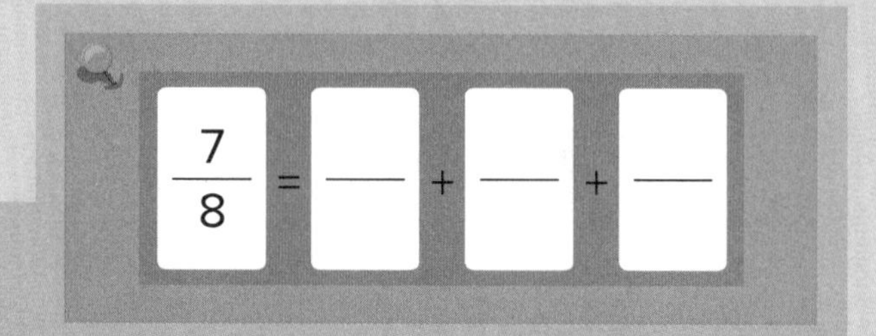

$\frac{7}{8} = \text{\_\_} + \text{\_\_} + \text{\_\_}$

Carrina shaded $\frac{4}{10}$ of this rectangle purple.

She then shaded $\frac{2}{10}$ orange.

What fraction of the shape did she shade in total?

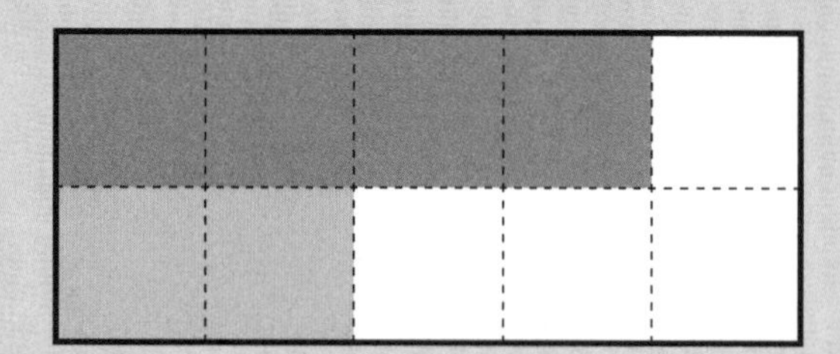

Complete this equation to match.

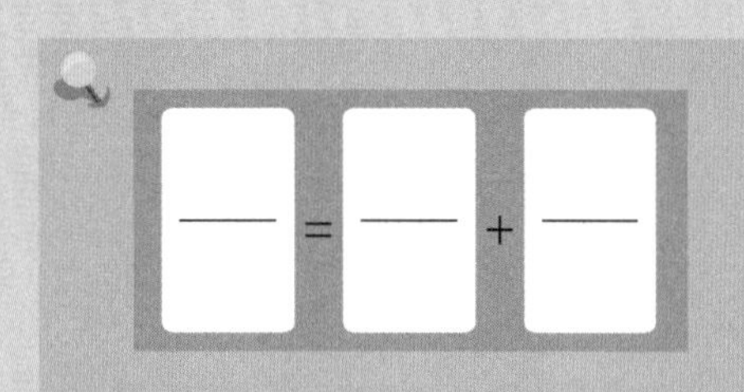

$\text{\_\_} = \text{\_\_} + \text{\_\_}$

Look at all of the equations you wrote.

When you add fractions, what part of the total stays the same?

What part changes? Why?

Step Up

1. Each large rectangle is one whole. Write fractions to complete true equations. Shade parts in different colors to show your thinking.

a.

$\frac{3}{5} = \text{\_\_} + \text{\_\_}$

b.

$\frac{8}{12} = \text{\_\_} + \text{\_\_}$

c.

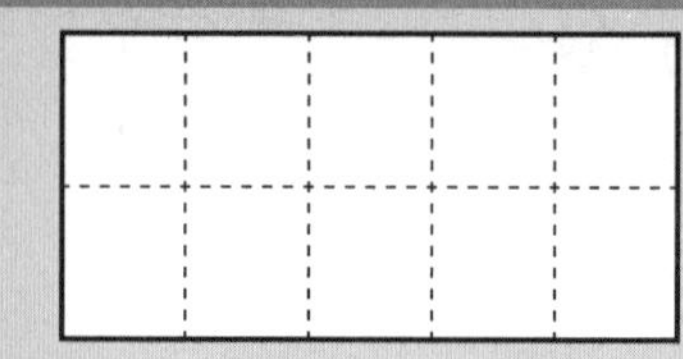

$\frac{8}{10} = \text{\_\_} + \text{\_\_} + \text{\_\_}$

2. Each large rectangle is one whole. Shade parts using different colors to show each fraction. Then write the total fraction that is shaded.

a. 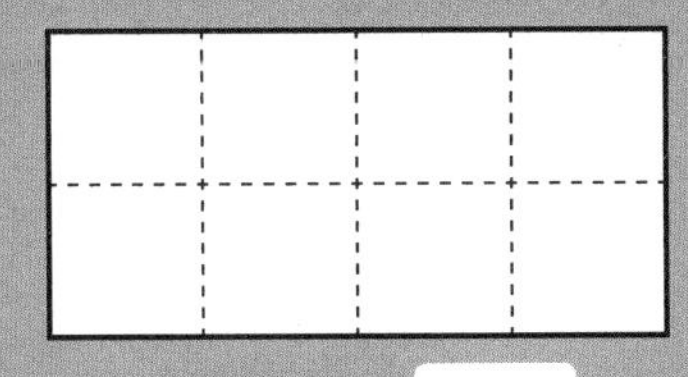

$\frac{3}{8} + \frac{4}{8} = \frac{}{}$

b. 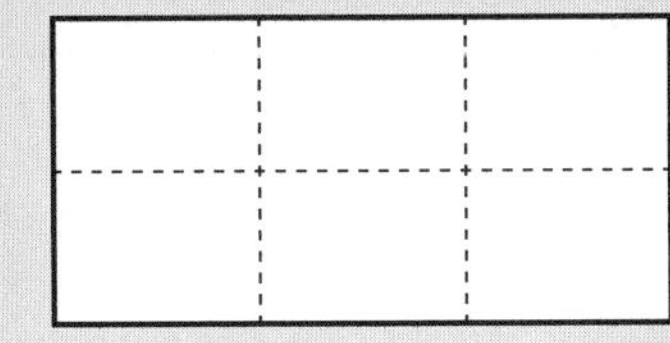

$\frac{1}{6} + \frac{3}{6} = \frac{}{}$

c. 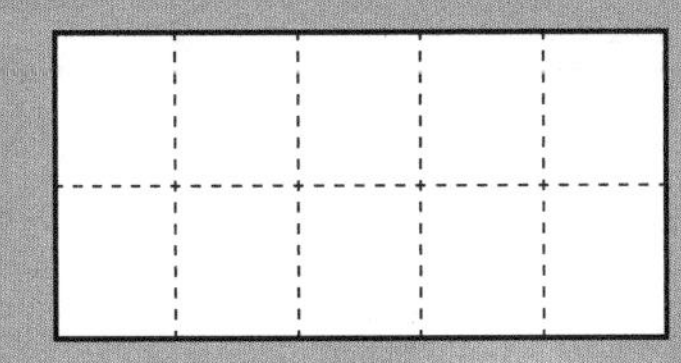

$\frac{4}{10} + \frac{2}{10} = \frac{}{}$

d. 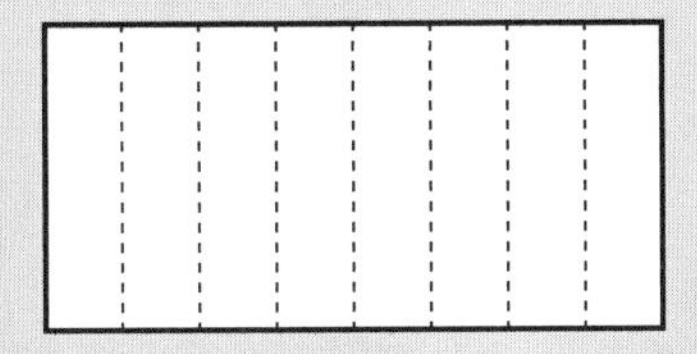

$\frac{3}{8} + \frac{2}{8} = \frac{}{}$

e. 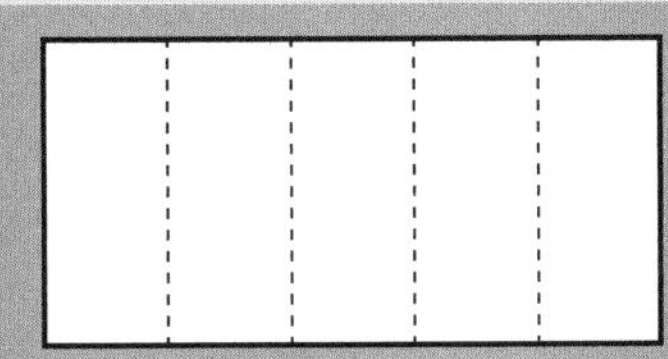

$\frac{3}{5} + \frac{1}{5} = \frac{}{}$

f. 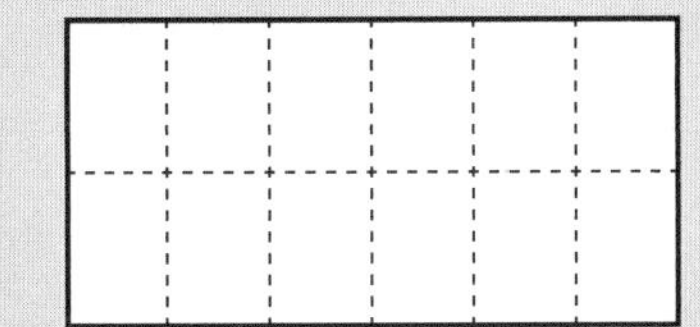

$\frac{5}{12} + \frac{6}{12} = \frac{}{}$

g. 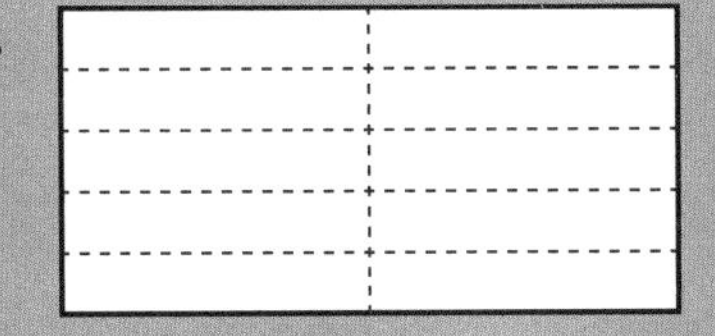

$\frac{2}{10} + \frac{3}{10} = \frac{}{}$

h. 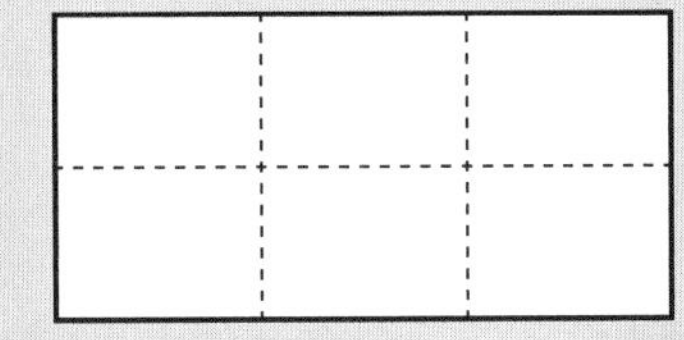

$\frac{4}{6} + \frac{1}{6} = \frac{}{}$

i. 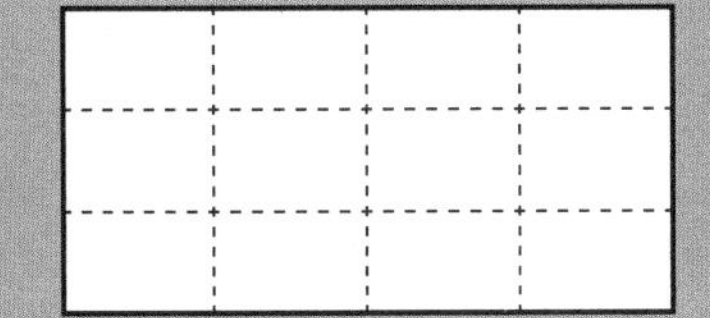

$\frac{7}{12} + \frac{3}{12} = \frac{}{}$

3. Complete each equation. Then draw a picture to match.

a. $\frac{4}{6} + \frac{1}{6} = \frac{}{}$

b. $\frac{2}{8} + \frac{5}{8} = \frac{}{}$

Step Ahead

1. In Question 2 above, loop the totals that have a numerator greater than 6.

2. Write the fractions you looped in the blue boxes below.
Then complete the equations to show a different way to make each total.

a. 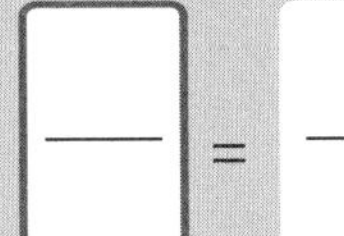 = 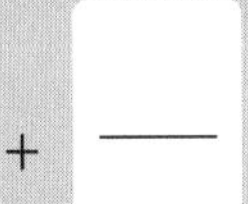 + 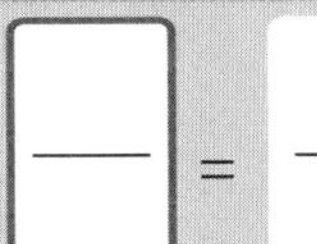

b. 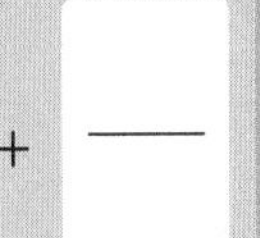

c. 

Step In Adding Common Fractions (Number Line Model)

One bottle of juice was $\frac{2}{4}$ full. Another bottle was $\frac{3}{4}$ full.

If the two amounts were combined, what would be the total?

What equation could you write?

When you add fractions, what happens to the numerator?
What happens to the denominator?

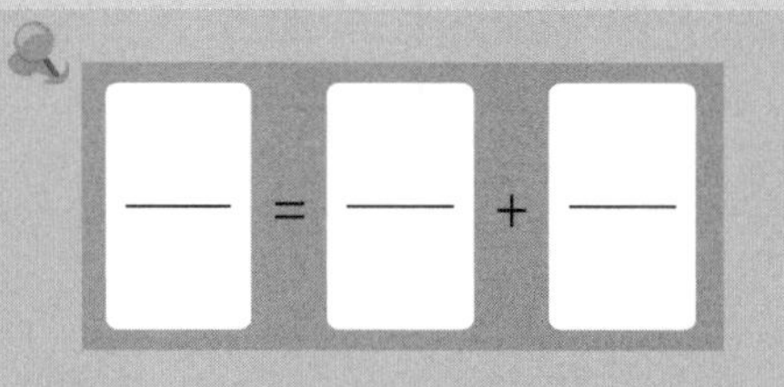

Could you fit all the juice into one bottle? How do you know?

How could you show the addition on this number line?

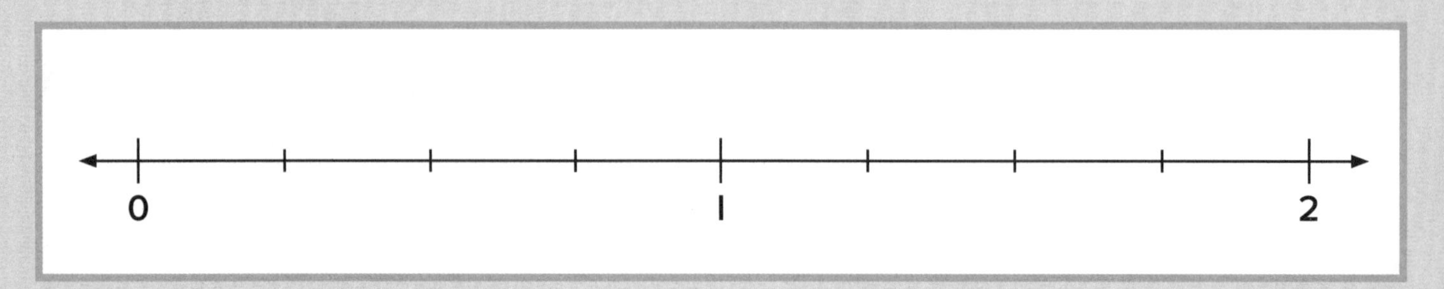

What fractions can you write at 0, 1, and 2 to show the equivalent number of fourths?

Step Up

1. Draw jumps to match each equation.

a. $\frac{5}{6} + \frac{4}{6} = \frac{9}{6}$

$\frac{0}{6}$ $\frac{6}{6}$ $\frac{12}{6}$

b. $\frac{8}{12} + \frac{6}{12} = \frac{14}{12}$

$\frac{0}{12}$ $\frac{12}{12}$ $\frac{24}{12}$

c. $\frac{7}{5} + \frac{4}{5} = \frac{11}{5}$

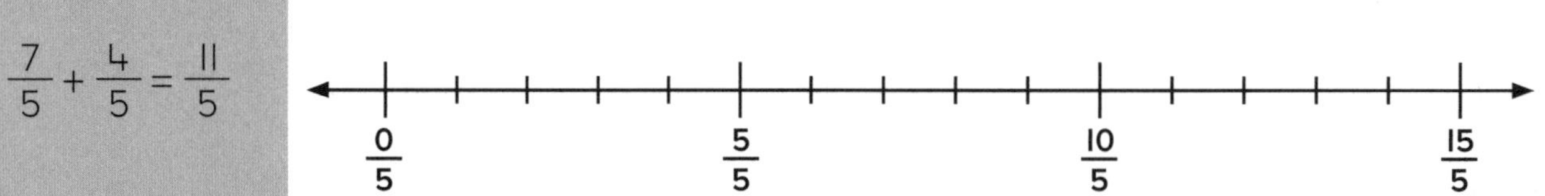

2. Use this number line to help you write the totals below.

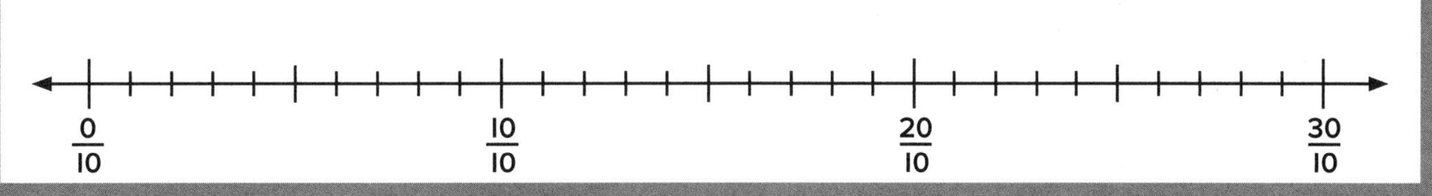

a. $\frac{4}{10} + \frac{5}{10} = $ ___	**b.** $\frac{6}{10} + \frac{2}{10} = $ ___	**c.** $\frac{1}{10} + \frac{5}{10} = $ ___
d. $\frac{12}{10} + \frac{7}{10} = $ ___	**e.** $\frac{5}{10} + \frac{18}{10} = $ ___	**f.** $\frac{14}{10} + \frac{13}{10} = $ ___

3. Use what you know about adding fractions to complete each equation.

a. $\frac{5}{8} + \frac{2}{8} = $ ___	**b.** $\frac{8}{6} + \frac{11}{6} = $ ___	**c.** $\frac{10}{4} + \frac{8}{4} = $ ___
d. $\frac{15}{12} + \frac{0}{12} = $ ___	**e.** $\frac{5}{3} + \frac{9}{3} + \frac{6}{3} = $ ___	**f.** $\frac{2}{8} + \frac{15}{8} + \frac{5}{8} = $ ___

4. Look at the totals in Question 3. Loop the totals that are greater than 3.

Step Ahead

1. Leonardo swims one mile over two days. Each day he swims a different distance. Write fractions of a mile to show two different possibilities for distances he could swim.

1 mi = ___ + ___ 1 mi = ___ + ___

2. Two quarts of juice is poured into three glasses. The amount in each glass is different. Write fractions of a quart to show two possibilities for each glass.

2 qt = ___ + ___ + ___ 2 qt = ___ + ___ + ___

Step In Solving Word Problems Involving Fractions

This recipe makes one batch of muffins.
Joel is making three batches.
He has about 2 cups of oats in the cupboard.

What amount of oats will he use in total?
Will he have enough oats?

What equation could you write to show how to calculate the total amount of oats needed?

What information will help you?

Oat and Banana Muffins

$\frac{1}{2}$ cup sugar
$\frac{2}{3}$ cup oats
1 cup flour
1 tsp baking soda
1 tsp cinnamon

How could this number line help you figure out the answer?

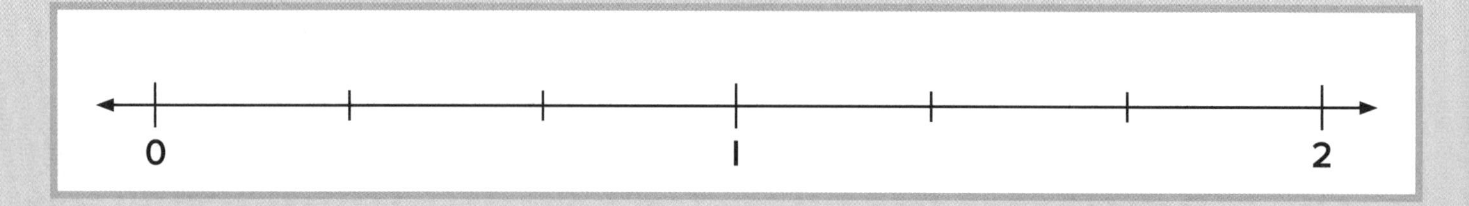

Step Up

1. Read each problem carefully. Color the ⬭ to estimate each answer.

a. Leon is making two small bags. He needs $\frac{3}{4}$ of a yard of fabric to make each bag. How much fabric will he use in total?

- ⬭ about one yard
- ⬭ between one and two yards
- ⬭ more than two yards

b. Marcela mixed $\frac{5}{8}$ of a quart of orange juice and $\frac{6}{8}$ of a quart of pineapple juice. How much juice did she mix in total?

- ⬭ less than one quart
- ⬭ between one and two quarts
- ⬭ more than two quarts

c. One piece of ribbon is $\frac{9}{6}$ of a foot long. Another is $\frac{6}{6}$ of a foot long. What is the total length of ribbon?

- ⬭ about one foot
- ⬭ about two feet
- ⬭ more than two feet

d. Four boxes are stacked on top of each other. Each box is about half a meter tall. How tall is the whole stack?

- ⬭ about one meter
- ⬭ between one and two meters
- ⬭ about two meters

2. Solve these word problems. Show your thinking.

a. Callum walks $\frac{3}{4}$ of a mile to school. It takes him about $\frac{1}{4}$ of an hour. How far does he walk in total to school and back?

miles

b. Two books are being packed into a box. One book is $\frac{7}{8}$ inch thick and one is $\frac{5}{8}$ inch thick. Their total mass is $\frac{6}{8}$ lb. If the books are stacked flat, how tall will the stack be?

inches

c. Dad bought $\frac{5}{8}$ lb of carrots, a green pepper that weighed $\frac{3}{8}$ lb, and some broccoli. The total mass was $\frac{14}{8}$ lb. How much did the broccoli weigh?

pound

d. Lea is $\frac{7}{10}$ of her dad's height. Her sister is $\frac{5}{10}$ of their dad's height. What is the girls' combined height compared to their dad's height?

of their dad's height

Step Ahead

Complete each equation so the total is **greater** than 2 but **less** than 3.

a. $\frac{10}{6} + \frac{\quad}{\quad} = \frac{\quad}{\quad}$

b. $\frac{\quad}{\quad} = \frac{3}{5} + \frac{\quad}{\quad}$

c. $\frac{\quad}{\quad} + \frac{16}{12} + \frac{\quad}{\quad} = \frac{\quad}{\quad}$

Step In Identifying Fractions of a Full Turn

A quarter-turn tester is a tool that measures a quarter of a full turn.

Other angle testers can be used to measure other fractions of a full turn.

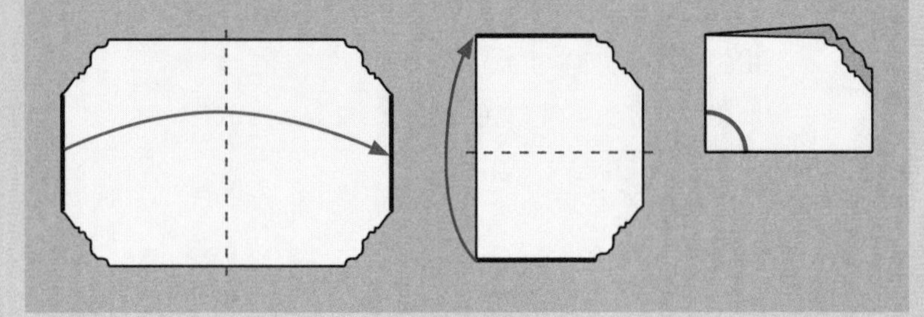

Cut out and fold the angle testers from the support page.

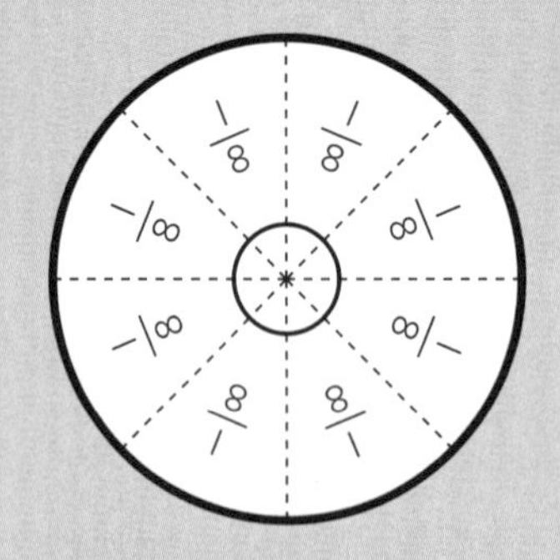

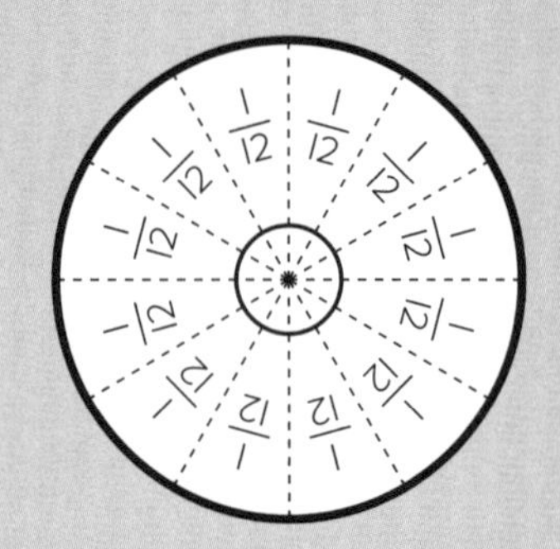

Into how many equal parts has each tester been divided?

When the testers are folded, what is the smallest fraction of a full turn each tester can measure?

Step Up

1. Use the eighth-turn tester to measure each angle inside the shapes below and those on page 121. Write the measurement beside each arc. Leave the angles blank if they cannot be measured using this tester.

a.

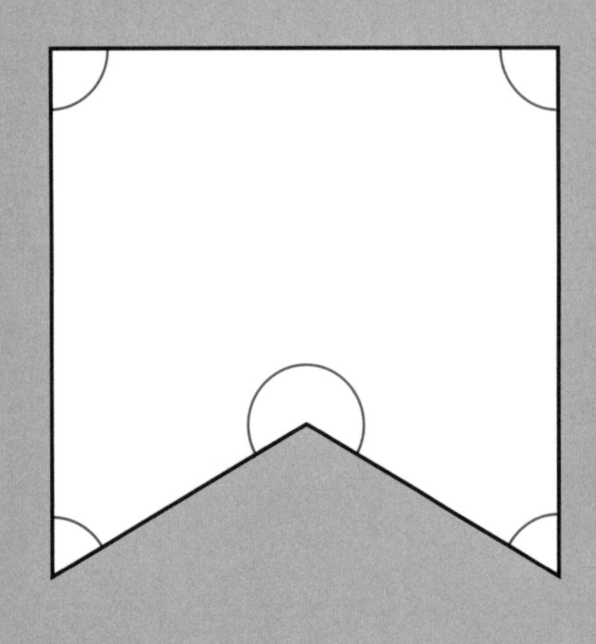

b.

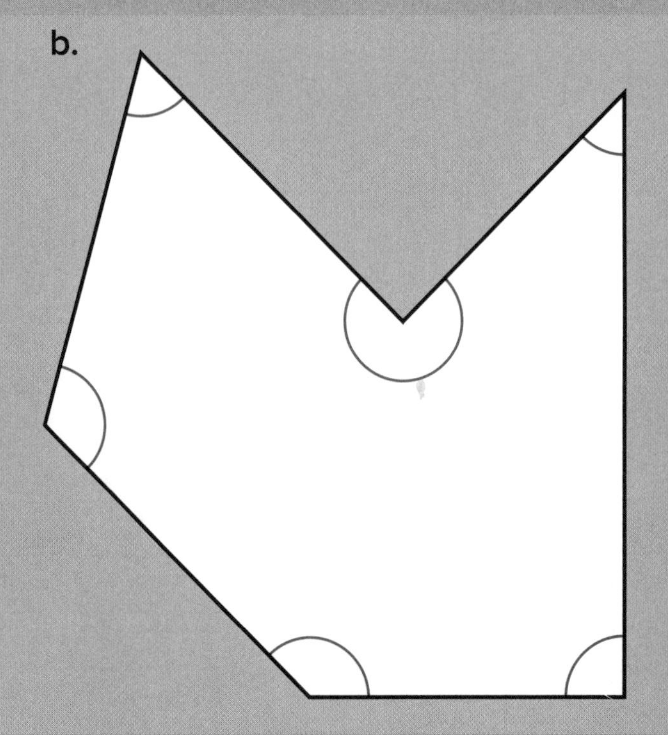

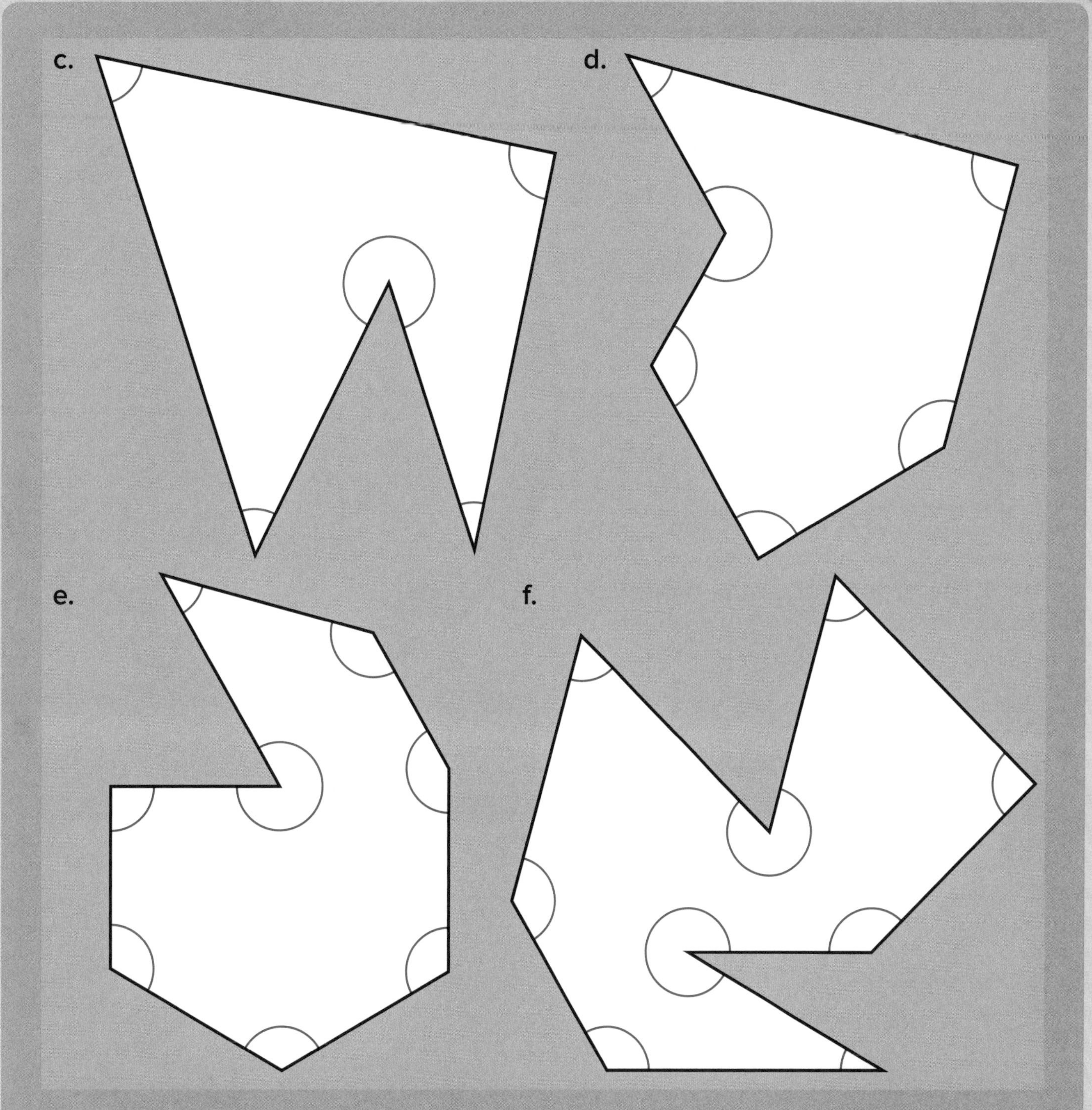

2. Use the twelfth-turn tester to measure each angle inside the shapes in Question 1. Write the measurement beside each arc. Some angles will already have a measurement marked so write beside them.

Step Ahead Use a tester to draw these shapes on a piece of paper.

a. A hexagon that has an eight-twelfths angle.

b. A pentagon that has a seven-twelfths angle.

Step In Using a Protractor

One full turn around a point can be divided into 360 parts.

Each part is called a **degree** and is $\frac{1}{360}$ of a full turn.

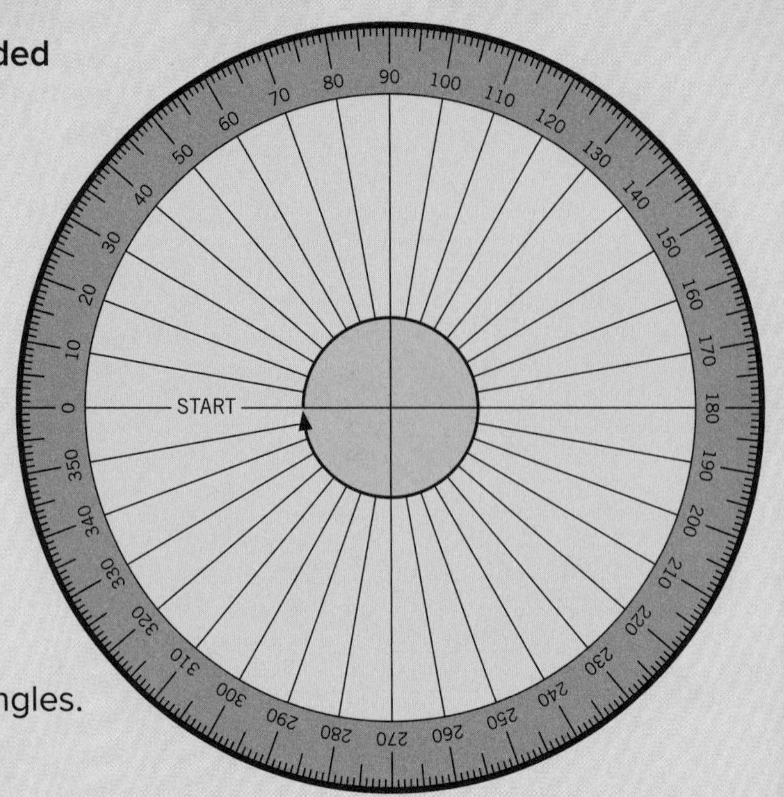

The symbol ° is used for degree. One full turn around a point is 360°.

Look at the protractor on the right.
A protractor is a tool used to measure angles.

Follow these steps to use your protractor.

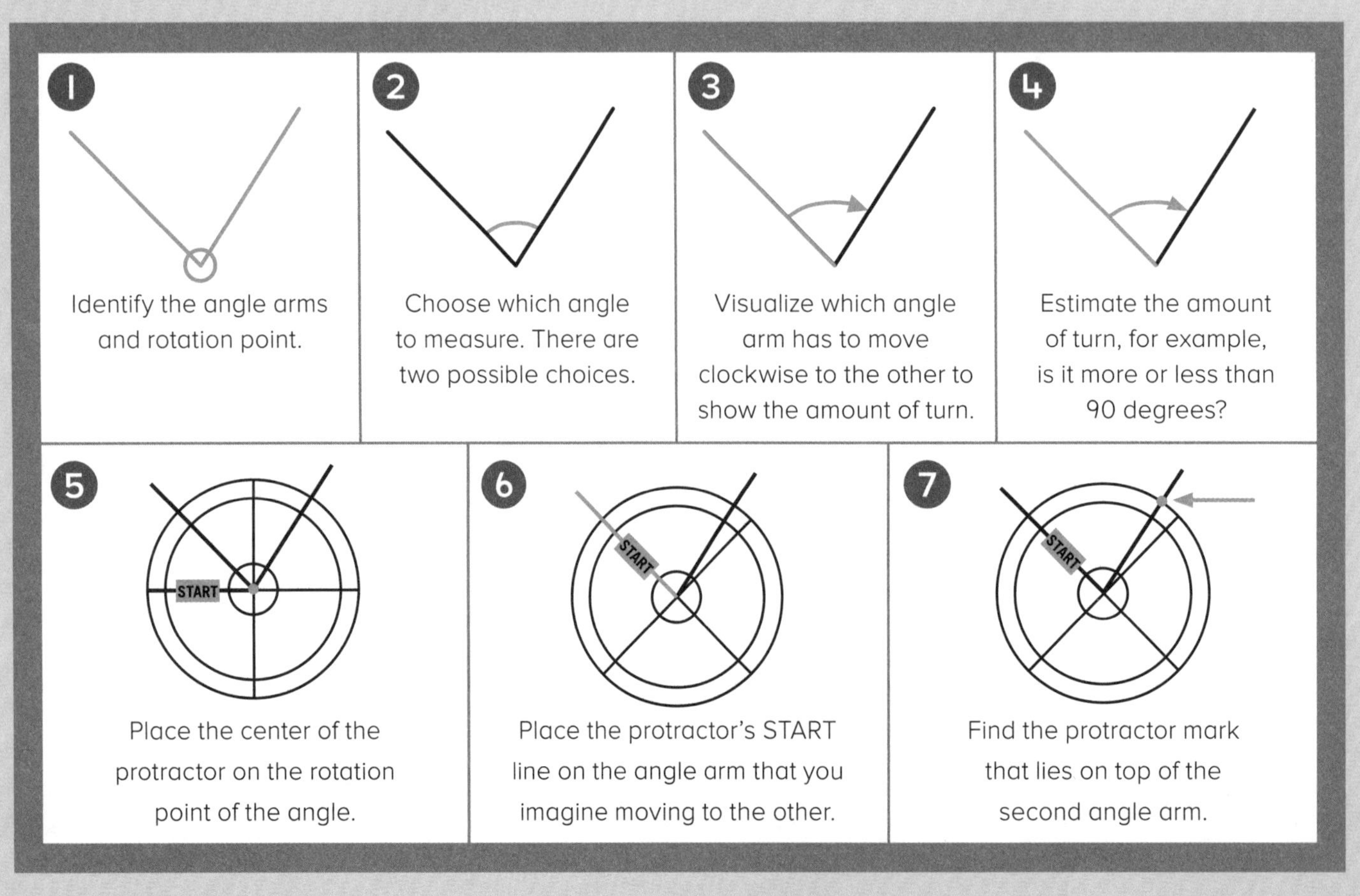

Step Up

Use a protractor to measure and label the inside angles of each shape.

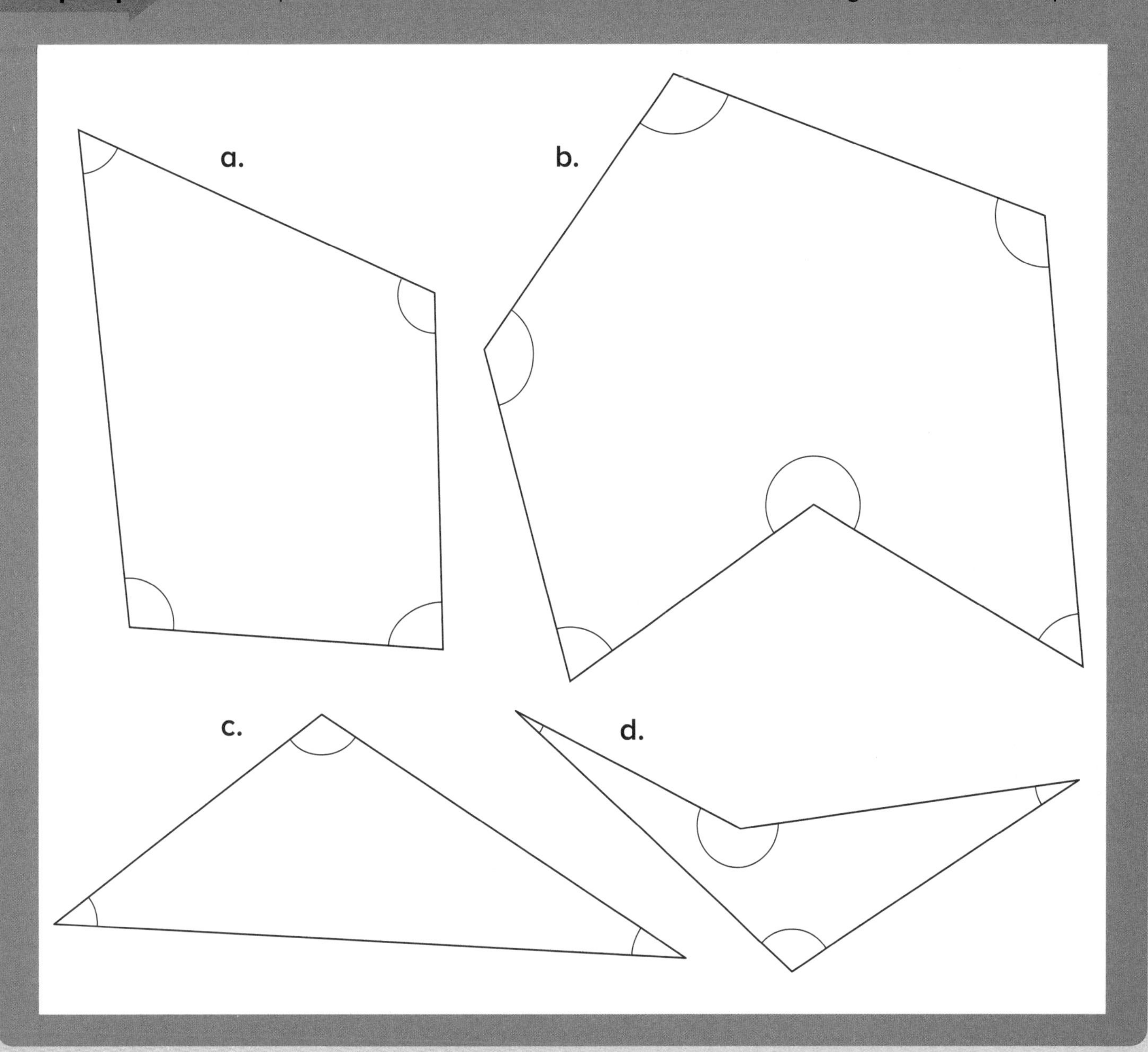

Step Ahead

a. Draw two connecting line segments that show an angle of 60° between them.

b. What fraction of a full turn is 60°?

Step In Identifying Acute, Right, and Obtuse Angles

A right angle is one-fourth of a full turn.
How many degrees does that equal? How do you know?
Find two right angles in the picture.
Mark them with a blue arc.

An acute angle is an angle that is less than a right angle.
Find two acute angles in the picture.
Mark them with a red arc.

An obtuse angle is angle that is greater than a right angle but less than a half turn.
Find two obtuse angles in the picture.
Mark them with a green arc.

Step Up

1. Use a protractor to help you find these angles.
- Write **A** next to the acute angles.
- Write **R** next to the right angles.
- Write **O** next to the obtuse angles.

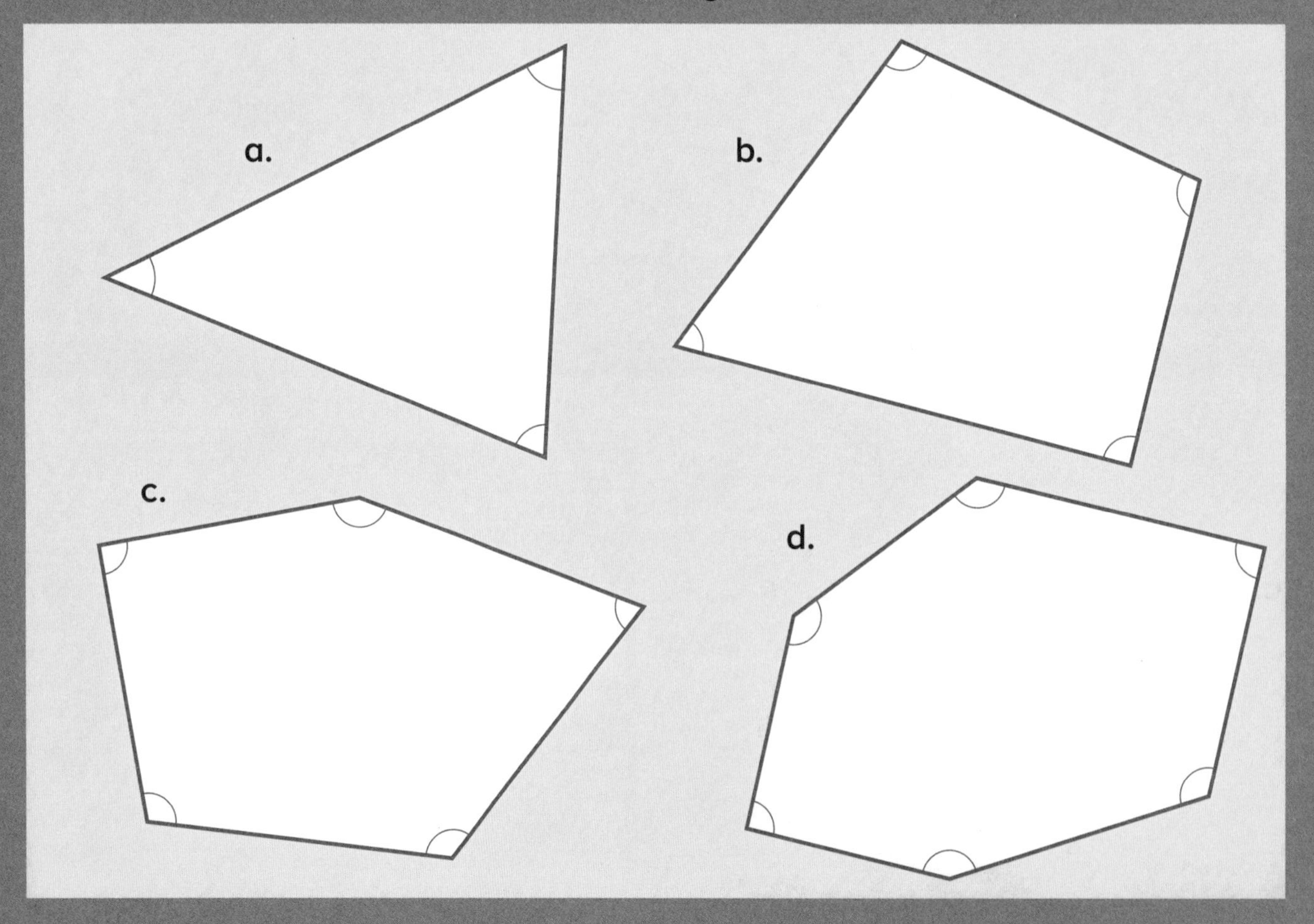

2. Triangles can be named acute, right, or obtuse based on the size of their greatest angle. In each triangle below, loop the greatest angle.

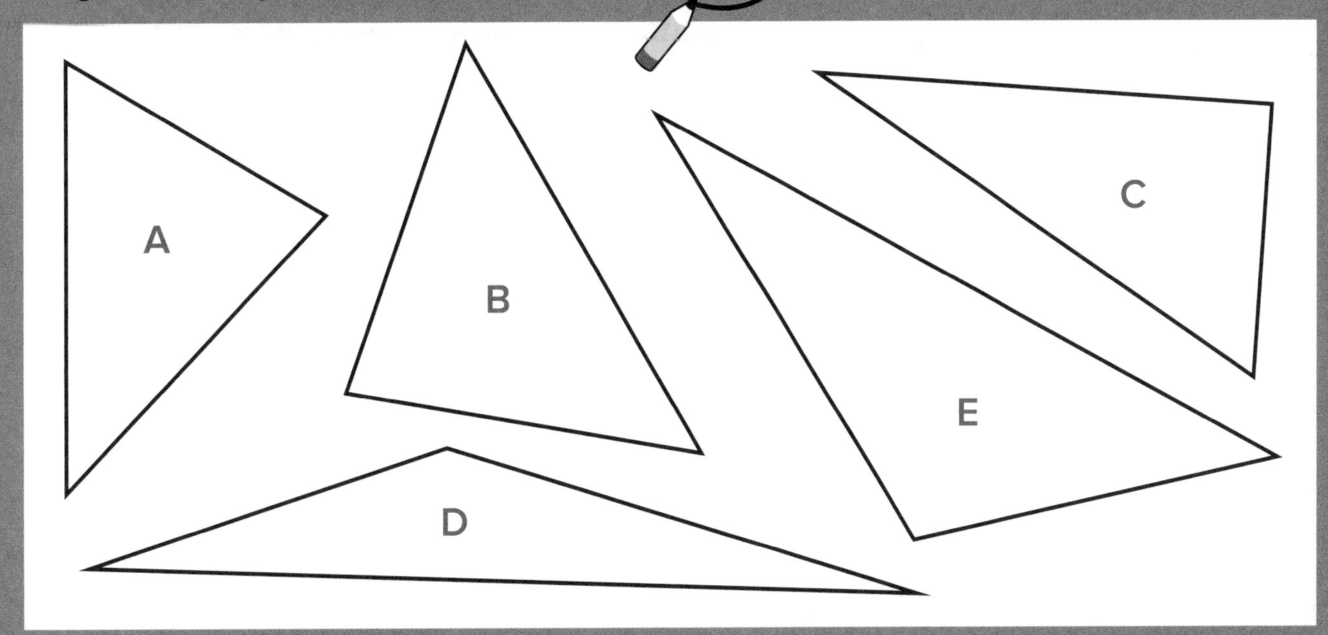

3. Measure then write the value of each angle you looped in Question 2.

A ____° B ____° C ____° D ____° E ____°

4. Use your measurements from Question 3 to answer these questions about the triangles in Question 2.

a. Which triangles are acute triangles? ____________

b. Which triangles are right triangles? ____________

c. Which triangles are obtuse triangles? ____________

Step Ahead For each of these, draw a triangle that shows the angle. Mark the angle with an arc.

a. one obtuse angle

b. one right angle

Step In Estimating and Calculating Angles

Angles can be identified by labeling the endpoints of their angle arms and the point where the arms meet. When using points to name an angle, the point that refers to the vertex must be in the middle.

This angle can be called Angle ROS.

What other name could be used?
How do you know?

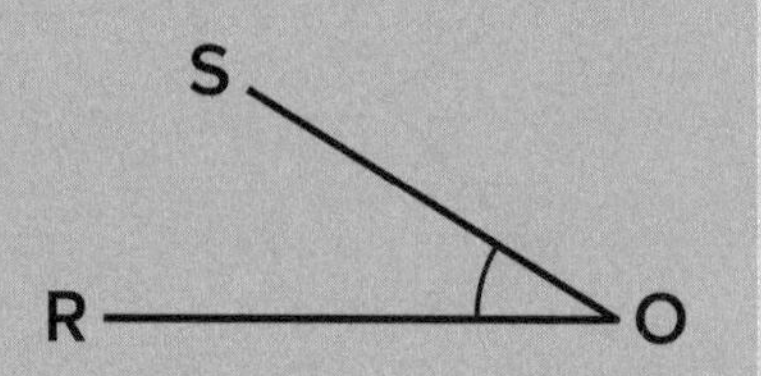

RO is one of the angle arms. What is the other angle arm?

Look at this diagram.
Imagine OA turned clockwise to finish at the same position as OB.

B
A O C
D

What fraction of a full turn would OA have made?

How many degrees would it have turned? How do you know?

What does that tell you about Angle AOB?

I think it is one-fourth of a full turn. A full-turn is 360 degrees so I need to figure out one-fourth of 360.

Step Up

1. Use the clues to calculate the size of each angle in the diagram. Do not use a protractor. Show your thinking.

Clues

- Angle **BOD** is 40°.
- Angle **COD** is half of Angle **BOD**.
- Angle **AOB** is the same size as Angle **BOD**.

A
B
C
O D

Angle **COD** is ________ °

Angle **AOB** is ________ °

Angle **AOD** is ________ °

Angle **AOC** is ________ °

2. Look at the diagram. Use the clues to calculate the size of each angle. Do not use a protractor. Show your thinking.

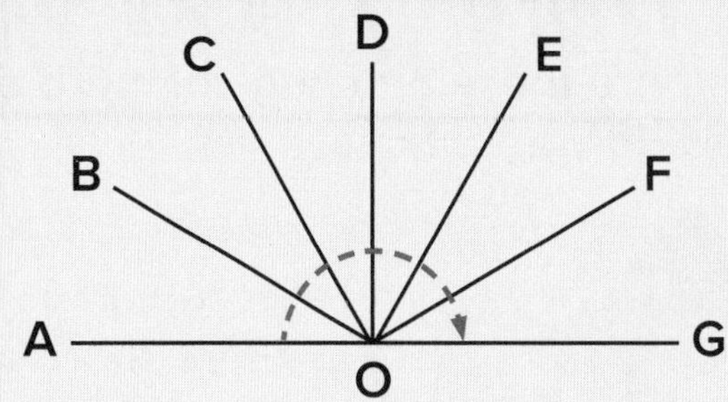

Clues

- Angle **AOB** is 30°.
- Angle **BOC** is 30°.
- Angle **COD** is 30°.
- Angle **DOE** is 30°.
- Angle **EOF** is 30°.
- Angle **FOG** is 30°.

Angle **AOC** is ________ °

Angle **AOD** is ________ °

Angle **EOG** is ________ °

Angle **AOE** is ________ °

Angle **BOE** is ________ °

Angle **AOG** is ________ °

3. Look at the diagram in Question 2. Name three angles that are **less than 90°**.

________ ________ ________

4. Look at the diagram in Question 2. Name three angles that are **greater than 90°**.

________ ________ ________

Step Ahead Look at the diagram in Question 2 above. Write these angle sizes.

Angle **BOD** is ________ °

Half of Angle **BOD** is ________ °

Angle **BOF** is ________ °

Half of Angle **BOF** is ________ °

Angle **BOC** is ________ °

One-third of Angle **BOC** is ________ °

Angle **DOG** is ________ °

One-third of Angle **DOG** is ________ °

Step In Reviewing the Comparison Model of Multiplication

Compare these two bags of marbles. What do you notice?

The purple bag has three **times as many** marbles as the orange bag.

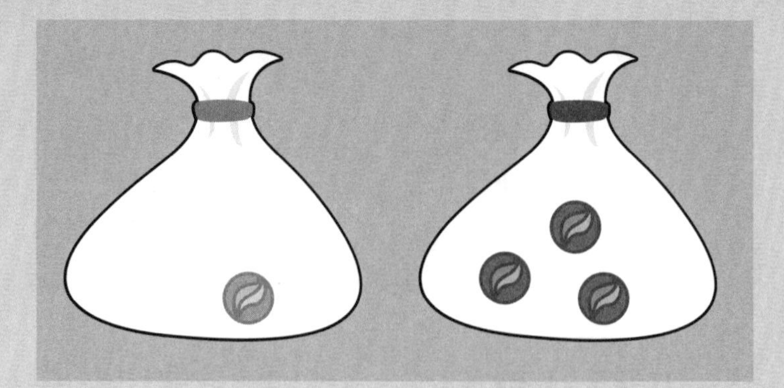

Draw more marbles so that one bag has four **times as many** marbles as the other.

What do you know about these two bags of marbles?

Draw more marbles so that one bag has three **times as many** marbles as the other.

How did you figure out the number of marbles to draw?

Complete the statement to match the marbles in the bag.

___ ___ many as ___

Step Up

1. Draw marbles in the empty bag to match the statement.

a. Bag B has 3 times as many marbles as Bag A.

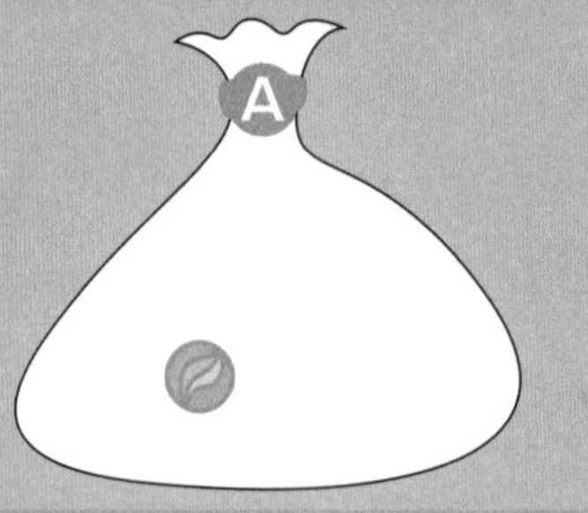

b. Bag C has 5 times as many marbles as Bag D.

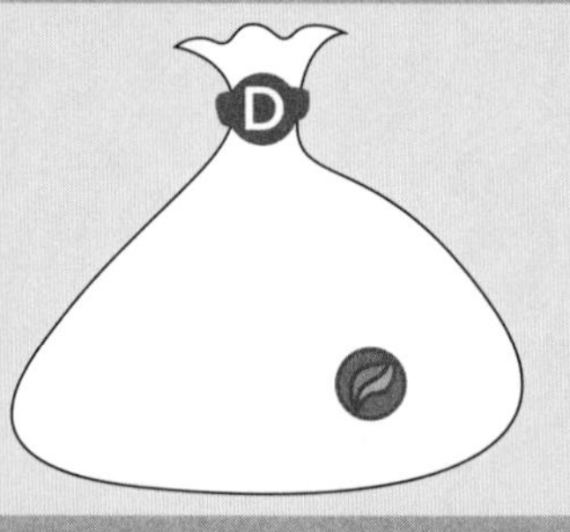

2. Loop the marbles to show one group. Then draw marbles in each empty bag to match the statement.

a. Bag E has 3 times as many marbles as Bag F.

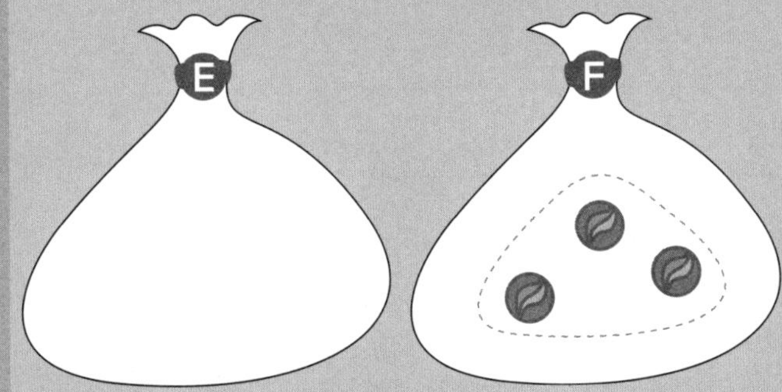

b. Bag H has 4 times as many marbles as Bag G.

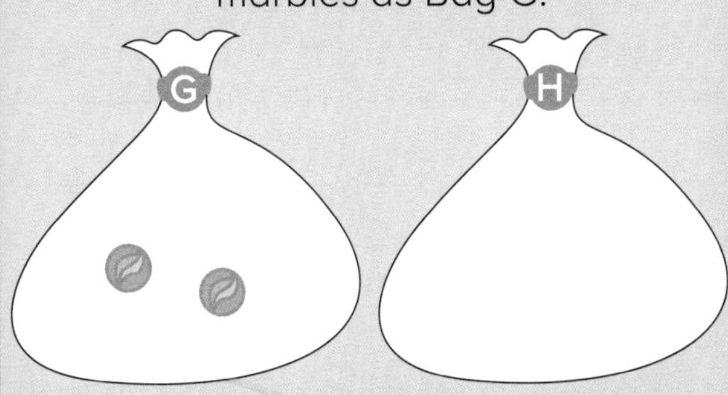

c. Bag J has 2 times as many marbles as Bag K.

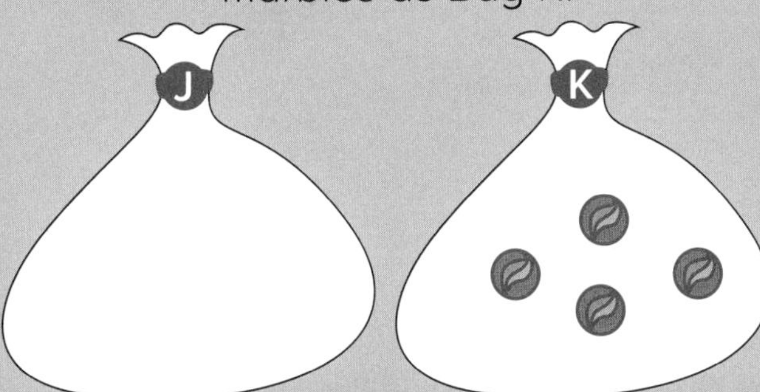

d. Bag L has 5 times as many marbles as Bag M.

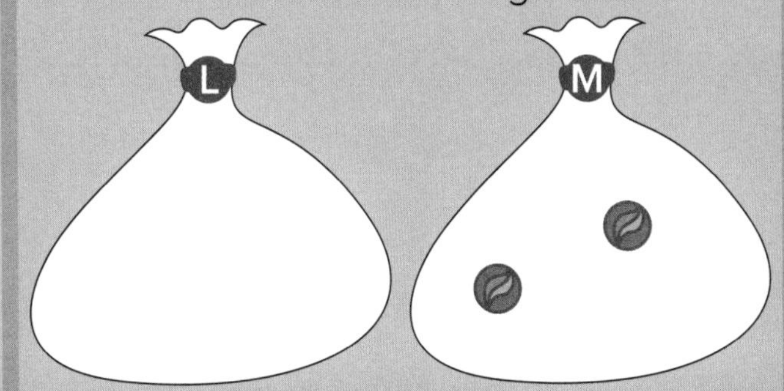

3. Complete each sentence.

a. 6 is 2 times as many as ____.

b. 10 is 5 times as many as ____.

c. ____ is 4 times as many as 1.

d. 15 is ____ times as many as 5.

e. 9 is 3 times as many as ____.

f. 24 is 6 times as many as ____.

g. ____ is 2 times as many as 8.

h. 18 is ____ times as many as 6.

Step Ahead Daniel is baking a cake. The recipe says to use 5 apricot pieces for every 1 walnut.

He used a total of 35 apricot pieces. How many walnuts did he use? ____

Step In — Using Strip Diagrams to Make Comparisons Involving Multiplication

How could you compare the length of these two strips?

5 yards		

How long is the longer strip?

How do you know?

I'll call the short strip **S**. I can figure out the length of the long strip by calculating 3 × **S**.

Complete this statement.

_____ yards is _____ times as long as _____ yards.

Step Up

1. Color the long strip to match each label.

a. 7 yards — **4 times as long**

b. 4 yards — **6 times as long**

c. 9 yards — **5 times as long**

2. Write numbers in the diagram to solve the problem. Then write the answer.

a. The old bridge was 15 yards long. The new bridge will be 6 times as long. What will be the length of the new bridge?

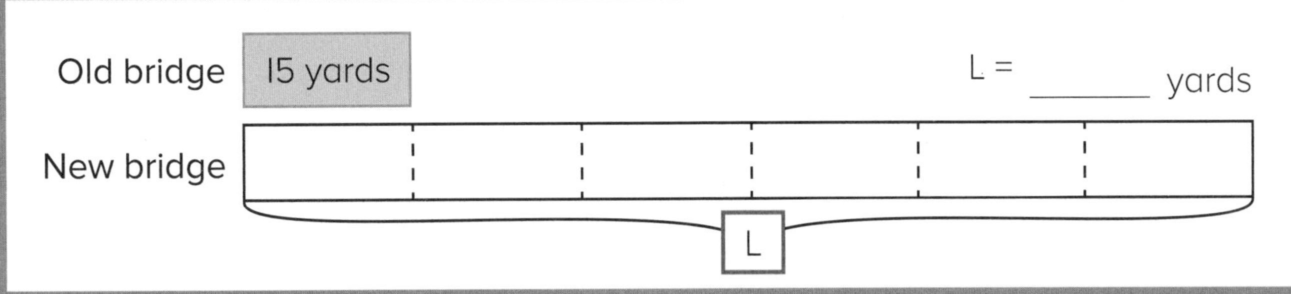

b. Kanti has $25 in savings. Peter has 5 times as much. How much does Peter have in savings?

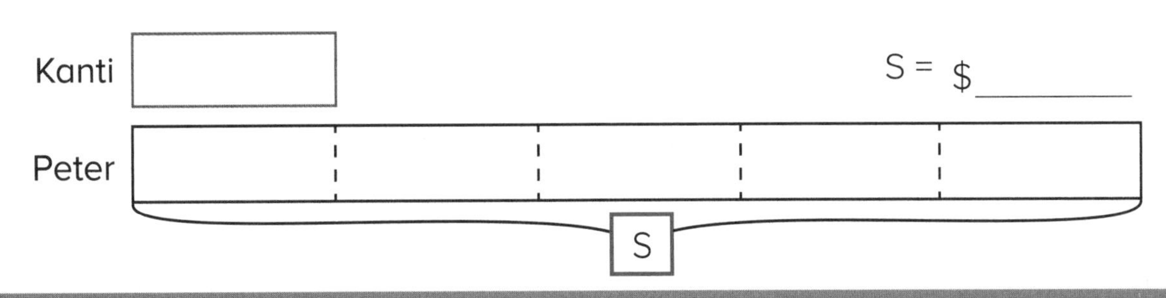

c. A small plane seats 35 passengers. A large plane seats 4 times as many passengers. What is the seating capacity of the large plane?

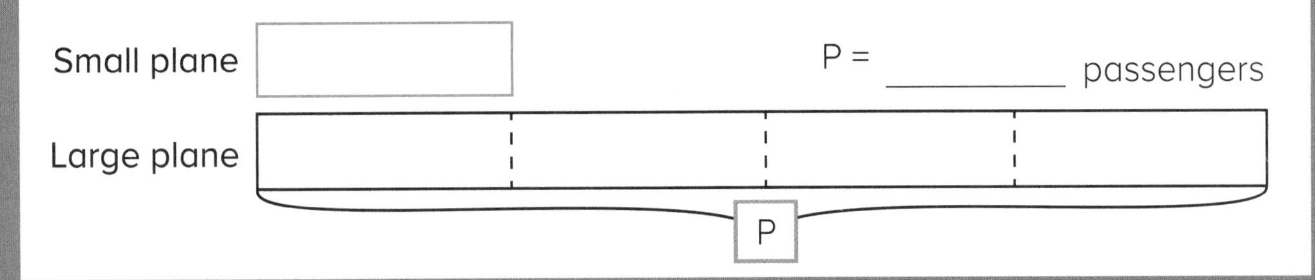

Step Ahead Draw a diagram to help solve this problem. Then write the answer.

There are 16 cards in each pack. Lorena buys 3 packs on Monday and another 2 packs on Tuesday. How many cards does she buy in total?

______ cards

Step In: Using Strip Diagrams to Make Comparisons Involving Multiplication and Addition

Michelle has 45 marbles in her collection.

Alberto has 3 more marbles than Michelle.

How many marbles does he have?
How do you know?

What numbers can you write in the diagram below to help figure out the total number?

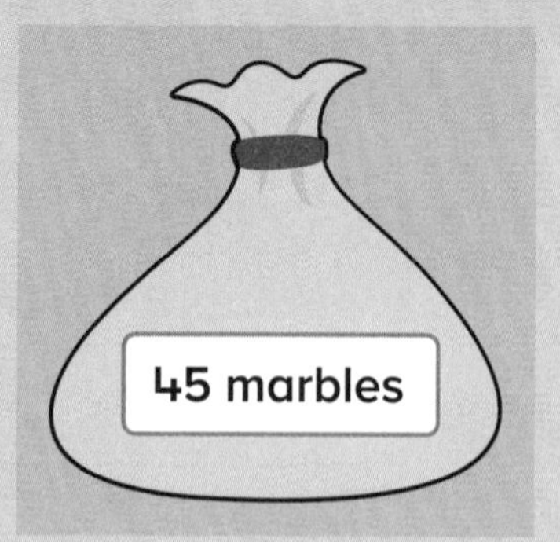

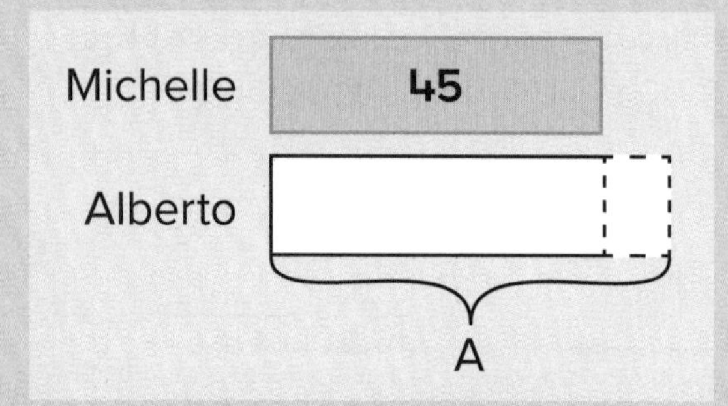

I'll call the number of marbles in Alberto's collection **A**.
A = 45 + 3

Darriel has 3 times as many marbles as Michelle.

Complete this diagram to figure out the number of marbles in her collection.

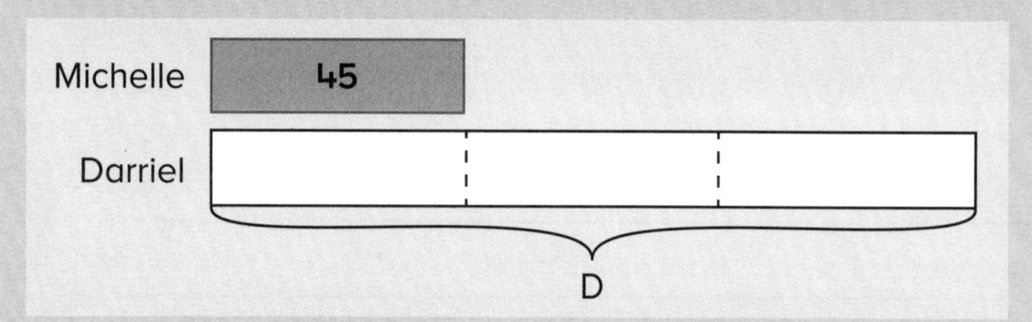

Think about the language of **3 more** and **3 times as many**.

How are the phrases different?

Step Up

1. Write **multiplication** or **addition** to show how you would solve each problem.

a. A plane ticket costs $245. It costs $35 more to reserve the seat. What is the total cost? ____________

b. An economy-class ticket costs $96. A ticket in first class costs 5 times as much. What is the cost of a first-class ticket? ____________

2. Write an equation to figure out each answer. Complete the diagram to show the answer.

a. 2,075 supporters watched the first game. 150 more supporters watched the second game. What was the attendance at the second game?

First game 2,075

Second game 150

b. Karen sold 789 copies of her book last month. She sold 420 copies this month. She has 45 copies left to sell. How many books has she sold?

Last month 789

This month

c. It takes 30 seconds to reheat a pie. If the pie is frozen it takes 6 times as long. How long does it take to heat a frozen pie?

Reheating 30

From frozen

Step Ahead Draw a diagram to help solve this problem. Then write the answer.

A coach orders uniforms for some of his players. Shirts cost $16 each and shorts cost $10 each. What is the total cost of 5 uniforms?

$ ______

Step In — Using Strip Diagrams to Explore the Relationship between Multiplication and Division

Hector has 35 pencils. He has 7 times as many pencils as his sister Claire.

How many pencils does his sister have?

How does this diagram match the word problem?

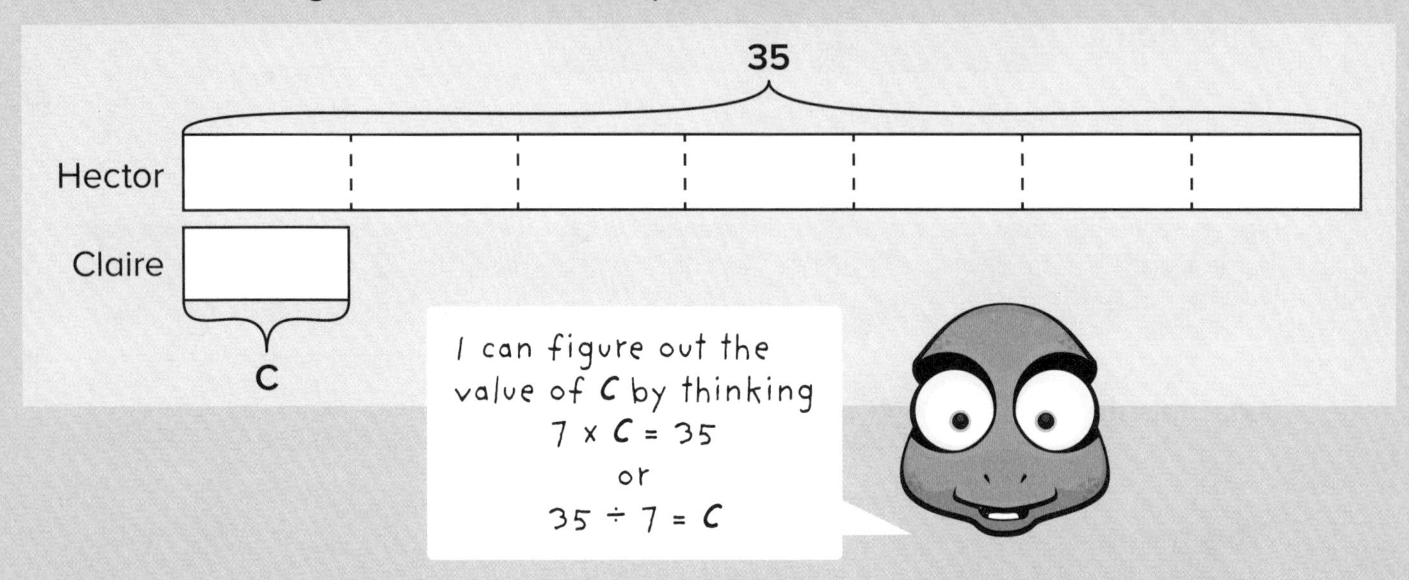

Complete these two equations to show the answer.

$7 \times$ ____ $= 35$

$35 \div 7 =$ ____

Step Up

1. Solve each problem. Write numbers in the diagram to show your thinking.

a. Chayton is 75 years old. He is 3 times as old as Sabrina. What is Sabrina's age?

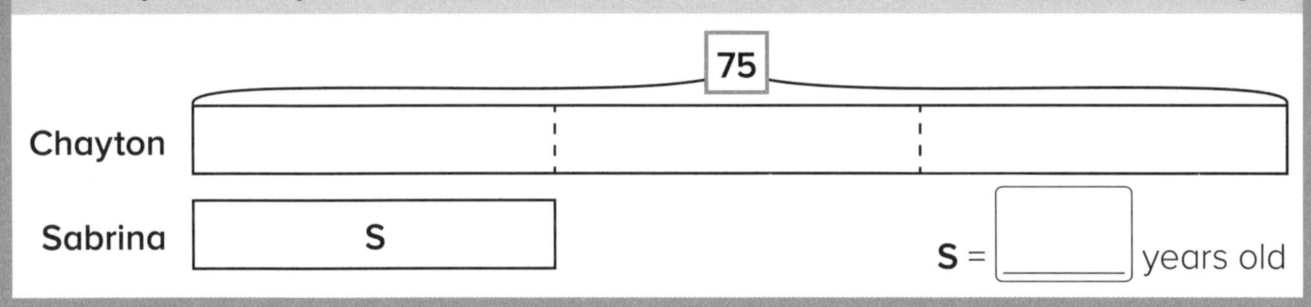

S = ____ years old

b. 5 tickets cost a total of $80. What is the cost of I ticket?

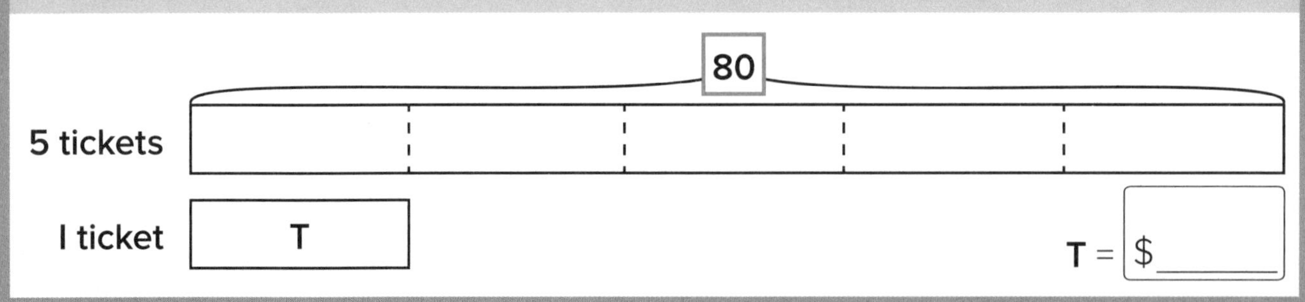

T = $____

2. Draw a diagram to solve each problem. Then write the answer.

a. Lorenzo has 60 stamps in his collection. He has 4 times as many stamps as Susan. How many stamps does Susan have?

________ stamps

b. Grade 4 raised $85 in cake sales. They raised 5 times as much as Grade 3. What amount did Grade 3 raise?

$________

c. 6 friends equally share the cost of a gift. The gift costs $90. What amount will each friend pay?

$________

Step Ahead Solve this problem. Draw diagrams or write equations to show your thinking.

Raleigh buys 5 bags of soil and 4 bags of fertilizer. The soil costs $75. The fertilizer costs $92. The next day she buys 2 more bags of soil and 1 more bag of fertilizer. What amount did she pay the second day?

$________

Step In — Using Strip Diagrams to Make Comparisons Involving Division and Subtraction

This picture shows the weight of Alma's bag.

Aiden's bag weighs 3 lb less than Alma's.

How does this diagram match the problem?

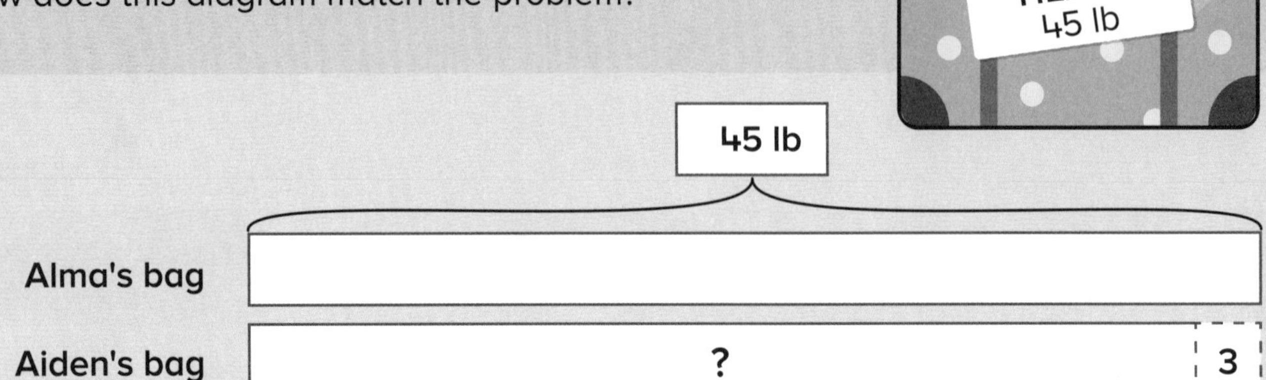

What is the weight of Aiden's bag? How do you know?

Look at this diagram. How would you describe the relationship of Luke's bag to Alma's bag?

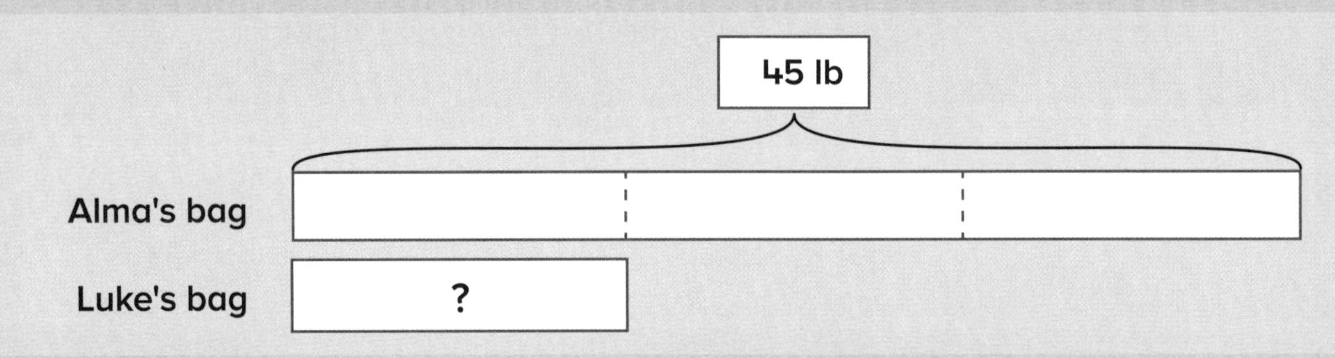

What thinking would you use to figure out the weight of Luke's bag?

Think about the language of **one-third** and **3 less**.
How are these phrases different?

Step Up

1. Write the number sentence you would use to figure out the answer. Complete the diagram to show your thinking.

A shirt costs $52. A tie costs one-fourth of the shirt. What is the cost of the tie?

Shirt — $52

Tie — $______

____

2. Write the number sentence that you would use to figure out each answer. Complete the diagram to show the answer.

a. Corey scored 96 points. He scored twice as many points as his brother. How many points did his brother score?

Corey	**96 points**
Brother	

____

b. A tiger weighs 385 lb. A lion weighs 90 lb less. How much does the lion weigh?

Tiger	**385 lb**
Lion	

____

c. Devon has $1,045 in her savings account. She buys a new couch and has $650 left. What is the cost of the couch?

Savings	**$1,045**
Couch	

____

d. Diego earned $95 in one month. He earned five times as much as his sister. How much did his sister earn?

Diego	**$95**
Sister	

____

Step Ahead

Two friends spent $40 in total at the movies.
The tickets cost three times as much as the snacks.

How much did the tickets cost?

$______

Step In Using Strip Diagrams to Solve Word Problems

This is a photo of Adan and his family when he was 8 years old. Adan has been circled.

Read the clues and figure out the age of each person in the photo.

CLUE 1	My dad is 10 times as old as my little brother.
CLUE 2	I am twice as old as my little brother.
CLUE 3	My dad is 4 years older than my mom.
CLUE 4	My mom is 4 times older than my sister.
CLUE 5	My grandpa is 5 years older than the combined age of my mom and dad.

How old is each person in the photo?

In what order did you use the clues?

Think about the ages of the people in your family. What clues could you write?

Step Up Write number sentences to solve each word problem.
You can draw pictures or diagrams to help your thinking.

a. A concert hall seats 2,450 people. 1,890 tickets have been sold.
How many more tickets are available?

_______ tickets

b. Lifen cycles 12 miles each day. Samuel cycles 15 miles each day.
How much farther has Samuel cycled after 5 days?

_______ miles

c. Four friends share the cost of a gift. They each pay $36.
How much did the gift cost?

$_______

d. It costs $72 to buy 6 yards of chain.
What is the cost of buying 5 yards of the same chain?

$_______

Step Ahead Eva spent $26 on drinks for a party. The cost of the food was 5 times as much as the cost of the drinks.

What is the total amount she spent on food and drinks?

$_______

Step In Exploring Whole Numbers and Common Fractions

Any whole number can be written as a common fraction.

What are some fractions that are equivalent to 3?

What helps you figure out they are equivalent?

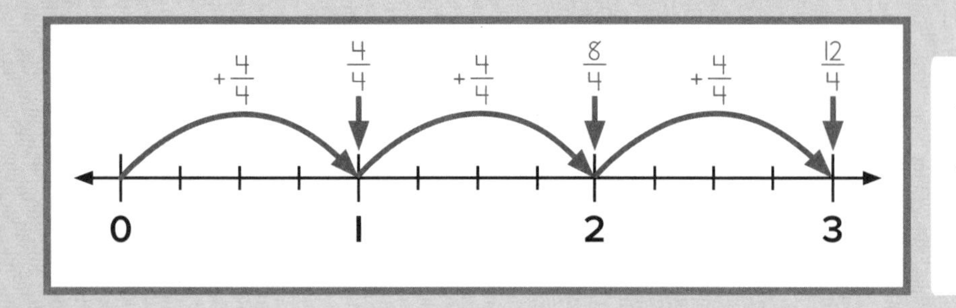

$\frac{4}{4}$ is 1 whole and $\frac{8}{4}$ is 2 wholes so $\frac{12}{4}$ is the same as 3 wholes. You make a jump of $\frac{4}{4}$ between each whole number.

Look at each fraction that is at the same mark as a whole number.

How are the fractions related to the whole numbers?

Each numerator is a multiple of 4.

When I multiply the whole number by the denominator the answer is the same as the numerator.

When I divide the numerator by the denominator the answer is the same as the whole number.

Label each mark on this number line with a common fraction.

Look at the common fractions you wrote at each whole number.

What relationships occur between the numbers?

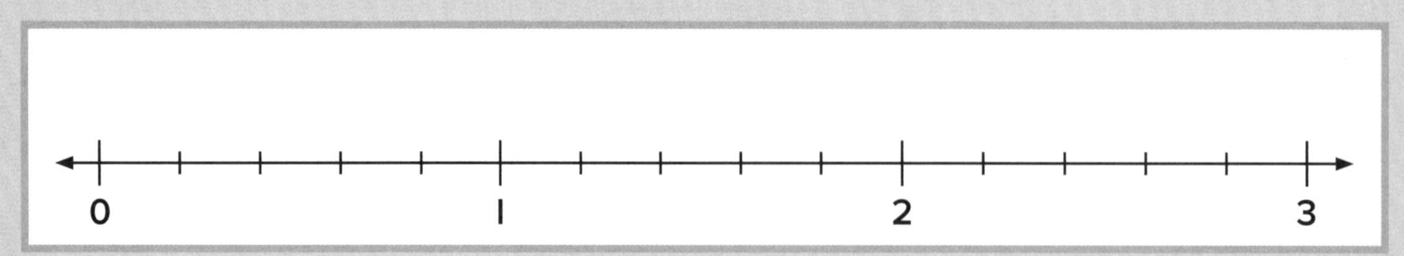

What is the closest whole number to $\frac{16}{5}$?

How could you figure it out?

I think that identifying which multiple of 5 is closest to 16 will help me figure it out quickly.

Step Up

1. Write each whole number as a fraction.
Use what you know about multiples to help you.

a. $1 = \frac{\_\_}{5}$ $2 = \frac{\_\_}{5}$ $3 = \frac{\_\_}{5}$ $4 = \frac{\_\_}{5}$ $5 = \frac{\_\_}{5}$

b. $1 = \frac{\_\_}{6}$ $2 = \frac{\_\_}{6}$ $3 = \frac{\_\_}{6}$ $4 = \frac{\_\_}{6}$ $5 = \frac{\_\_}{6}$

c. $1 = \frac{\_\_}{8}$ $2 = \frac{\_\_}{8}$ $3 = \frac{\_\_}{8}$ $4 = \frac{\_\_}{8}$ $5 = \frac{\_\_}{8}$

2. Write each fraction as a whole number.

a. $\frac{6}{3} =$ ____ $\frac{21}{3} =$ ____ $\frac{15}{3} =$ ____ $\frac{30}{3} =$ ____ $\frac{24}{3} =$ ____

b. $\frac{40}{4} =$ ____ $\frac{20}{4} =$ ____ $\frac{28}{4} =$ ____ $\frac{16}{4} =$ ____ $\frac{36}{4} =$ ____

3. Write the whole number that is closest to each fraction. Show your thinking.

a.  is closest to $\frac{25}{4}$

b.  is closest to $\frac{20}{6}$

c.  is closest to $\frac{37}{5}$

Step Ahead

Write each total as a **whole number.** Use what you know about equivalence between whole numbers and fractions to help you.

a. $\frac{6}{3} + \frac{8}{8} =$ ____

b. $\frac{21}{3} + \frac{10}{5} =$ ____

c. $\frac{40}{4} + \frac{42}{6} =$ ____

Step In — Introducing Mixed Numbers

Ruby and Raman share 5 licorice sticks.
If they share the sticks equally, how much will each person have?

They will need to break one of the sticks to share it. Then they will have two whole pieces each, plus half a piece each.

A **mixed number** is a **whole number** and a **common fraction** added together and written as a single number without the addition symbol.

$2 + \frac{1}{2} \rightarrow 2\frac{1}{2}$

Imagine all the licorice sticks were broken in half before sharing. How would you write each share as a fraction? $\frac{\square}{\square}$

Will each person still have the same amount as before? How do you know?

Mixed numbers can be made by joining together amounts in different ways.

$3\frac{2}{5}$ is the same as $3 + \frac{1}{5} + \frac{1}{5}$

$3\frac{2}{5}$ is the same as $2 + 1 + \frac{2}{5}$

How could you show $4\frac{3}{8}$ as the sum of other numbers?

Step Up

1. Read each story and look at the picture. Write the total as a mixed number.

a. Felix bought two sandwiches. The shaded parts show how much he ate. How much did Felix eat?

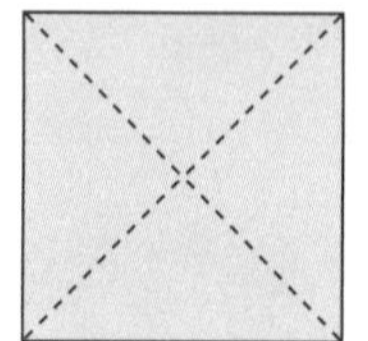
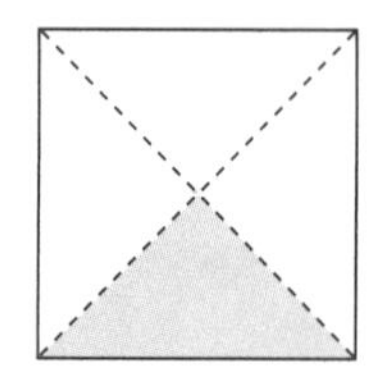

Felix ate ________ sandwiches.

b. Kylie's family bought three pizzas. The shaded parts show how much they ate. How much did they eat?

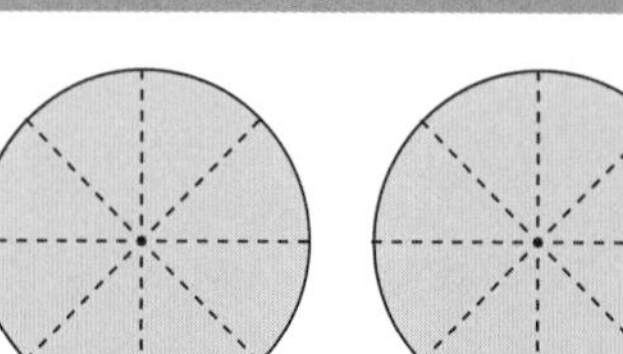
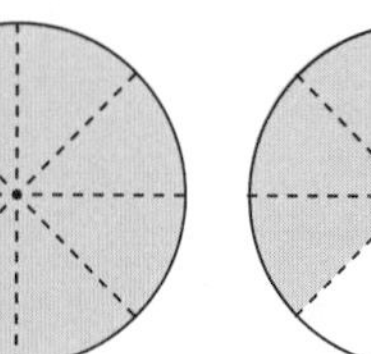

They ate ________ pizzas.

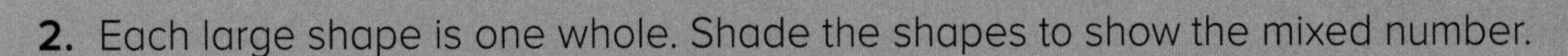

2. Each large shape is one whole. Shade the shapes to show the mixed number.

a. $3\frac{1}{5}$

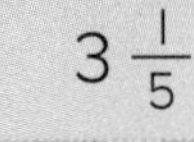

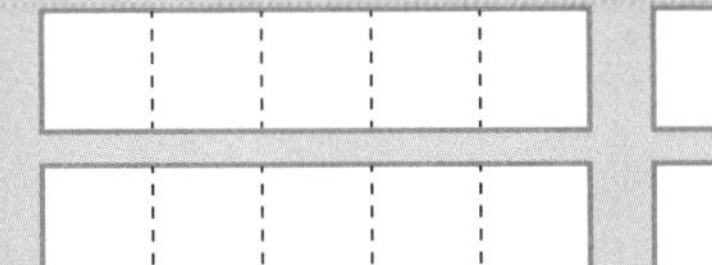

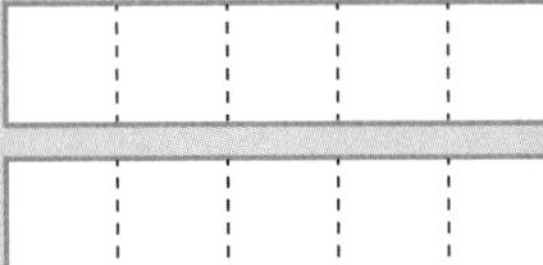

b. $2\frac{3}{6}$

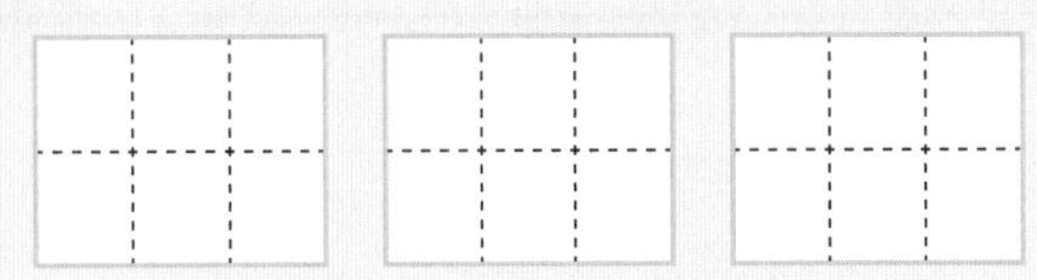

c. $1\frac{5}{8}$

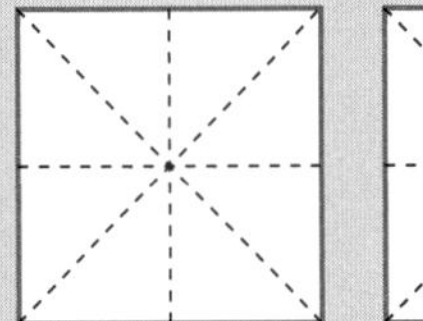

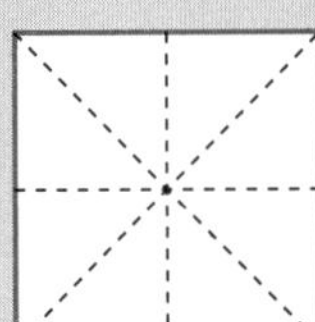

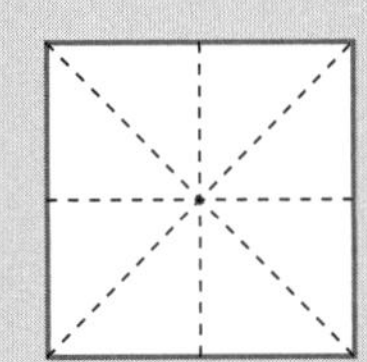

d. $3\frac{2}{4}$

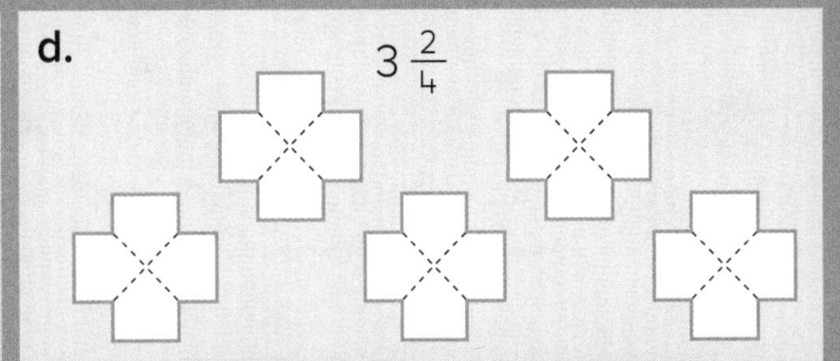

3. Each large shape is one whole. Complete each equation to show how much is shaded. Write the total as a **common fraction** then as a **mixed number**.

a.

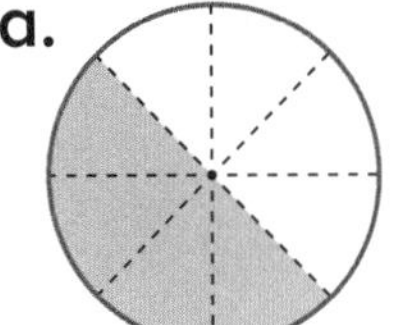

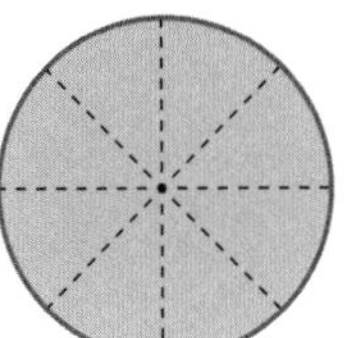

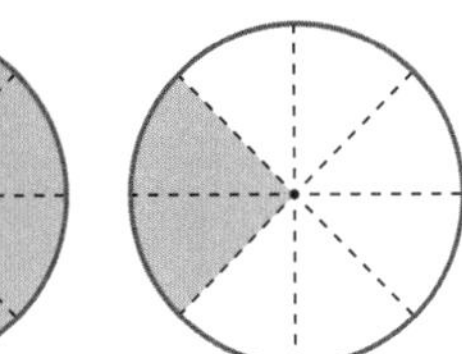

___ + ___ + ___ = ___ =

b.

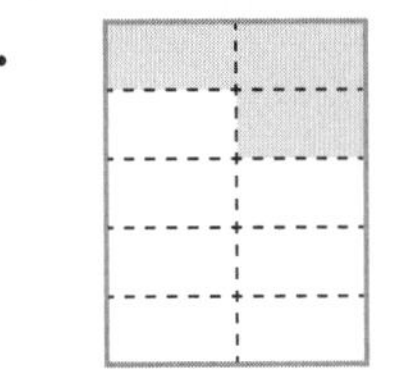

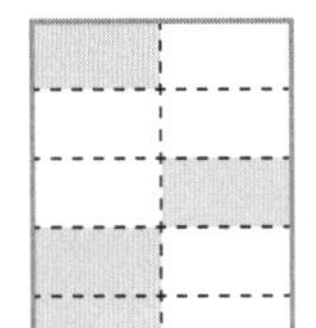

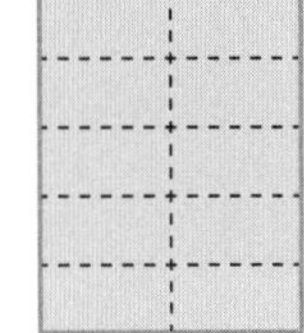

___ + ___ + ___ = ___ =

c.

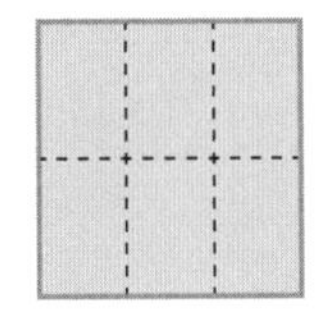

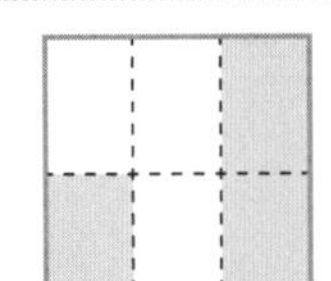

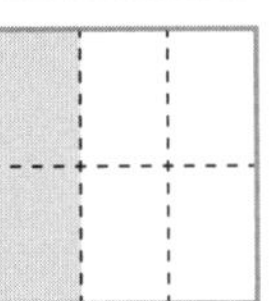

___ + ___ + ___ = ___ =

d.

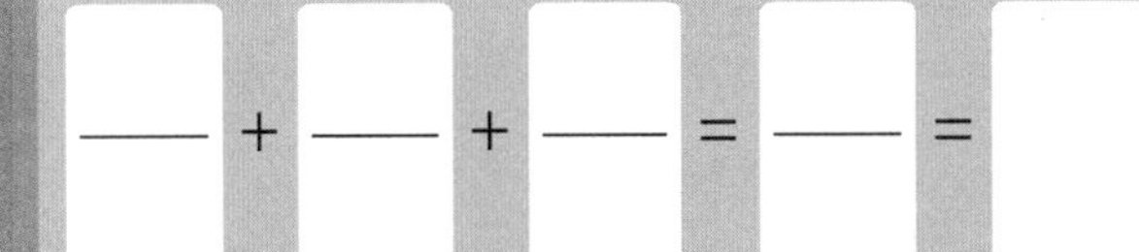

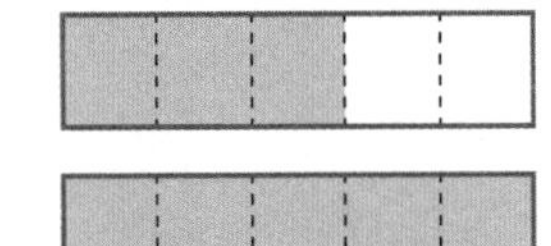

___ + ___ + ___ = ___ =

Step Ahead

Write three different ways to make a total of $3\frac{6}{8}$.
You can draw pictures on scrap paper to help.

$= 3\frac{6}{8}$ $= 3\frac{6}{8}$ $= 3\frac{6}{8}$

Step In — Exploring Equivalence between Mixed Numbers and Common Fractions

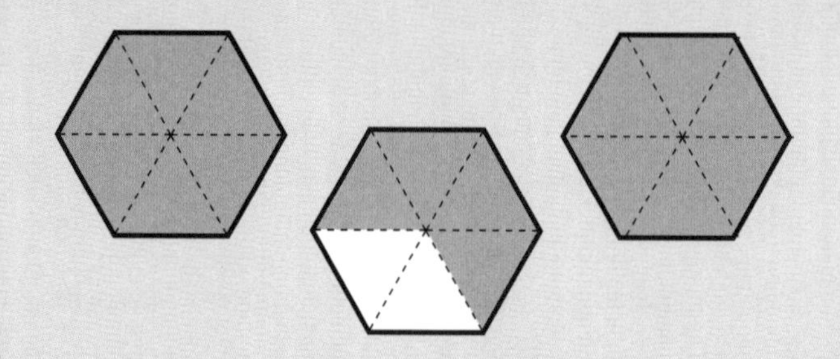

Anna says this picture shows $2\frac{4}{6}$.

Nancy says it shows $\frac{16}{6}$.

Who is correct? Why?

A number line can be used to show the position of both amounts.

What do you notice about their position?

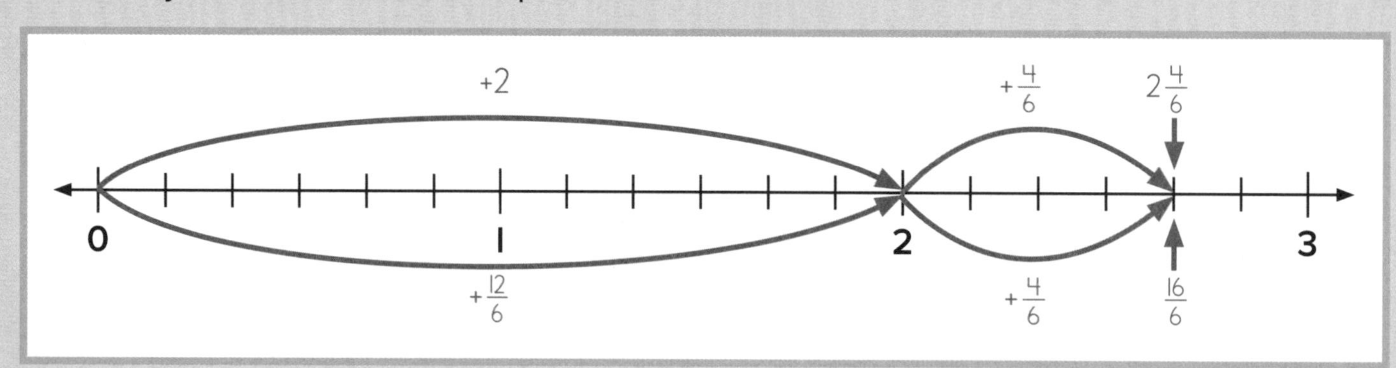

Loop the mark for $\frac{8}{6}$.

What is the equivalent mixed number?

How do you know?

Loop the mark for $1\frac{5}{6}$.

What is the equivalent common fraction?

Mixed numbers and common fractions are two different ways to represent the same amount. Could you use mixed numbers to describe amounts less than 1? Why or why not?

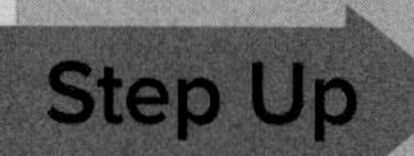

1. Write the equivalent mixed number and common fraction that describes the parts that are shaded. Each purple shape is one whole.

a.

☐ is the same as $\frac{\square}{\square}$

b.

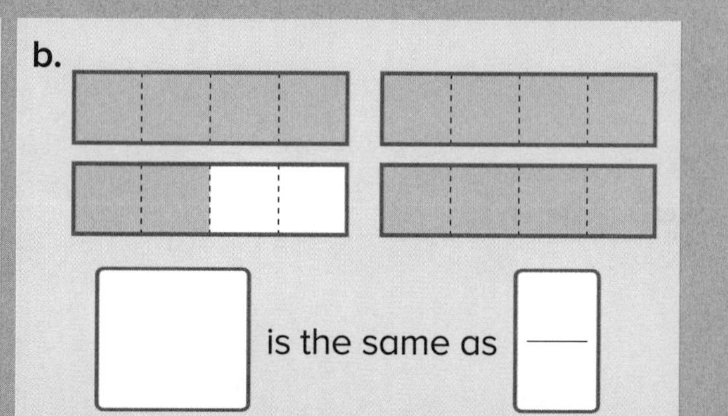

☐ is the same as $\frac{\square}{\square}$

2. Complete the common fractions and mixed numbers.

a.

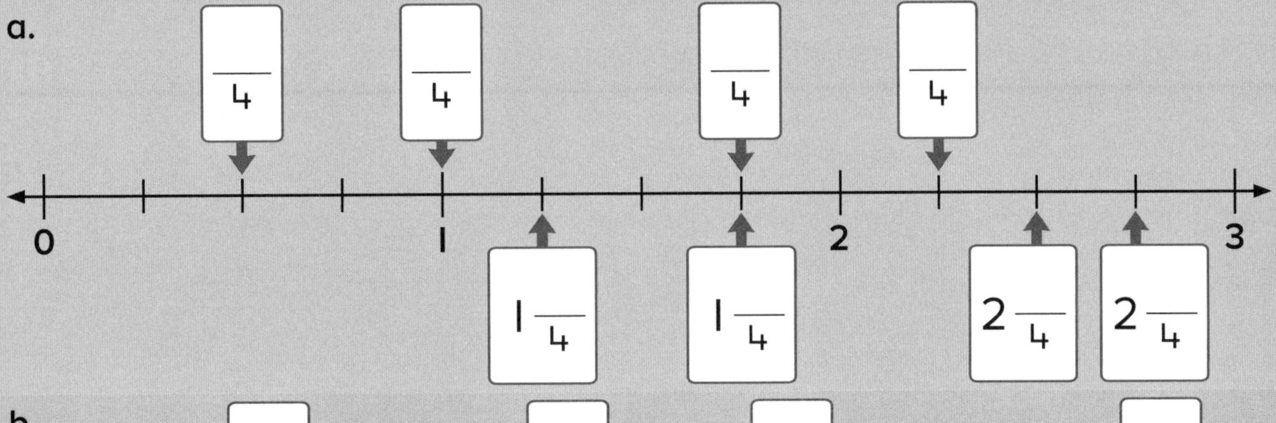

b.

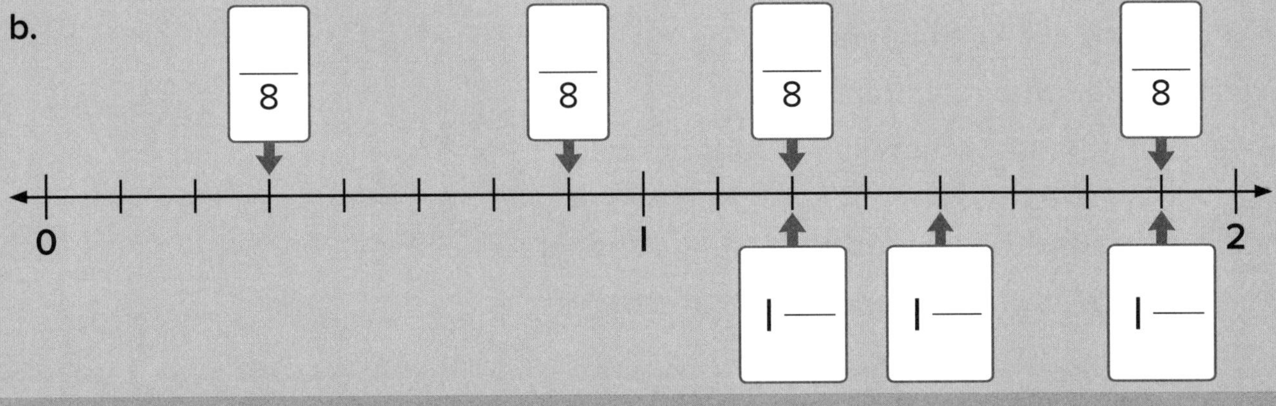

3. Use the number line in Question 2b to write these mixed numbers as common fractions.

a. $1\frac{10}{8} = \frac{}{}$	b. $1\frac{14}{8} = \frac{}{}$	c. $1\frac{9}{8} = \frac{}{}$	d. $1\frac{12}{8} = \frac{}{}$	e. $1\frac{16}{8} = \frac{}{}$

4. Write **<**, **>**, or **=** to complete each number sentence.
Use the number line in Question 2b to help you.

a. $\frac{8}{8}$ ◯ $1\frac{1}{8}$	b. $\frac{11}{8}$ ◯ $1\frac{3}{8}$	c. $1\frac{7}{8}$ ◯ $1\frac{2}{8}$	d. $1\frac{10}{8}$ ◯ $\frac{16}{8}$
e. $\frac{14}{8}$ ◯ 2	f. $\frac{13}{8}$ ◯ $1\frac{1}{8}$	g. $1\frac{4}{8}$ ◯ $\frac{12}{8}$	h. $1\frac{2}{8}$ ◯ 1

Step Ahead Loop the greater fraction.

$1\frac{2}{5}$ or $\frac{16}{10}$

Show your thinking.

Step In Adding Mixed Numbers

How could you figure out the total amount of water in these pitchers?

Daniela thought $2\frac{3}{8}$ is the same as $2 + \frac{3}{8}$, and $1\frac{4}{8}$ is the same as $1 + \frac{4}{8}$.

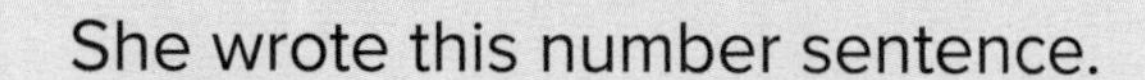

She wrote this number sentence.

She added the whole numbers first.

Next she added the fractions.

Then she added the two totals. What is the total?

$$2 + \frac{3}{8} + 1 + \frac{4}{8} = \square$$

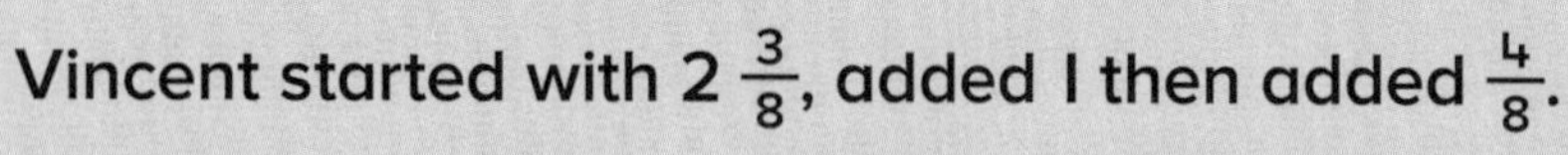

Vincent started with $2\frac{3}{8}$, added 1 then added $\frac{4}{8}$.

How can you show his method on this number line?

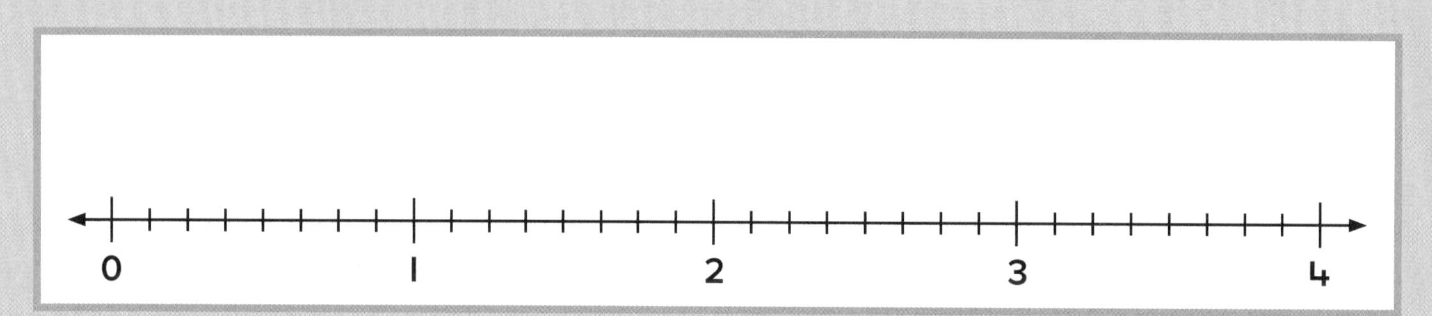

Step Up

1. Use Vincent's method to add these mixed numbers. Show your thinking on the number line.

a. $2\frac{2}{4} + 1\frac{1}{4} =$ ______

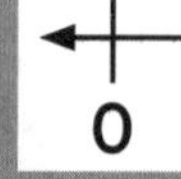

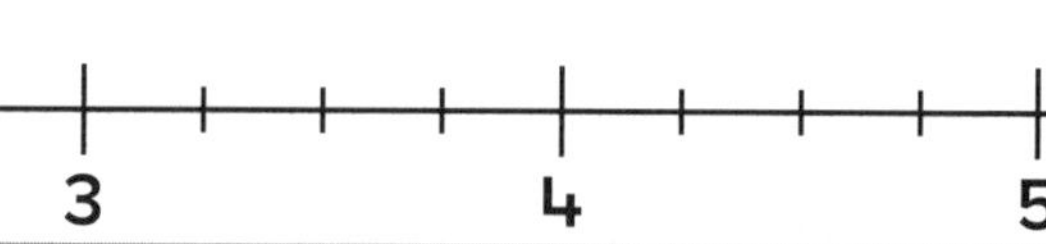

0 1 2 3 4 5

b. $2\frac{1}{5} + 1\frac{3}{5} =$ ______

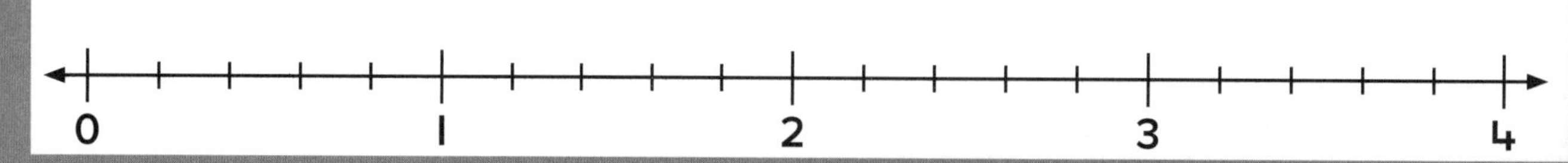

2. Use the same method to add these. Show your thinking on the number line.

a. $1\frac{3}{10} + \frac{5}{10} =$ ________

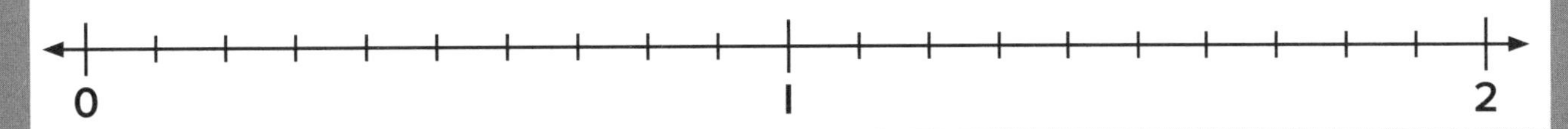

b. $1\frac{4}{8} + 1\frac{3}{8} =$ ________

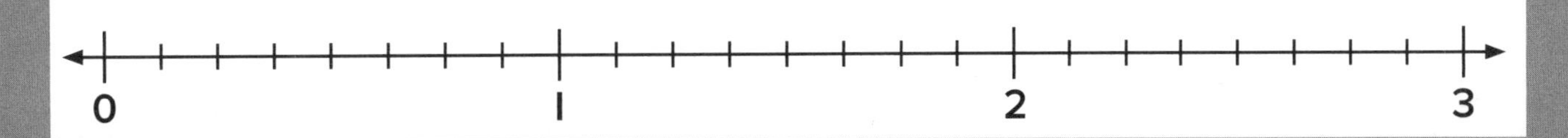

3. Use Daniela's method to add these mixed numbers. Show your thinking.

a. $3\frac{4}{8} + 2\frac{3}{8} =$ ________

b. $4\frac{3}{6} + 2\frac{2}{6} =$ ________

c. $3\frac{4}{12} + 5\frac{5}{12} =$ ________

d. $2\frac{6}{10} + 5\frac{2}{10} =$ ________

e. $4\frac{7}{12} + 1\frac{3}{12} =$ ________

f. $6\frac{1}{8} + 7\frac{5}{8} =$ ________

Step Ahead Write the missing numbers on this addition trail.

$3\frac{1}{12}$ → $+2\frac{3}{12}$ → ______ → $+5\frac{1}{12}$ → ______ → $+3\frac{4}{12}$ → ______ → $+8\frac{2}{12}$ → ______

Step In Adding Mixed Numbers (Composing Whole Numbers)

The owner of a cafe estimated that there were about $1\frac{5}{8}$ gallons of strawberry ice cream in one container and $2\frac{6}{8}$ gallons of lemon ice cream in another.

What is the total amount of ice cream in the two containers?

Do you think that it is more or less than 4 gallons?

How could you figure it out?

I could count on from $2\frac{6}{8}$.

I could split each mixed number into wholes and fractions. I know that $\frac{5}{8} + \frac{6}{8}$ will be greater than $\frac{8}{8}$. What can I do about that total?

In a standard mixed number, the fractional part has a numerator that is less than the denominator.

How would you change the total to show a standard mixed number?

What will be the new total? Will it still represent the same amount? How do you know?

Step Up

1. Count on from one mixed number to figure out the total. Draw jumps on the number line to show your thinking.

a. $2\frac{4}{5} + 1\frac{3}{5} =$ ________

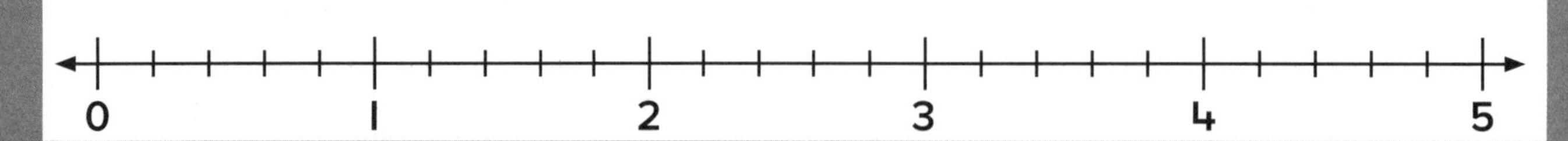

b. $1\frac{5}{6} + 1\frac{4}{6} =$ ________

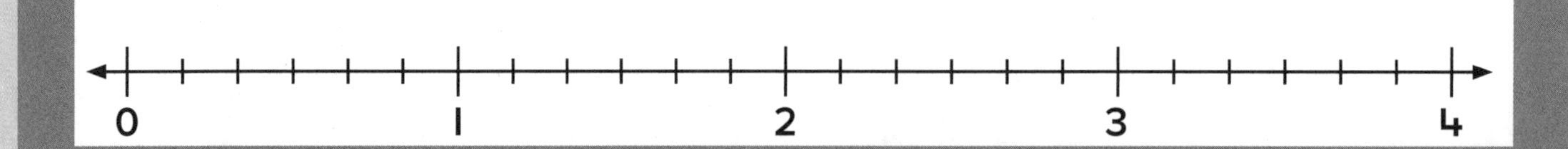

2. Split each mixed number into whole numbers and fractions before adding. Then write the total. Show your thinking.

a. $5\frac{3}{4} + 2\frac{2}{4} =$ ________

b. $3\frac{6}{8} + 4\frac{3}{8} =$ ________

c. $8\frac{2}{6} + 4\frac{5}{6} =$ ________

d. $6\frac{4}{12} + 3\frac{10}{12} =$ ________

e. $7\frac{3}{5} + 4\frac{3}{5} =$ ________

f. $2\frac{6}{8} + 4\frac{7}{8} =$ ________

g. $4\frac{5}{8} + 2\frac{3}{8} =$ ________

h. $5\frac{8}{12} + 14\frac{6}{12} =$ ________

Step Ahead

Figure out which pairs of mixed numbers add to make a whole number and color them the same. Some mixed numbers do not have a match.

$3\frac{11}{12}$ $2\frac{3}{12}$ $3\frac{6}{12}$ $1\frac{7}{12}$

$4\frac{9}{12}$ $4\frac{1}{12}$ $6\frac{5}{12}$ $5\frac{4}{12}$

Step In Solving Word Problems Involving Mixed Numbers

A gold necklace weighs 25 $\frac{5}{10}$ grams. One gold bracelet weighs 14 $\frac{3}{10}$ grams and another weighs 8 $\frac{9}{10}$ grams.

What is the total weight of the bracelets?

What do you need to find out? What information will help you?

How could you figure out the answer?

I could write number sentences to show how I would add on a number line.

I would split the mixed numbers into wholes and fractions. I think I will need to regroup.

Step Up

1. Figure out the answer to each problem. Show your thinking.

a. Asila drives to work each day. After she drives 4 $\frac{1}{2}$ miles, she still has another 3 $\frac{1}{2}$ miles to go. How far is it from her home to her work?

_______ miles

b. Two statues are being packed into a box. One weighs 7 $\frac{3}{8}$ lb and the other weighs 9 $\frac{4}{8}$ lb. What is their total weight?

_______ pounds

c. Tyler has a soup recipe that fills $\frac{6}{8}$ of a saucepan. If he makes double the quantity, how much more than one saucepan will he have?

_______ saucepan

d. A movie marathon has three movies. Each movie is 1 $\frac{3}{4}$ hours long. If they play one after another, how long will the marathon take?

_______ hours

2. Solve these problems. Show your thinking.

a. A seedling was in a pot that was $\frac{6}{8}$ full of soil. On Day 7, the seedling was $\frac{5}{8}$ of an inch tall. By Day 14, it had grown an extra $1\frac{2}{8}$ inches. How tall was the seedling on Day 14?

_______ in

b. Two full 2-liter bottles of water were in the fridge. After four days, one bottle was half full. The other had $1\frac{3}{10}$ liters left in it. How much water was there in total?

_______ L

c. Teresa ran one lap around the park in $1\frac{2}{4}$ minutes. Her second lap took $1\frac{3}{4}$ minutes. How many minutes did it take her to complete two laps?

_______ min

d. A chain was $8\frac{5}{12}$ feet long. It was joined to another chain so the total length was $10\frac{9}{12}$ feet. How long was the extra piece of chain?

_______ ft

Step Ahead

The sum of two mixed numbers is $3\frac{4}{10}$. Complete the equations to show six different pairs of numbers that will each add to that sum.

a. $3\frac{4}{10}$ = _______ + _______

b. $3\frac{4}{10}$ = _______ + _______

c. $3\frac{4}{10}$ = _______ + _______

d. $3\frac{4}{10}$ = _______ + _______

e. $3\frac{4}{10}$ = _______ + _______

f. $3\frac{4}{10}$ = _______ + _______

Step In Reviewing Factors and Multiples

Figure out each product. What do you notice?

1 × 30	______	3 × 10	5 × 6

Write the multiplication expression that is missing.

How did you decide what to write?

I looked for factors that I could double and halve.
1 x 30 is the same as 2 x 15.

What do you know about factors and multiples?

Look at the diagram on the right.

Write 40 in the first box. What numbers could you write in the second box so that the relationship is true?

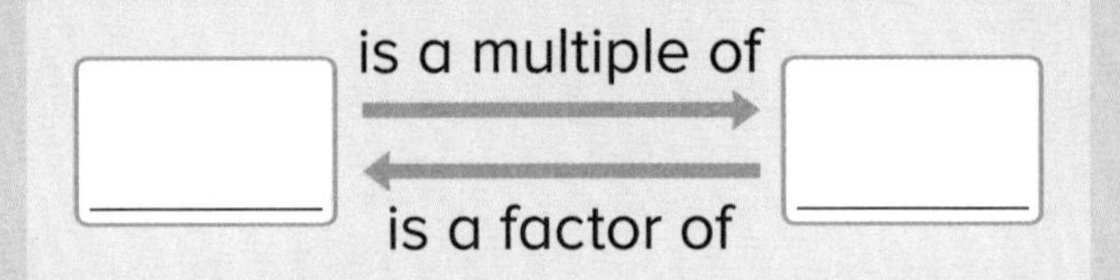

What are some other numbers that you could write in the second box?

Step Up

1. Write numbers to complete these.

a. 15 — is a multiple of → / ← is a factor of — ______

b. 56 — is a multiple of → / ← is a factor of — ______

c. ______ — is a multiple of → / ← is a factor of — 4

d. ______ — is a multiple of → / ← is a factor of — 9

e. 64 — is a multiple of → / ← is a factor of — ______

f.

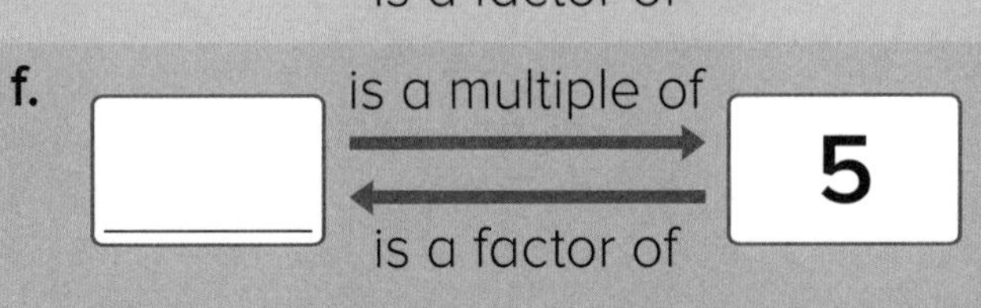

2. Complete these to show pairs of possible factors.

a. 40 is the same as
___ × ___
___ × ___
___ × ___
___ × ___

b. 54 is the same as
___ × ___
___ × ___
___ × ___
___ × ___

c. 70 is the same as
___ × ___
___ × ___
___ × ___
___ × ___

d. 88 is the same as
___ × ___
___ × ___
___ × ___
___ × ___

e. 60 is the same as
___ × ___
___ × ___
___ × ___
___ × ___
___ × ___

f. 80 is the same as
___ × ___
___ × ___
___ × ___
___ × ___
___ × ___

g. 72 is the same as
___ × ___
___ × ___
___ × ___
___ × ___
___ × ___

h. 48 is the same as
___ × ___
___ × ___
___ × ___
___ × ___
___ × ___

Step Ahead Write at least three numbers to match each label. One is done for you.

Numbers 1 to 100		
2 factors	3 factors	6 factors
11	___	___
___	___	___
___	___	___

Step In — Reviewing Strategies to Multiply One- and Two-Digit Numbers

Owen is planning a party.

He buys 6 bags of potato chips. There are 18 small packets of chips inside each bag.

How many small packets of chips has he bought?

How did you figure out the total?

Owen then buys 5 packs of apple juice. There are 24 juice boxes in each pack. How many boxes did he buy?

Owen needs at least 70 granola bars. How many boxes should he buy?

Step Up

1. Write the total cost. Show your thinking.

a. Buy 4 tickets — $56

$ ______

b. Buy 7 tickets — $35

$ ______

2. Write the products. Show your thinking.

a. 6 × 45 = ______

b. 72 × 8 = ______

c. 5 × 84 = ______

d. 55 × 3 = ______

3. Write the anwers that you can figure out in your head.

a. 35 × 8 = ______	**b.** 5 × 18 = ______	**c.** 60 × 9 = ______	**d.** 4 × 27 = ______
e. 0 × 99 = ______	**f.** 45 × 8 = ______	**g.** 3 × 52 = ______	**h.** 25 × 9 = ______

Step Ahead Write the missing number in each algorithm.

a.

	H	T	O
		4	7
×			8
	3		6

b.

	H	T	O
		6	2
×			
	2	4	8

c.

	H	T	O
			3
×			9
	5	6	7

Step In — Using the Associative Property to Multiply Two-Digit Numbers (Double and Halve)

I want to lay turf in an area that measures 12 yd by 15 yd. How many square yards of turf will I need?

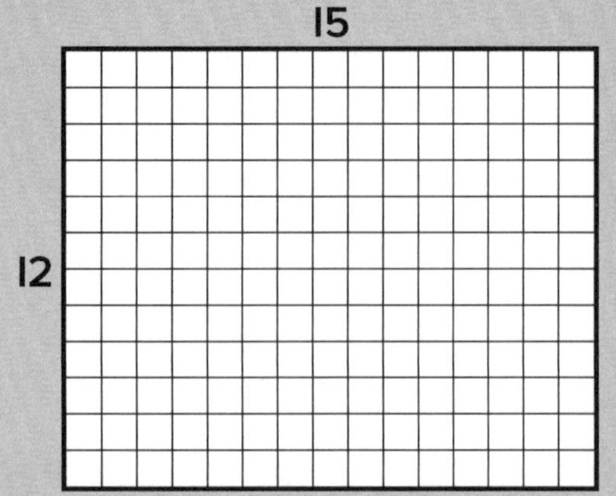

Look at this array. How could you figure out the number of square yards without counting all the squares?

There are 30 squares in 2 rows. 30 + 30 + 30 + 30 + 30 + 30 = 180.

You could also double and halve.
Imagine the array above is cut in half and rearranged like this.

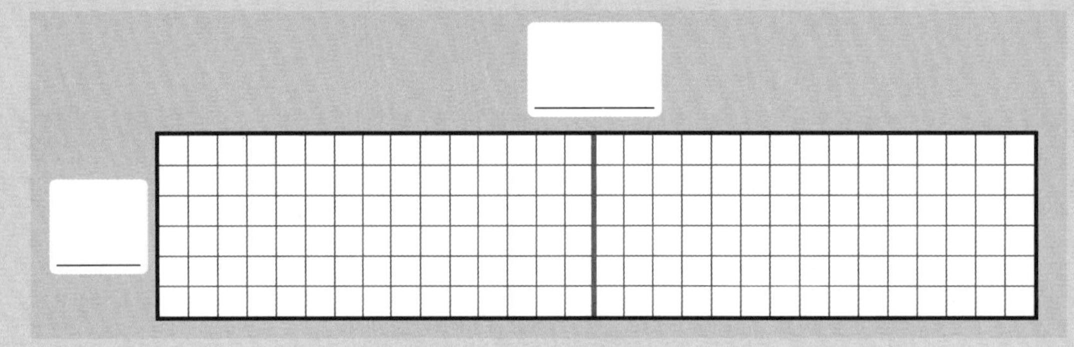

Has the total number of squares changed? Label the new dimensions.

Are these numbers easier to multiply in your head?

How will 6 × 30 change if you doubled and halved it again?

Step Up

1. Double one number and halve the other to make a problem that is easier to solve. Then write the product.

a. 15 × 14	b. 16 × 15	c. 35 × 8
____ × ____	____ × ____	____ × ____
15 × 14 = ____	16 × 15 = ____	35 × 8 = ____

2. Double and halve twice to solve each of these.

a. **15 × 28**

_____ × _____

_____ × _____

15 × 28 = _____

b. **13 × 16**

_____ × _____

_____ × _____

13 × 16 = _____

c. **28 × 25**

_____ × _____

_____ × _____

28 × 25 = _____

3. Calculate the products. Show the steps you use.

a. 25 × 24 = _____

b. 45 × 16 = _____

c. 18 × 4 = _____

d. 35 × 16 = _____

e. 12 × 75 = _____

f. 12 × 55 = _____

Step Ahead

Loop the expression that you **would not** use the double-and-halve strategy to solve. Then explain your reasoning.

45 × 12 **35 × 15** **16 × 25** **18 × 5**

_____

_____

_____

Step In Using the Associative Property to Multiply Two-Digit Numbers (Use Factors)

There are 15 small boxes inside each of these large boxes.

Write a multiplication sentence you could use to figure out the total number of small boxes in all the large boxes.

____

How would you calculate the total in your head?

I used factors to make the multiplication easier.

$15 \times 6 \times 4$

is the same as

$3 \times 5 \times 6 \times 4$

How would you multiply $3 \times 5 \times 6 \times 4$?
Which factors would you multiply first? Why?

What is the total number of small boxes?

Rozene counted 36 pine trees in one square of this field.

How could Rozene estimate the total number of trees in the whole field if there are the same number in each square?

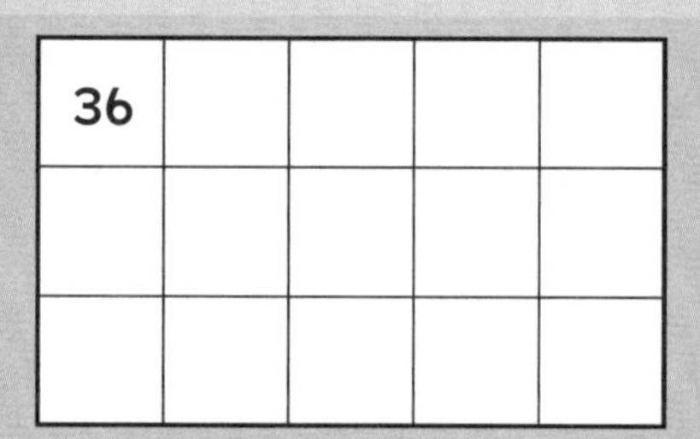

Step Up

1. Break **one** number into two factors to make it easier to multiply. Then complete the equation.

a. 35×8 is the same as ___ × ___ × ___ = ___

b. 6×35 is the same as ___ × ___ × ___ = ___

c. 25×28 is the same as ___ × ___ × ___ = ___

d. 45×4 is the same as ___ × ___ × ___ = ___

e. 12×15 is the same as ___ × ___ × ___ = ___

2. Break **both** numbers into two factors. Then write an equation showing the four factors in the order you would multiply them to figure out the product.

a. 40 × 18 **is the same as** 4 × 10 × 9 × 2

10 × 9 × 4 × 2 = ______

b. 36 × 15 **is the same as** ____ × ____ × ____ × ____

______ = ______

c. 12 × 24 **is the same as** ____ × ____ × ____ × ____

______ = ______

d. 14 × 45 **is the same as** ____ × ____ × ____ × ____

______ = ______

e. 25 × 16 **is the same as** ____ × ____ × ____ × ____

______ = ______

Step Ahead

For each of these, write the product. Then write the different pairs of **two-digit** numbers that may have been factored to create these equations.

a. 5 × 2 × 6 × 9 = ______

12 × 45

______

b. 3 × 5 × 8 × 7 = ______

24 × 35

______

Step In Investigating Perfect Squares

Look at this growing pattern. How many squares are in the first picture? How many squares have been added to make the second picture?

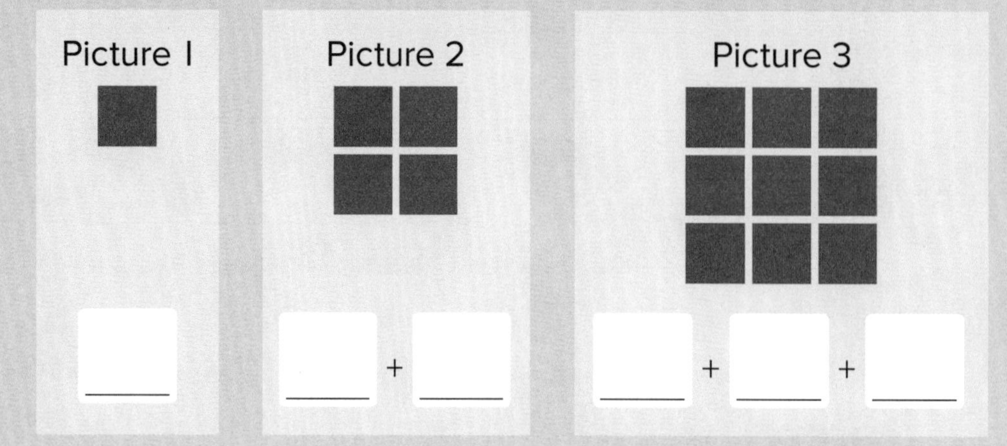

How many squares have been added to make the third picture?

What do you think the fourth and fifth pictures will look like? How many squares will be added each time?

Color squares to show your thinking. Then write the addition sentences to match.

Picture 4 ___ + ___ + ___ + ___

Picture 5 ___ + ___ + ___ + ___ + ___

What do you notice about the numbers being added each time?

Step Up

1. Complete the addition sentences to describe each picture on page 160. Then write the related multiplication sentence.

Picture 1	1	=	1	=	1 × 1
Picture 2	1 + 3	=	___	=	___ × ___
Picture 3	1 + ___ + ___	=	___	=	___ × ___
Picture 4	___ + ___ + ___ + ___	=	___	=	___ × ___
Picture 5	___ + ___ + ___ + ___ + ___	=	___	=	___ × ___

2. Imagine there were two more pictures in the pattern from Question 1. Write the matching addition and multiplication sentences.

Picture 6	___	=	___	=	___ × ___
Picture 7	___	=	___	=	___ × ___

Step Ahead

This table shows a square number pattern.

a. Complete the table

Picture (Input)	2	4	6		10	12	15
Squares (Output)		16	36	64			

b. Write an equation to show the process for figuring out any square number.

___

7.6

Step In — Solving Word Problems Involving Multiplication (Two-Digit Numbers)

The Bay City Tigers need to buy 25 pairs of shorts.

How could you figure out the total cost of the shorts?

Abraham wrote the partial products to figure out the total.

25 × 27

20 × 20 = 400
20 × 7 = 140
5 × 20 = 100
5 × 7 = 35

What is the total cost of the shorts? How do you know?

The Mountain Warriors need to buy 12 team shirts and 12 pairs of shorts. What will be the total cost?

I will call the total cost of the shirts and shorts T.
T = (35 + 27) × 12

Step Up

1. Use the uniform prices above. The Cincinnati Chargers need to buy 16 complete uniforms. What is the total cost?

Working Space

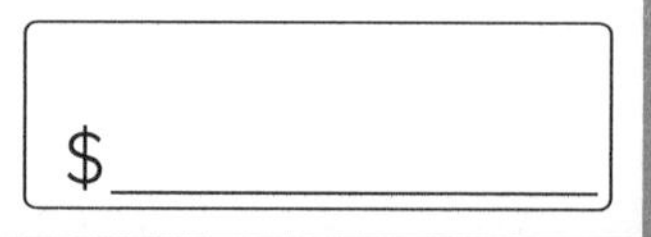

2. Solve these word problems. Show your thinking.

a. Sweaters cost $47 each. This is $15 more than the price of a cap. 25 of these caps were sold at one game. What was the total amount made in sales from caps?

$ ______

b. A stadium parking lot has 38 rows. There are 42 spaces in each row. 200 spaces are reserved for staff. How many spaces are there for supporters?

______ spaces

c. Sports bags cost $29 each. If this price was reduced by $3, how much would be **saved** when buying 24 bags?

$ ______

d. A club has $500 to spend. It buys 5 footballs at $49 each and 3 helmets at $75 each. How much money is left over?

$ ______

Step Ahead

Write a word problem to match this equation. Then figure out the product.

42 × 13 = ______

______

______

______

Step In Subtracting Common Fractions (Number Line Model)

Terek went to the movies and bought a small box of popcorn.
At the start of the movie, the box was $\frac{7}{8}$ full.
At the end of the movie, there was $\frac{2}{8}$ of the box left over.

How much popcorn did Terek eat during the movie?

What equation could you write?

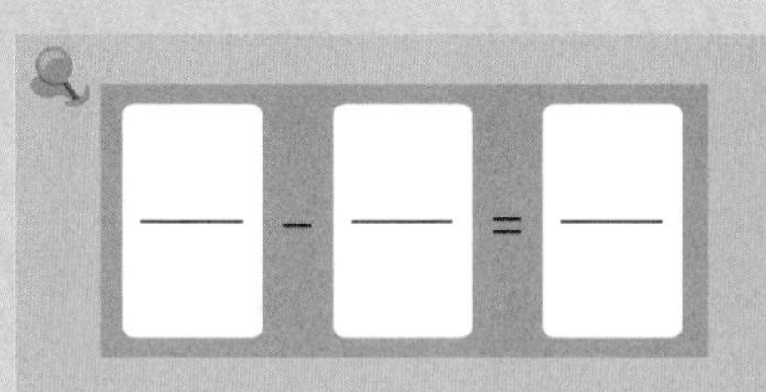

When you subtract fractions what happens to the numerator?
What happens to the denominator?

How could you show the difference on this number line?

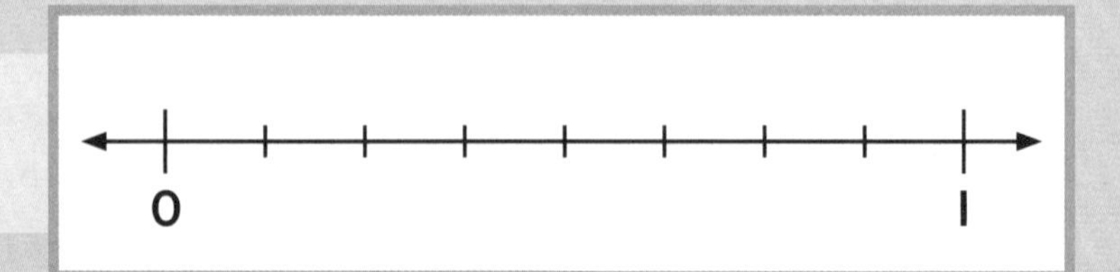

Grace and her friend bought a box of popcorn to share.
They each ate $\frac{3}{8}$ of the popcorn in the box.
How much popcorn was left over? How could you figure out the amount?

Step Up

1. Draw and label jumps to match each equation.

a. $\frac{11}{6} - \frac{7}{6} = \frac{4}{6}$

$\frac{0}{6}$ $\frac{6}{6}$ $\frac{12}{6}$

b. $\frac{13}{8} - \frac{4}{8} = \frac{9}{8}$

$\frac{0}{8}$ $\frac{8}{8}$ $\frac{16}{8}$

c. $\frac{16}{4} - \frac{12}{4} = \frac{4}{4}$

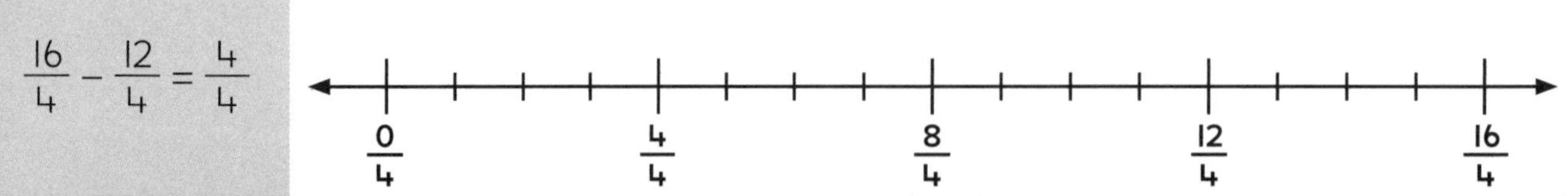

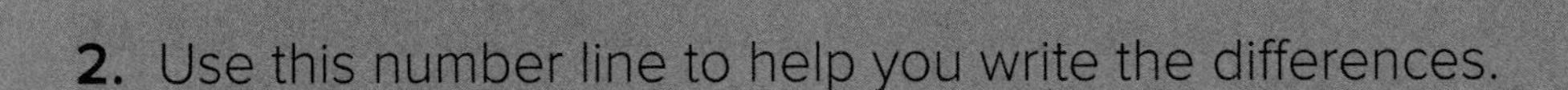

2. Use this number line to help you write the differences.

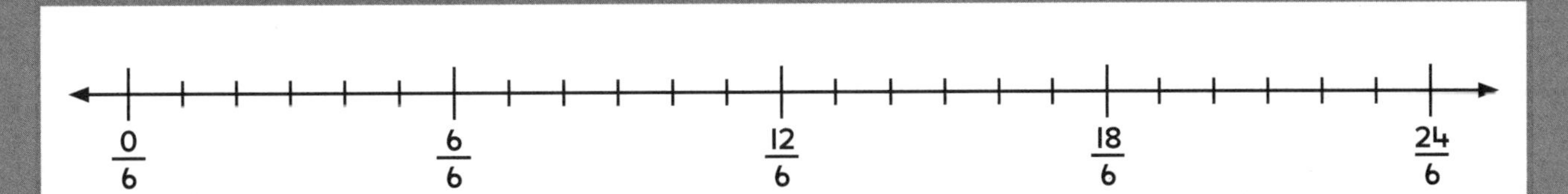

a. $\frac{15}{6} - \frac{4}{6} = \frac{\square}{\square}$	**b.** $\frac{\square}{\square} = \frac{20}{6} - \frac{8}{6}$	**c.** $\frac{17}{6} - \frac{2}{6} = \frac{\square}{\square}$
d. $\frac{\square}{\square} = \frac{23}{6} - \frac{9}{6}$	**e.** $\frac{21}{6} - \frac{16}{6} = \frac{\square}{\square}$	**f.** $\frac{\square}{\square} = \frac{18}{6} - 1$

3. Use what you know about subtracting fractions to calculate the difference between each pair of numbers.

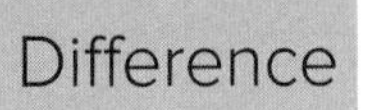

a. $\frac{9}{10}$ $\frac{4}{10}$	**b.** $\frac{15}{4}$ $\frac{12}{4}$	**c.** $\frac{5}{8}$ $\frac{23}{8}$	**d.** 1 $\frac{3}{8}$
Difference $\frac{\square}{\square}$	Difference $\frac{\square}{\square}$	Difference $\frac{\square}{\square}$	Difference $\frac{\square}{\square}$

4. Write the missing fraction in each equation.

a. $\frac{11}{12} = \frac{18}{12} - \frac{\square}{\square}$	**b.** $\frac{34}{8} - \frac{\square}{\square} = \frac{26}{8}$	**c.** $\frac{2}{3} = \frac{\square}{\square} - \frac{14}{3}$

Step Ahead

Complete each equation so that the difference is **between 2 and 3**. Use the number lines on pages 164 and 165 to help you.

a. $\frac{16}{4} - \frac{\square}{\square} = \frac{\square}{\square}$	**b.** $\frac{25}{6} - \frac{\square}{\square} = \frac{\square}{\square}$
c. $\frac{20}{8} - \frac{\square}{\square} = \frac{\square}{\square}$	**d.** $\frac{22}{4} - \frac{\square}{\square} - \frac{\square}{\square}$

Working Space

Step In Calculating the Difference between Mixed Numbers

One bunch of bananas weighs $5\frac{3}{4}$ pounds.
Another bunch weighs $3\frac{2}{4}$ pounds.
How could you figure out the difference in mass between the two bunches?

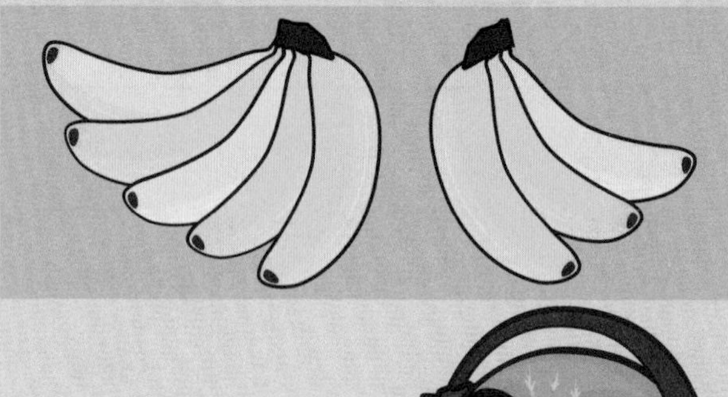

I would start with $5\frac{3}{4}$ then take away $3\frac{2}{4}$ in smaller jumps. One jump would be 3 and the next jump would be $\frac{2}{4}$.

When I add mixed numbers, I add the whole numbers and fractions separately then combine their totals. I think this will work for subtraction too.

How was addition used to calculate the difference on this number line?

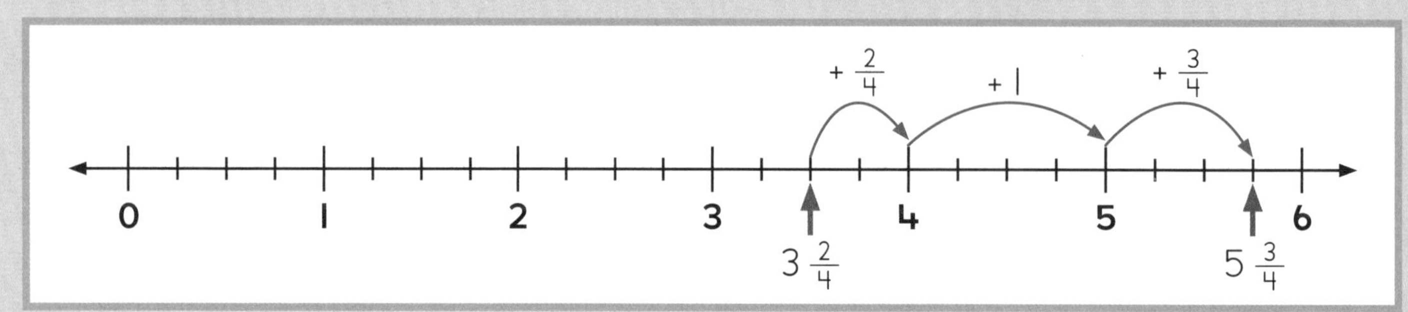

How could subtraction be used to find the difference?

Step Up

1. Calculate the difference. Draw jumps on the number line to show your thinking.

a. $3\frac{4}{6} - 1\frac{2}{6} =$

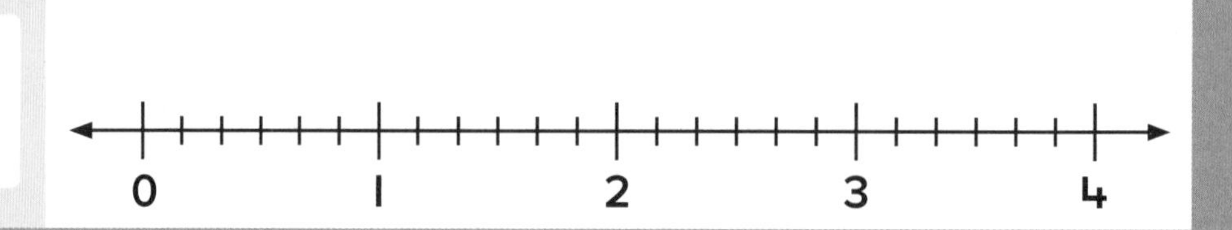

b. $4\frac{4}{5} - 3\frac{3}{5} =$

2. Calculate the difference. Draw jumps on the number line to show your thinking.

a. $3\frac{2}{4} - 1\frac{1}{4} =$ ☐

b. $2\frac{6}{8} - 1\frac{3}{8} =$ ☐

3. Calculate the difference. Show your thinking.

a. $6\frac{7}{8} - 2\frac{4}{8} =$ ☐

b. $5\frac{4}{10} - 4\frac{2}{10} =$ ☐

c. $6\frac{10}{12} - 1\frac{7}{12} =$ ☐

d. $10\frac{5}{6} - 2\frac{3}{6} =$ ☐

e. $9\frac{8}{12} - 8\frac{2}{12} =$ ☐

f. $6\frac{7}{10} - 1\frac{7}{10} =$ ☐

Step Ahead Write the missing numbers on this trail.

Step In — Calculating the Difference between Mixed Numbers (Decomposing Whole Numbers)

Morgan has two pet lizards. One is $3\frac{4}{8}$ inches long and the other is $1\frac{7}{8}$ inches long. How could you figure out the difference between their lengths?

Yara figured it out like this.
What did she do to make the subtraction easier?

$3\frac{4}{8} - 1\frac{7}{8}$

is the same as

$2\frac{12}{8} - 1\frac{7}{8}$

$2 - 1 = 1$

$\frac{12}{8} - \frac{7}{8} = \frac{5}{8}$

The difference is $1\frac{5}{8}$ inches.

How could you use addition to help you calculate the difference?

Look at the number lines below.

What is the same about the two methods shown?
What is different?

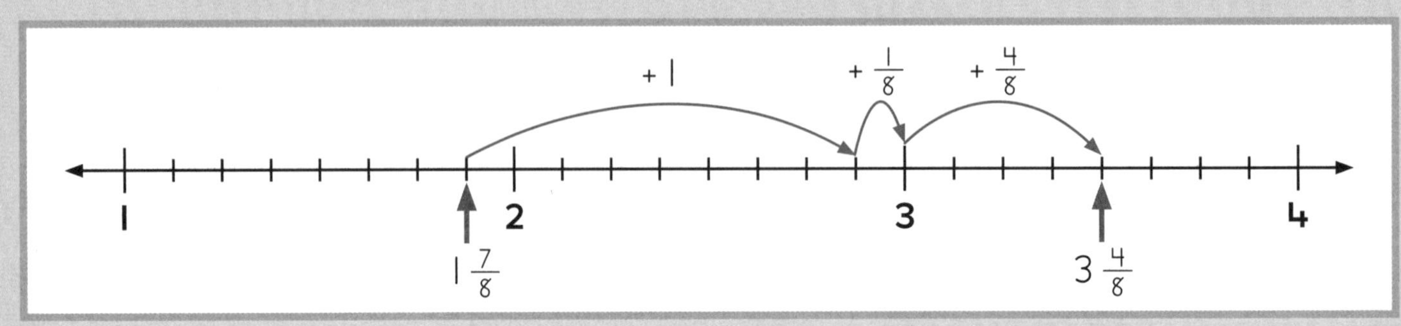

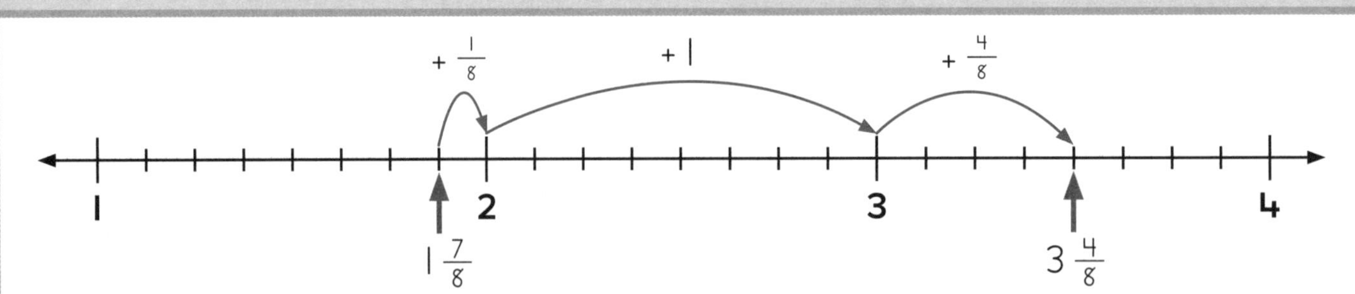

Step Up

1. Calculate the difference. Draw jumps on the number line to show your thinking.

$3\frac{2}{6} - 2\frac{5}{6} =$ ☐

2. Calculate the difference. Draw jumps on the number line to show your thinking.

a. $5\frac{1}{3} - 2\frac{2}{3} =$ ☐

b. $4\frac{1}{5} - 3\frac{3}{5} =$ ☐

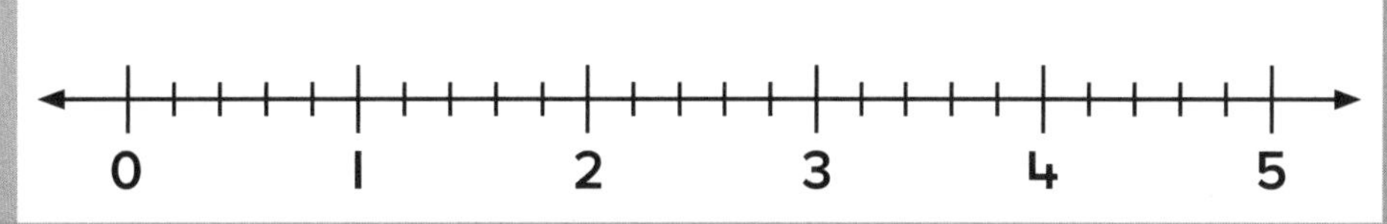

3. Calculate the difference. Show your thinking.

a. $7\frac{1}{6} - 2\frac{4}{6} =$ ______

b. ______ $= 6\frac{2}{5} - 5\frac{4}{5}$

c. $9\frac{3}{10} - 4\frac{3}{10} =$ ______

d. ______ $= 14\frac{2}{8} - 1\frac{3}{8}$

e. $16\frac{4}{12} - 11\frac{9}{12} =$ ______

f. ______ $= 5 - 3\frac{6}{8}$

Step Ahead

Look at these related equations.

$4 + 2 = 6$ $2 + 4 = 6$ $6 - 2 = 4$ $6 - 4 = 2$

Each sentence describes the same two parts (4 and 2) that make a total (6).

Write the related equations for the equation shown.

$3\frac{7}{8} + 2\frac{4}{8} = 6\frac{3}{8}$ ______

______ ______

Step In Solving Word Problems Involving Mixed Numbers and Common Fractions

Abel used a watering can and poured $3\frac{3}{4}$ quarts of water onto his seedlings which were in a garden bed that was $5\frac{3}{4}$ feet long. Afterward, the watering can had $4\frac{3}{4}$ quarts of water left in it.

How much water was in the watering can at the start? How could you figure it out?

Which information is important?

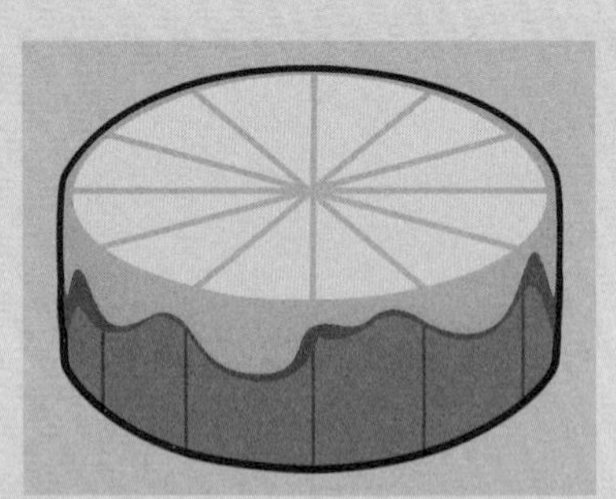

Two identical cakes were baked for a big party. Each cake was cut into twelfths. Halfway through the party, $\frac{3}{12}$ of one cake had been eaten. The other cake had 4 pieces missing and 5 people were standing near it.

How much cake was still left?
Which operations will you use to figure it out?

Step Up

1. Figure out the answer to each problem. Show your thinking.

a. Bixy and Boxy are cats. Bixy weighs $4\frac{1}{10}$ kilograms. The total weight of the cats is $9\frac{7}{10}$ kilograms. How much does Boxy weigh?

_______ kg

b. A bucket held $3\frac{1}{2}$ gallons of water. $1\frac{1}{2}$ gallons were used for watering lettuce and $\frac{1}{2}$ gallon was used for carrots. How much water was left?

_______ gal

c. A builder cut $2\frac{7}{8}$ inches off a length of lumber. The piece left was $5\frac{3}{8}$ inches long. How long was the piece of lumber at the start?

_______ in

d. Lily visited her dad. It took $2\frac{1}{4}$ hours to get there. It usually takes $1\frac{3}{4}$ hours. How much later than usual did she arrive?

_______ hr

2. Solve these problems. Show your thinking.

a. Wendell cut 5 oranges into sixths for a picnic. Afterward, there was only $\frac{4}{6}$ of an orange left. How many oranges and part oranges were eaten?

_______ oranges

b. A baker used $3\frac{7}{12}$ sticks of licorice and had $1\frac{5}{12}$ sticks left so she ate $\frac{4}{12}$ of a stick. How many sticks did the baker have at the start?

_______ sticks

c. Mom had $7\frac{2}{6}$ yards of fabric rolled up. She cut off $\frac{3}{6}$ yards for a quilt she was making. Some squares on that quilt were $\frac{1}{6}$ yard long on each side. She also cut $2\frac{4}{6}$ yards off the roll to make a second quilt. How much fabric was left on the roll?

_______ yd

Step Ahead

Write a subtraction word story that involves mixed numbers and common fractions.

____

____

____

____

____

____

____

Step In Solving Word Problems Involving Dot Plots

Two friends are training for a triathlon.

The dot plots below show the distances they ran.

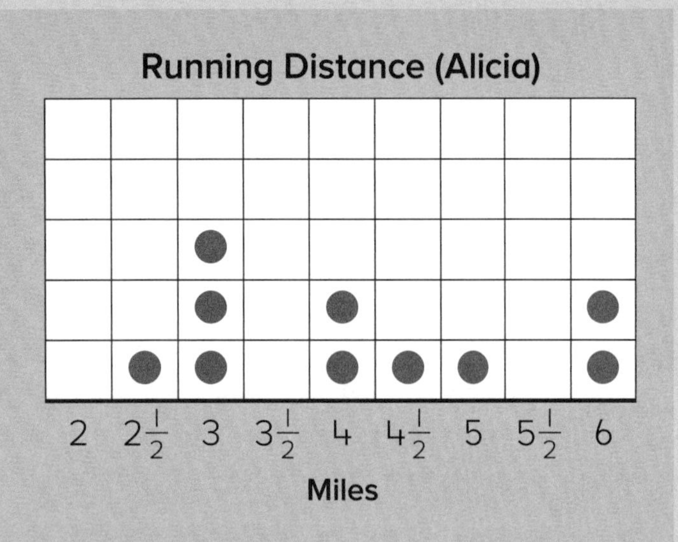

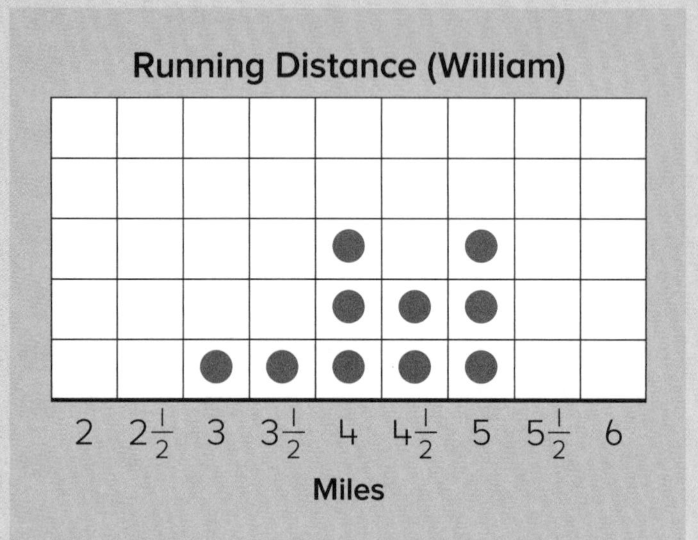

How many times did each person go running?

Who ran the greatest distance **in one run**?

What was the most common distance that each person ran?

Who ran the greater **total** distance?

What is the difference between the total distances that each person ran?

How did you figure out the answer?

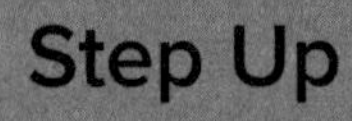

Step Up

1. Your teacher will give you a support page. Draw ● on the dot plot below to show the distance that Riku cycled each day.

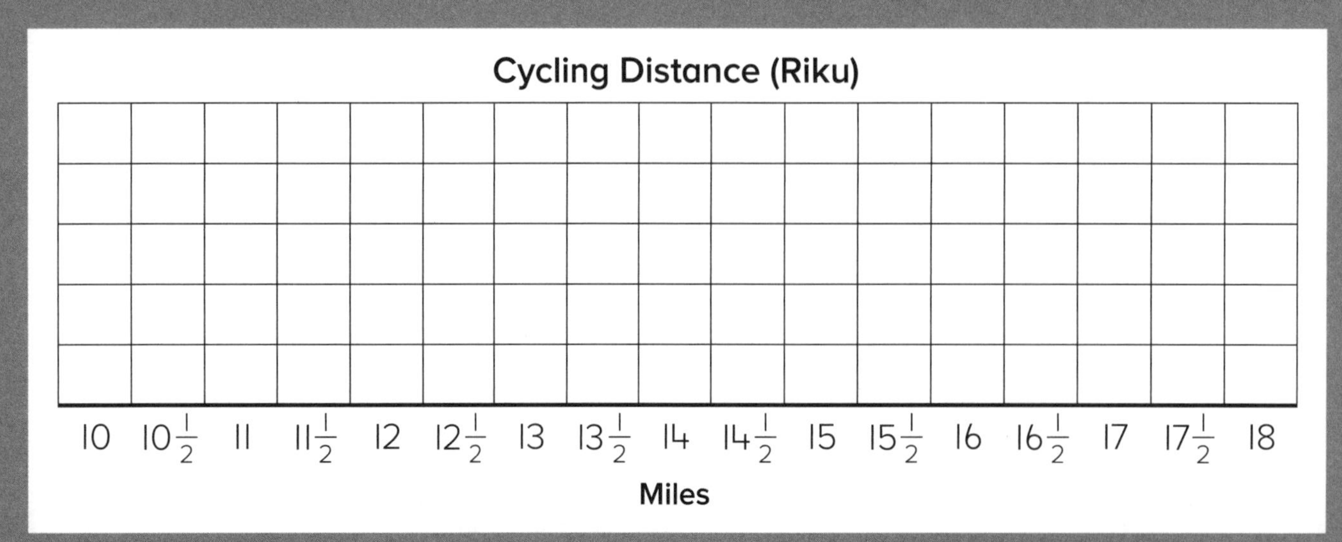

2. Your teacher will give you a support page. Draw ● on the dot plot below to show the distance that Fernando cycled each day.

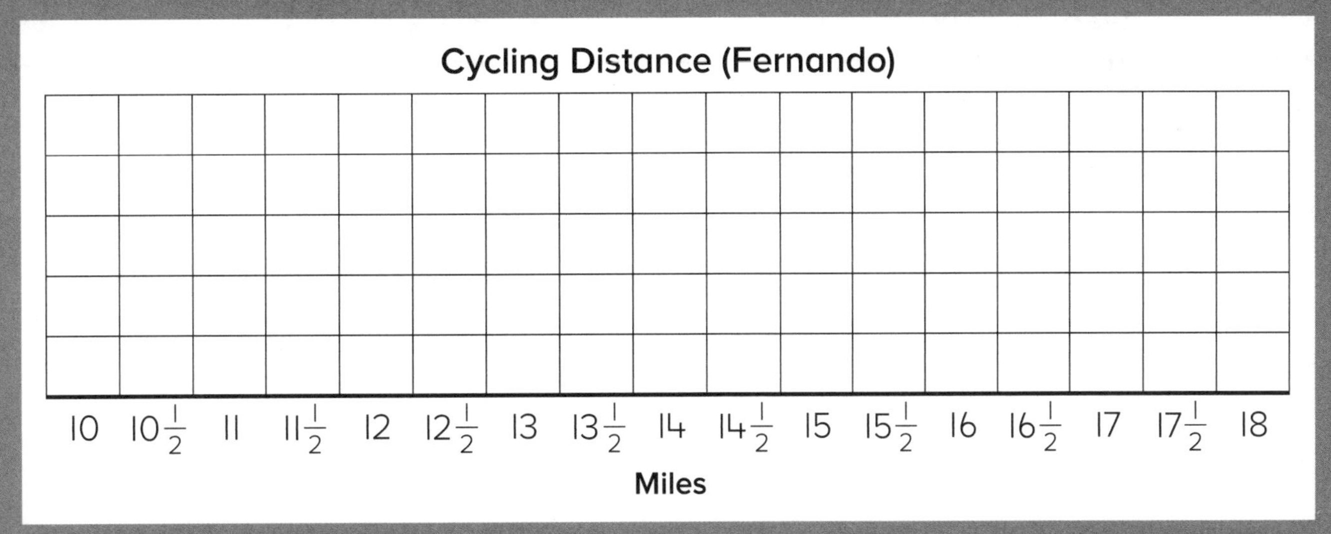

3. Refer to the dot plots in Questions 1 and 2 to answer these questions.

a. How many times did each person go cycling? ______

b. Who cycled the greatest distance in one ride? ______

c. What distance did Riku cycle most often? ______ miles

d. What is the difference between greatest distances each person cycled? ______ mile

Step Ahead

Refer to the dot plot in Question 2. Figure out the total distance Fernando cycled. Show your working.

______ miles

Step In Introducing Stem-and-Leaf Plots

This stem-and-leaf plot shows the number of points that Henry scored in his last 12 basketball games.

Points Scored					
Stem	Leaf				
0	3	4			
1	2	3	3	6	7
2	0	1	5	7	
3	1				

Key
3 | 1 means 31

His highest score was 31 points.

What are some other scores that he has recorded? How do you know?

What is the lowest score that he recorded?

What score did he record more than once?

The stem shows the digits in the tens place.
The leaf shows the digits in the ones place.
So, in the stem-and-leaf plot above, 3 | 1 means 31.

Read the scores in each row from left to right. What do you notice?

The scores are ordered from least to greatest.

Henry scored 18 points in his last game of the season. Write this score in the plot.

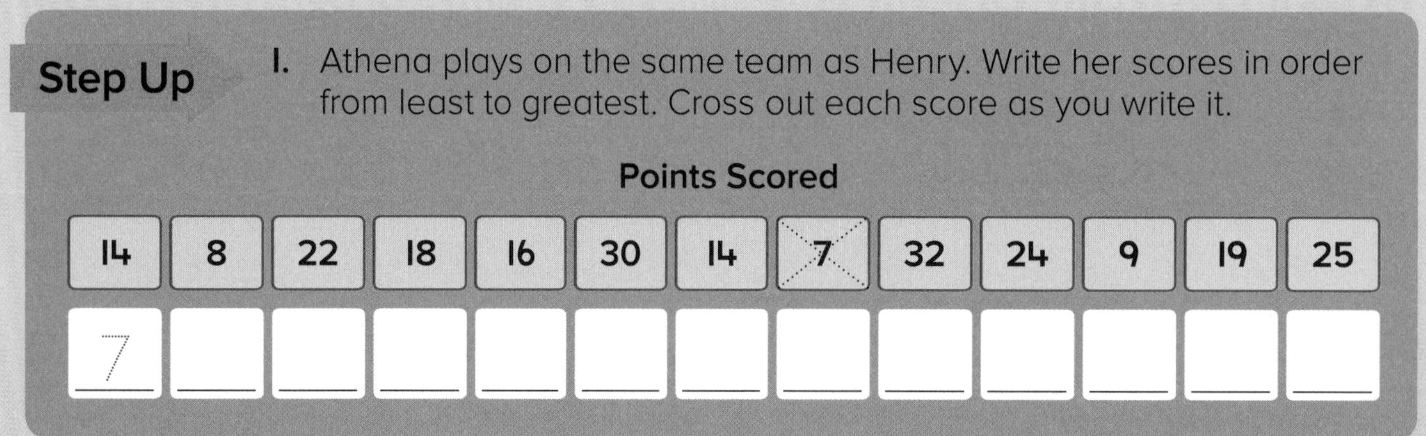

Step Up

1. Athena plays on the same team as Henry. Write her scores in order from least to greatest. Cross out each score as you write it.

Points Scored

14	8	22	18	16	30	14	~~7~~	32	24	9	19	25
7												

2. Record Athena's scores from Question 1 in this stem-and-leaf plot.

Points Scored									
Stem	Leaf								
0									
1									
2									
3									

3. Refer to the stem-and-leaf plot above to answer these questions.

a. What was Athena's lowest score? ______ points

b. Which score was recorded more than once? ______ points

c. How many times did she score more than 15 points? ______ times

d. How many times did she score fewer than 10 points? ______ times

e. What is the difference between her highest and lowest scores? ______ points

Step Ahead Use the stem-and-leaf plots on pages 174 and 175. Figure out the difference between the total points scored by Henry and Athena. Show your working.

______ points

Step In Introducing Decimal Fractions

Look at this picture.

Each square is one whole.
What amount is shaded?

What are the different ways you can write this number without using words?

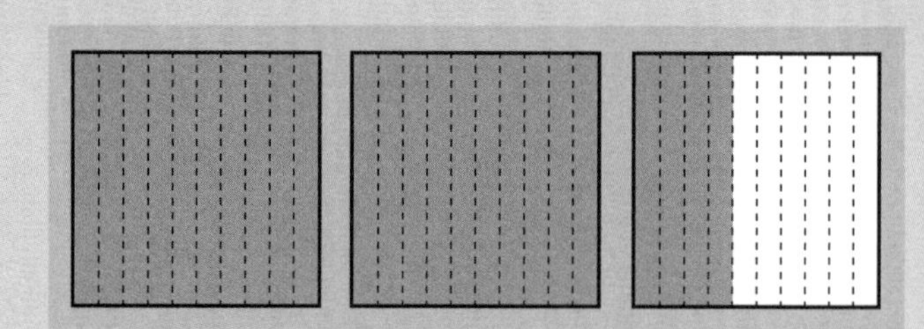

When fractions have a denominator that is a power of 10 they can easily be written in a place-value chart. Powers of 10 include numbers such as 10, 100, 1,000 and so on.

A number such as $2\frac{4}{10}$ can be written like this.

Ones	tenths
2 •	4

The red dot is called a **decimal point**. The decimal point is a mark that identifies the ones place.

Where have you seen numbers written with a decimal point?

Prices like $3.99 use a decimal point.

I've seen a decimal point used for weights like 3.5 lb on packets of food.

Look at the expanders below.

How would you say the number that each expander shows?

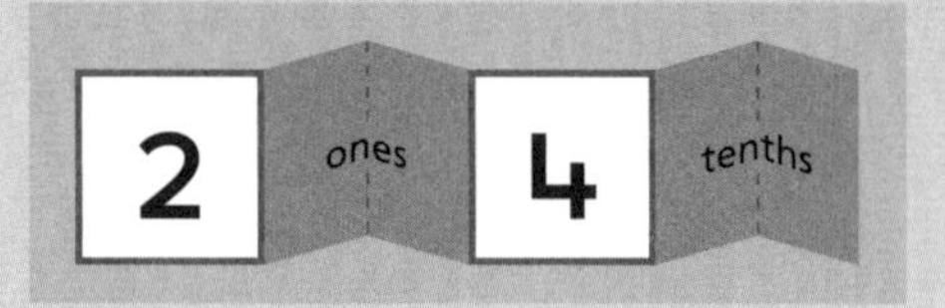

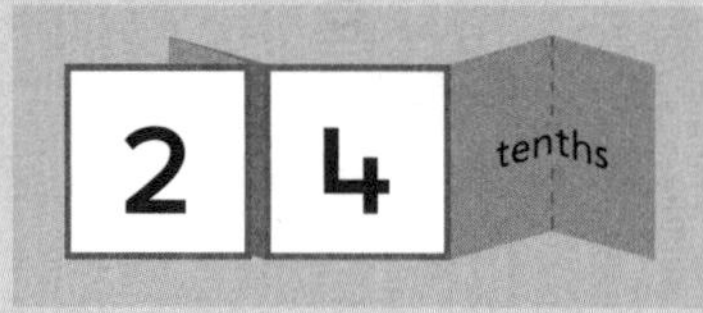

A **decimal fraction** is a fraction that is written with no denominator visible. The position of a digit after the decimal point tells what the invisible denominator is.

How do these numbers relate to mixed numbers and common fractions?

Why do you need to show the decimal point when the expander is completely closed?

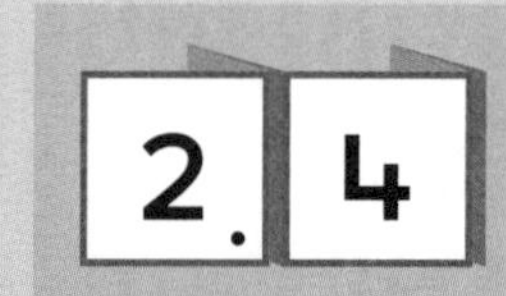

Step Up

1. Each square is one whole. Read the fraction name and shade the squares to match. Write the decimal fraction on the open expander.

a. two and five-tenths

b. one and seven-tenths

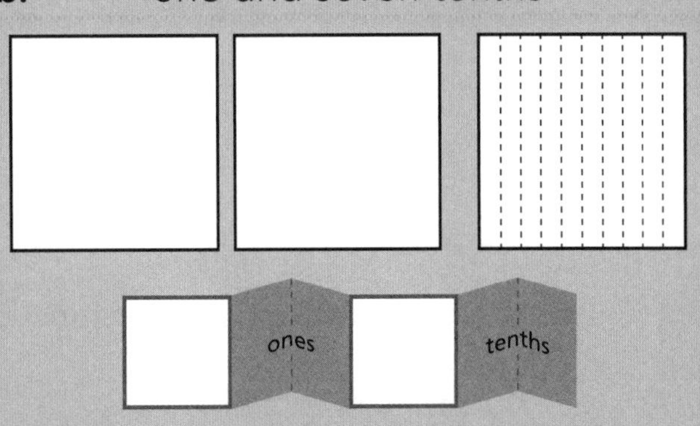

c. one and three-tenths

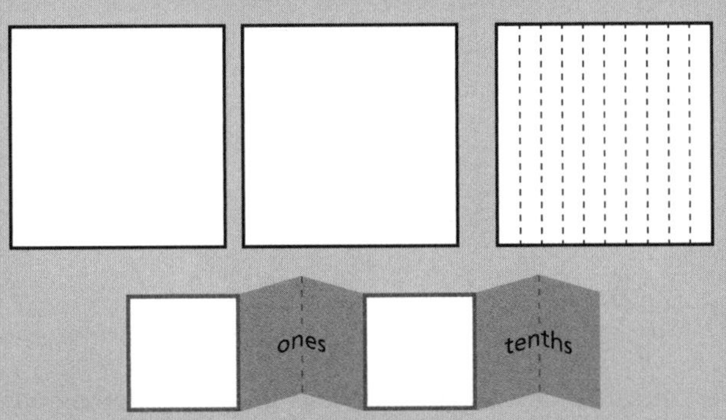

d. two and six-tenths

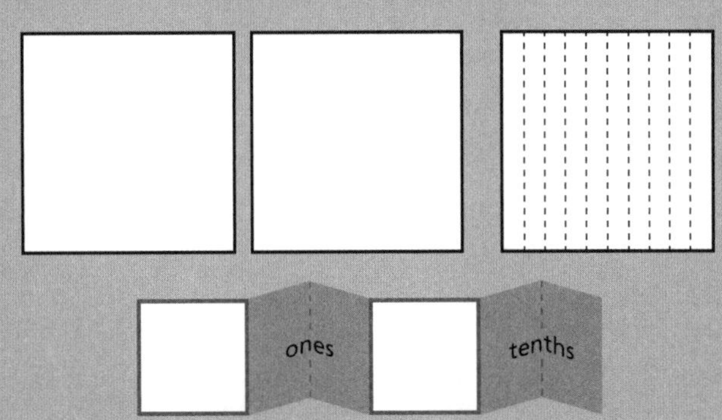

2. Read the fraction name. Write the amount as a common fraction or mixed number. Then write the matching decimal fraction on the expander.

a. four and two-tenths

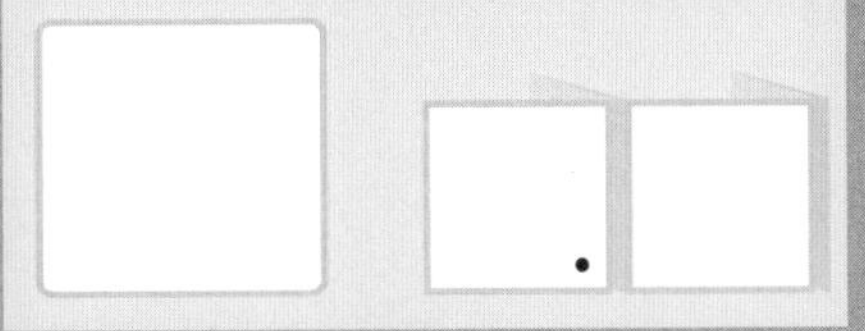

b. sixty-three tenths

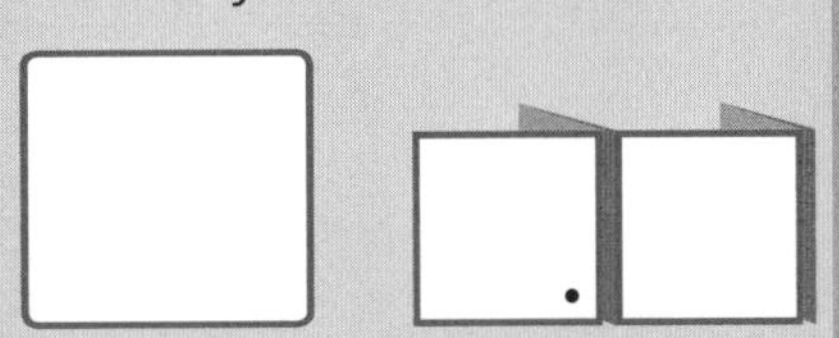

c. five and eight-tenths

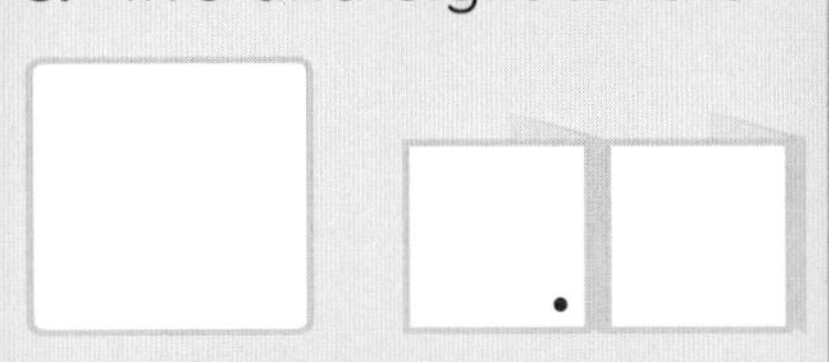

Step Ahead

Read the clues. Write the number on the expander to match.

a. I am greater than three and less than four. The digit in my tenths place is less than the digit in my ones place.

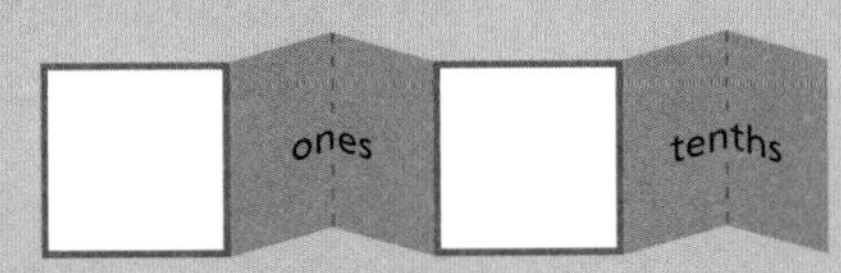

b. I am less than five and greater than one. The digit in my ones place is twice the value of the digit in my tenths place.

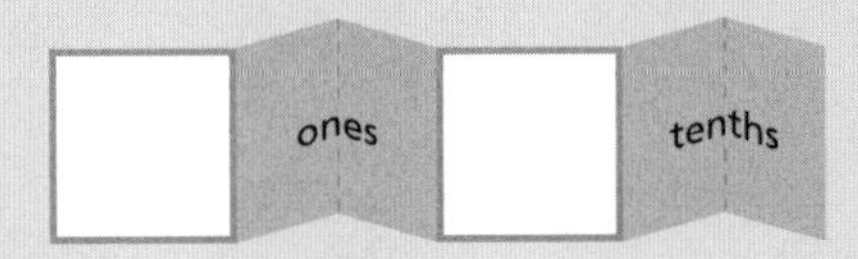

Step In Locating and Comparing Tenths

Look at the number line below. The distance between each whole number is one whole.

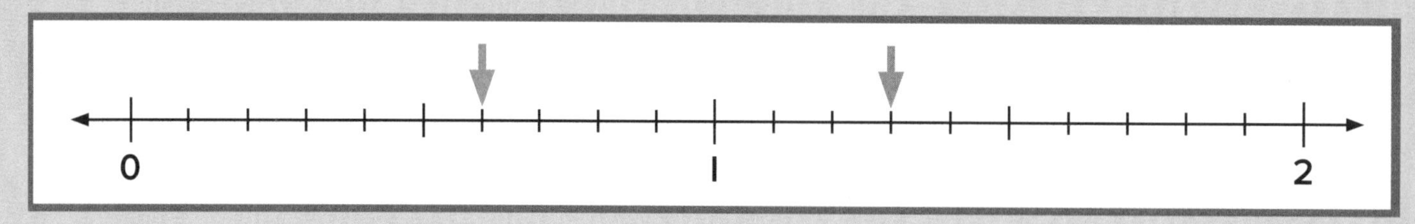

What fraction is the orange arrow pointing to? How do you know?

Write it as a common fraction and as a mixed number.

Complete these expanders to show the same fraction.

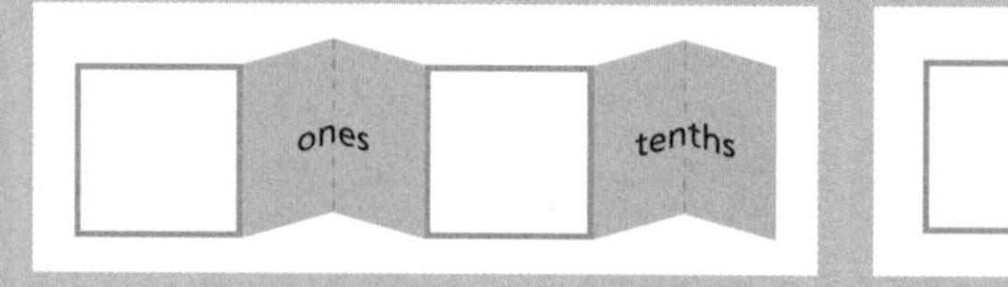

What fraction is the green arrow pointing to?
Can you write it as a common fraction and as a mixed number? Why?
What would it look like on an expander?

A zero is used in the ones place when the amount is less than 1. This makes it easy to quickly see whether it is a whole number or a fraction.

Think about how you compare 267 and 305 to figure out which number is greater.
Which place do you look at first?

Think about the fractions indicated by the arrows on the number line above.
What do they look like as decimal fractions?
Which is greater?
How can you tell by looking at their places?

Step Up

1. On this number line, the distance between each whole number is one whole. Write the decimal fraction that is shown by each arrow.

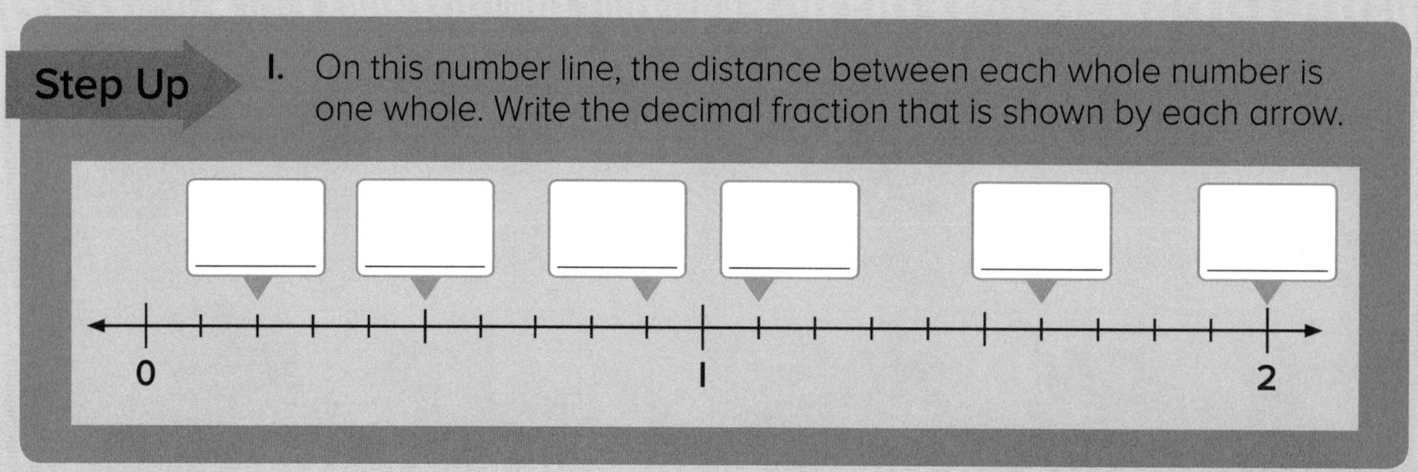

Use the masses of these fruit and vegetables to answer the questions on this page.

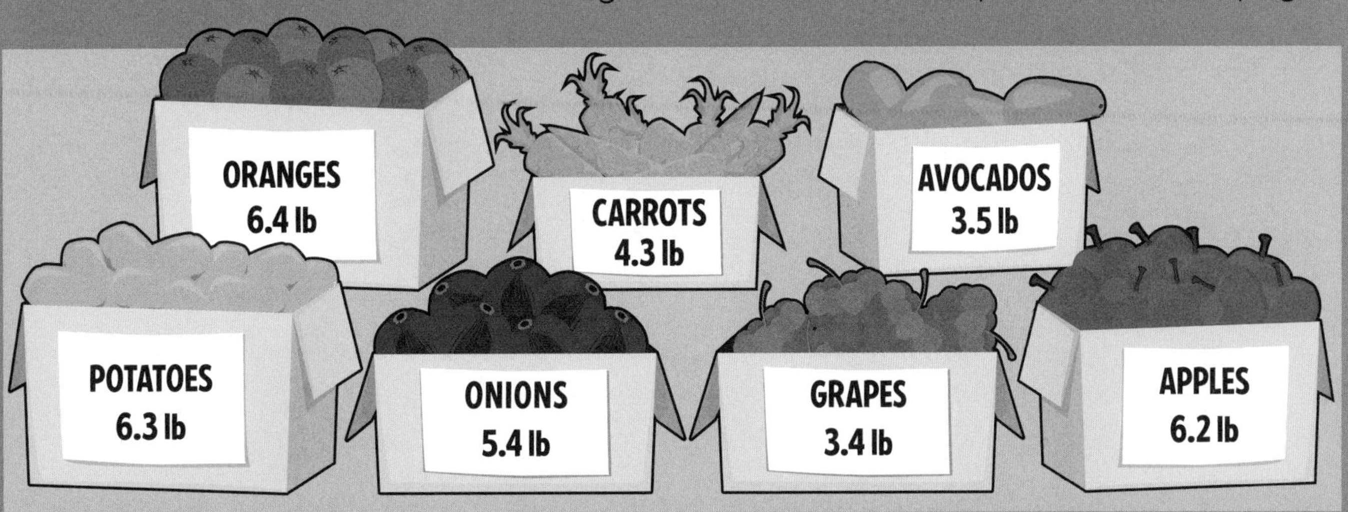

2. In each pair below, loop the box of fruit or vegetables that is **heavier**.

a. apples **or** onions

b. oranges **or** potatoes

c. apples **or** avocados

d. carrots **or** grapes

3. Write the masses. Then write **<** or **>** to make the sentence true.

a. avocados ____ lb ◯ potatoes ____ lb

b. onions ____ lb ◯ grapes ____ lb

c. oranges ____ lb ◯ apples ____ lb

d. avocados ____ lb ◯ onions ____ lb

Step Ahead

Write the masses of the fruit and vegetables in order from **least** to **greatest**. Then draw a line to connect each mass to its approximate position on the number line.

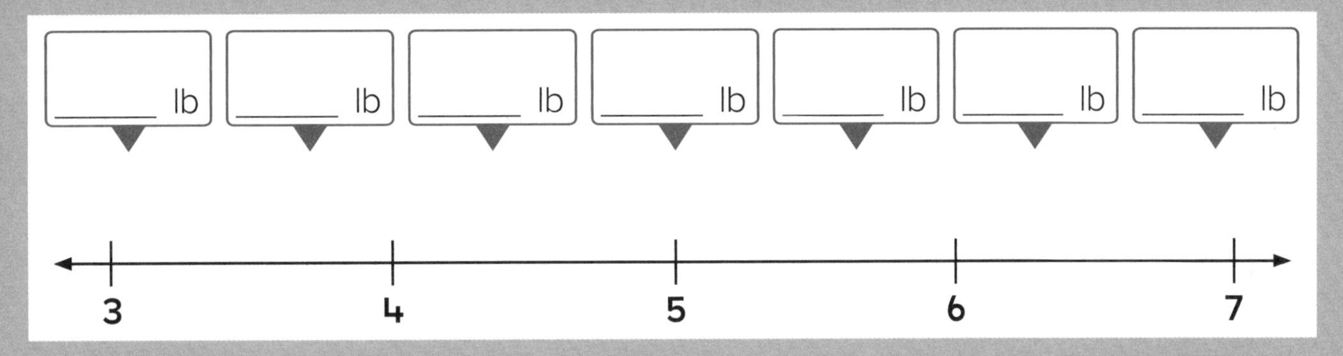

Step In Exploring Hundredths

Each large square represents one whole.

How many columns are in the shaded square?
What fraction of one whole does each column show?

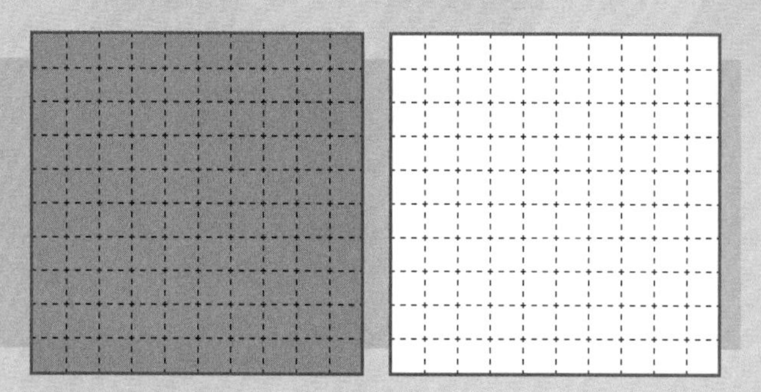

Shade the first four columns of the other square. What is the total shaded now?
Start from the bottom and shade five small squares in the next column.
How much is shaded now? What number is now shown by the shaded parts?

How many hundredths are in one whole? How do you know?

Step Up

1. Each large square represents one whole. Write the missing numbers to describe the shaded part of each large square.

a.

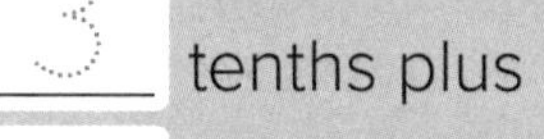

3 tenths plus

2 hundredths

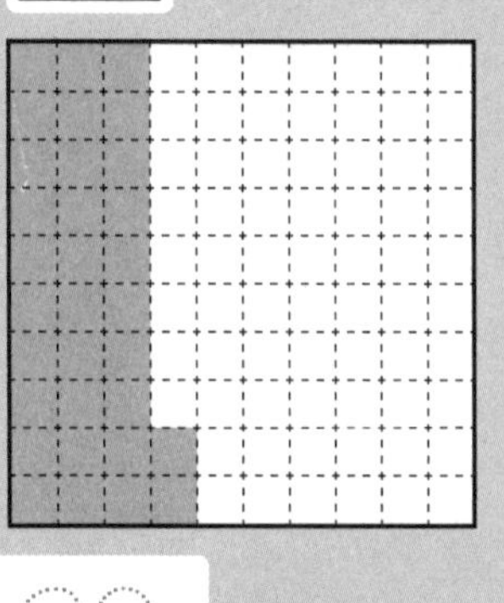

32 hundredths

b.

_____ tenths plus

_____ hundredths

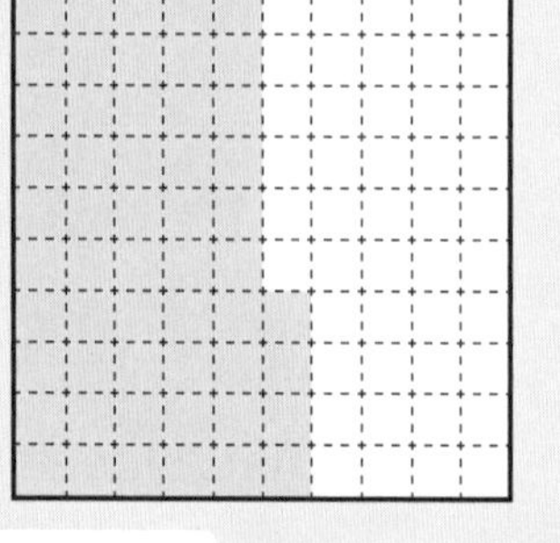

_____ hundredths

c.

_____ tenths plus

_____ hundredths

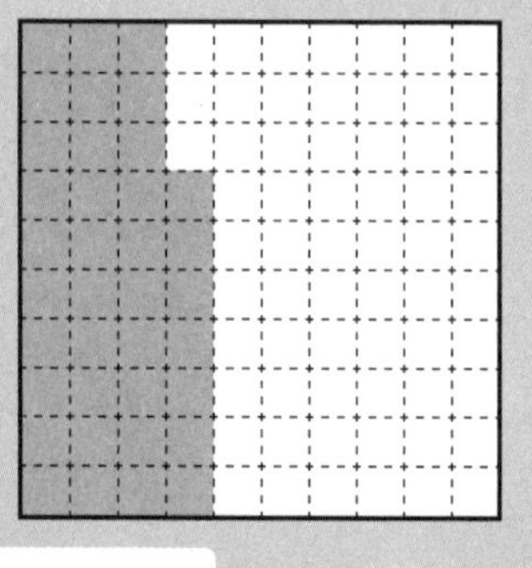

_____ hundredths

d.

_____ tenths _____ hundredths

_____ hundredths

e.

_____ tenths _____ hundredths

_____ hundredths

2. Shade each picture to match the description. Then write **how much more** needs to be shaded to make one whole.

a. **2** tenths plus
4 hundredths

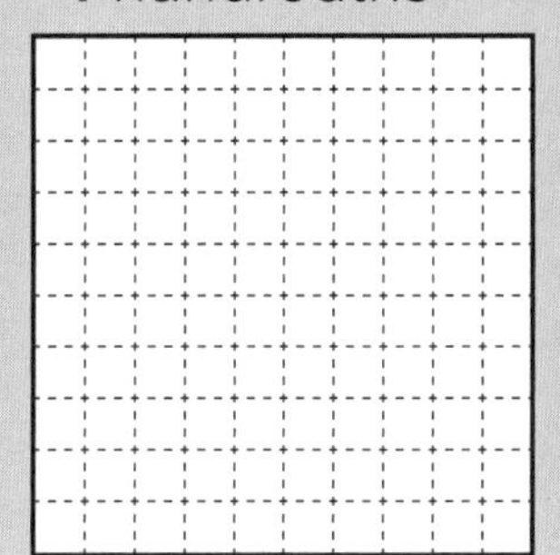

_____ tenths plus

_____ hundredths

b. **4** tenths plus
9 hundredths

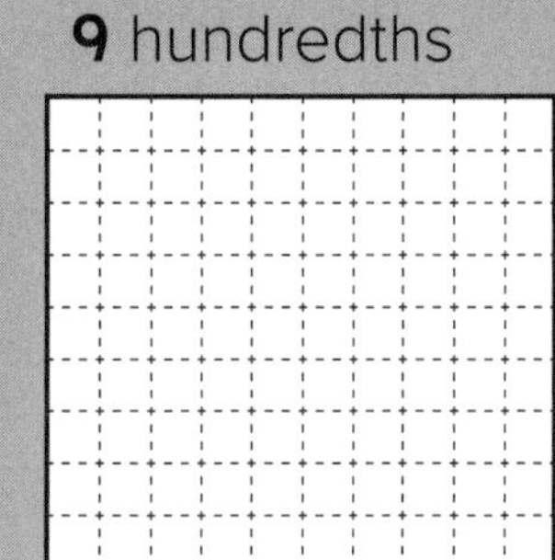

_____ tenths plus

_____ hundredths

c. **9** tenths plus
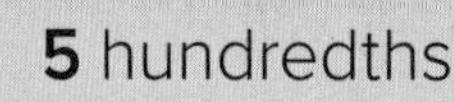
5 hundredths

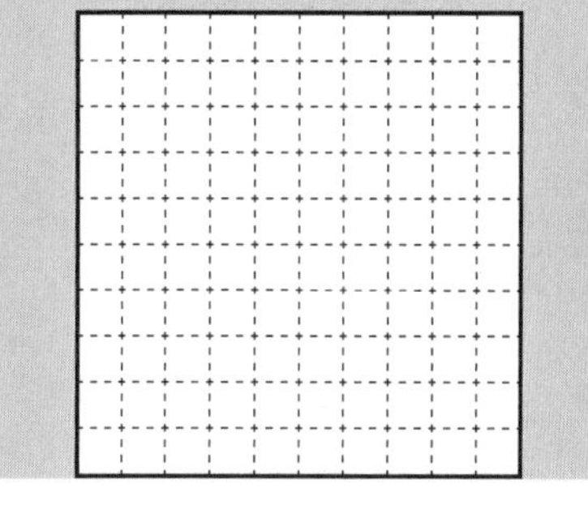

_____ tenths plus

_____ hundredths

d. **0** tenths plus
3 hundredths

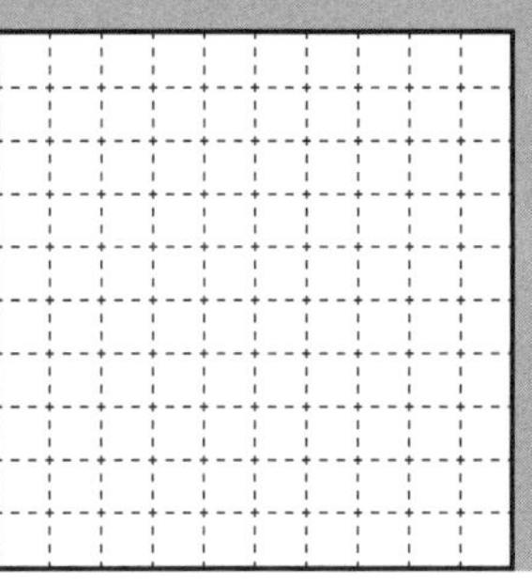

_____ tenths plus

_____ hundredths

e. **6** tenths plus
0 hundredths

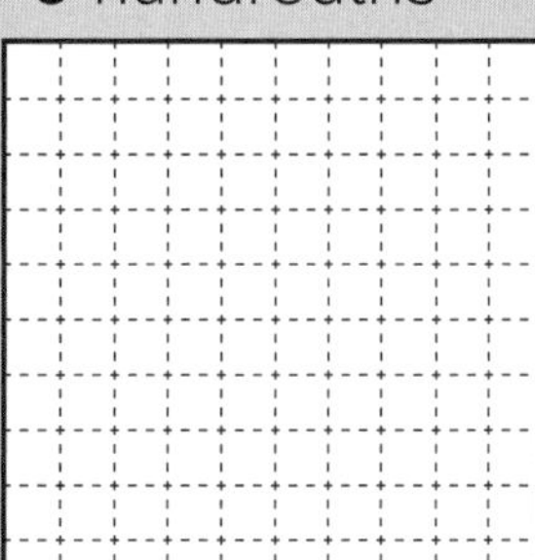

_____ tenths plus

_____ hundredths

f. **4** tenths plus
15 hundredths

_____ tenths plus

_____ hundredths

Step Ahead Draw lines to match the numbers. Some numbers do not have a match.

63 hundredths	7 tenths	28 hundredths	10 tenths	7 hundredths
70 hundredths	2 tenths 8 hundredths	6 tenths 3 hundredths	70 tenths	1

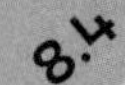

Step In — Writing Hundredths as Decimal Fractions (without Teens or Zeros)

Each large square represents one whole. How can you color them to show **one and seventy-six hundredths** without counting each hundredth?

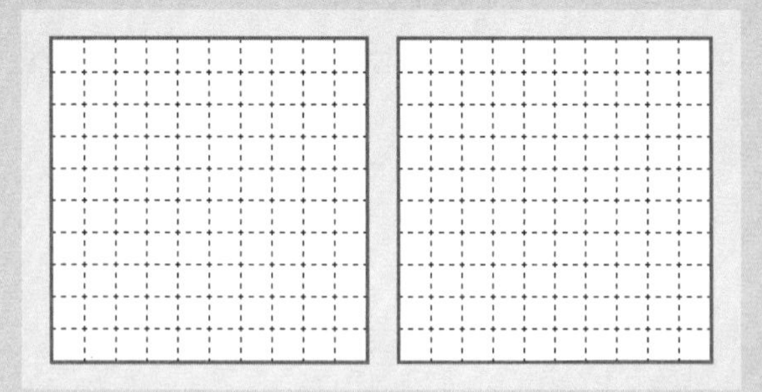

I would color all the first square to show one whole. Then I'd color 7 columns to show 7 tenths and then color 6 small squares to show 6 hundredths.

Write the number above on these two expanders.

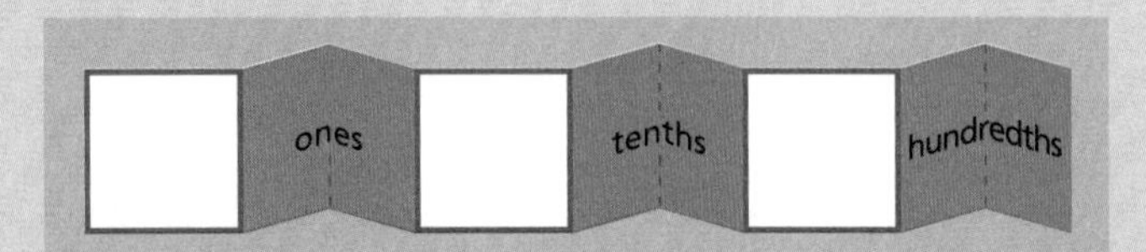

Which expander helps you to read the number? Why?

Which digit is in the tenths place? ... hundredths place?

Look at this place-value chart.

What do you notice about the places on either side of the ones place?

Write one and seventy-six hundredths on the chart.

Ten Thousands	Thousands	Hundreds	Tens	Ones	tenths	hundredths		
				•				

Step Up

1. Each large square is one whole. Color the squares to show the number. Then write the number on the expanders and as a mixed number.

two and twenty-eight hundredths

ones hundredths

.

$\frac{\quad}{100}$

2. Complete the missing parts. Each large square is one whole.

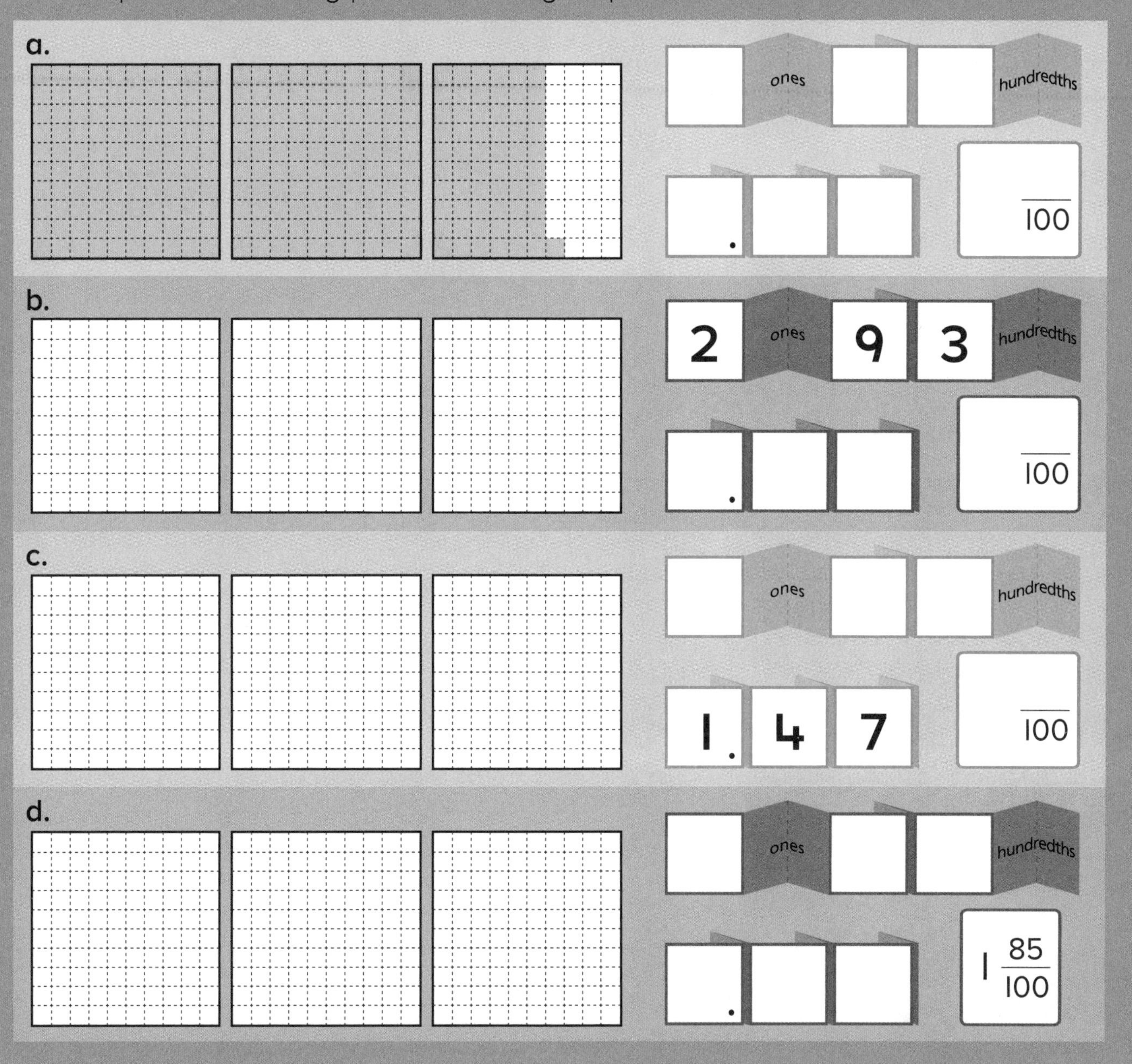

Step Ahead

Read the clues. Write a matching number on the expander.

a. I am greater than five and less than seven. I have more in the tenths place than in the hundredths place. I have more in the ones place than in the tenths place.

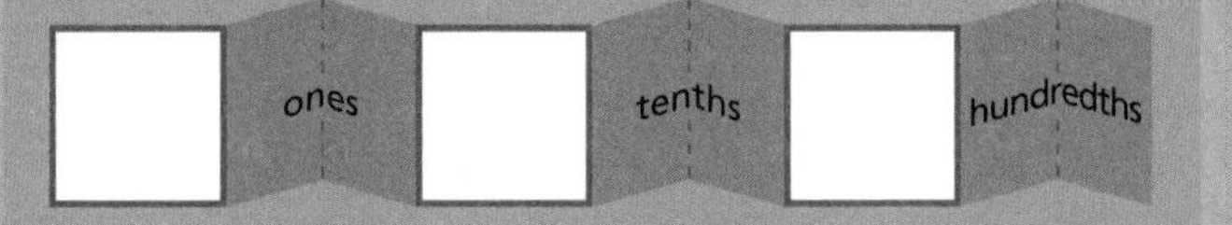

b. I am less than nine and greater than four. The digit in the tenths place is a multiple of 3. The digit in the hundredths place is greater than the digit in the ones place.

ones | tenths | hundredths

Step In Writing Hundredths as Decimal Fractions (with Teens and Zeros)

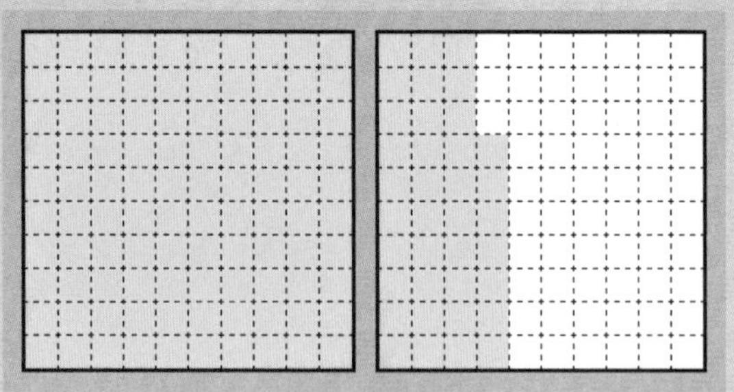

Each large square represents one whole.

How much has been shaded?

Write the amount on each expander below.

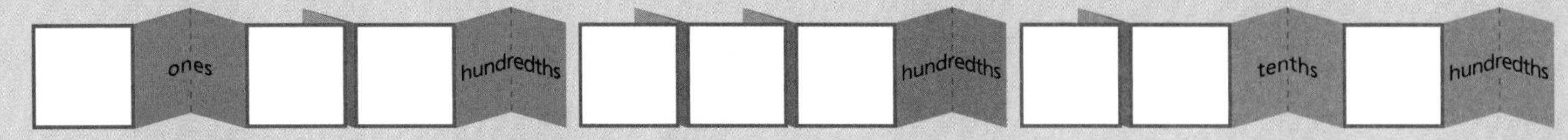

Which of these labels matches each expander above?

How do you know?

$\frac{137}{100}$ | $1 + \frac{37}{100}$ | $\frac{13}{10} + \frac{7}{100}$

What numbers are shaded below?

How will you write each number on the expander?

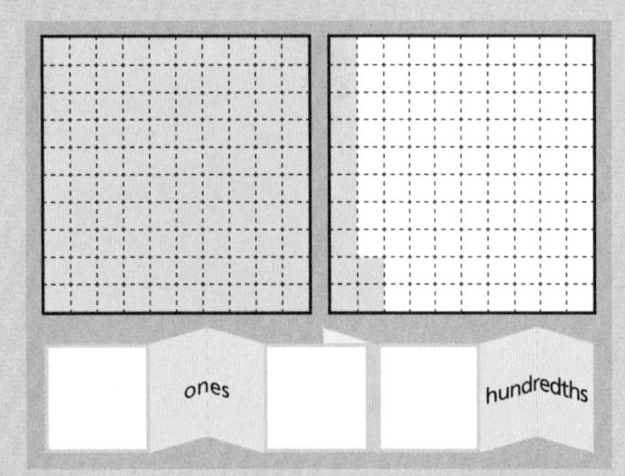

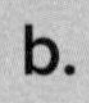

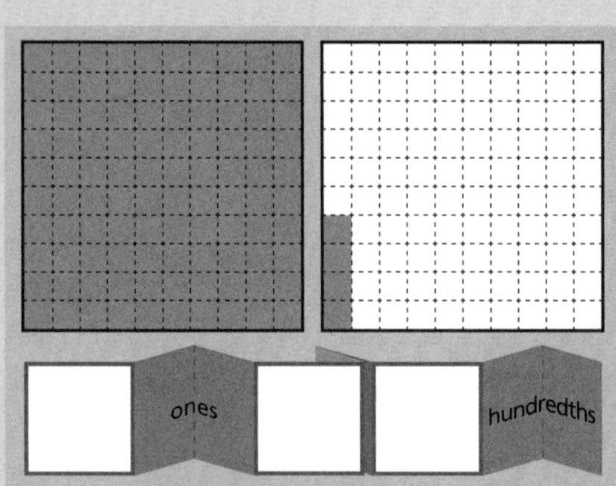

Step Up

1. Complete the missing parts.

a.

two and five hundredths

b.

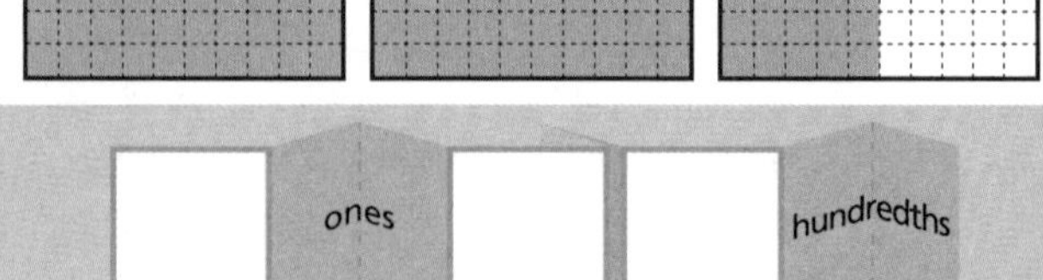

2. Read the number name. Then write the number on the expander.

a. two and fourteen hundredths

b. six and two hundredths

c. ninety-four hundredths

d. four and twenty hundredths

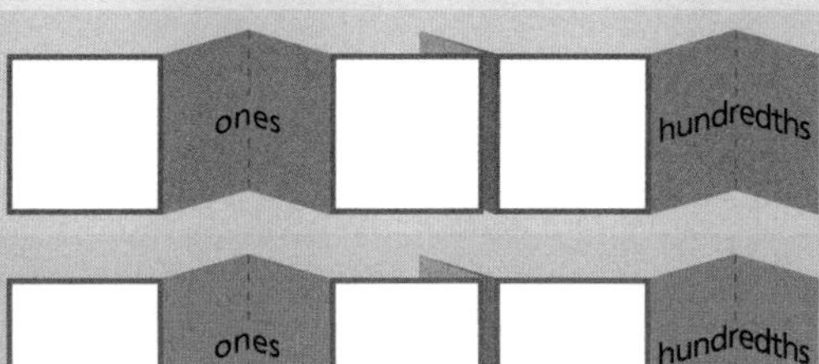

3. Write each number in words.

a. 3.19 ____________________

b. 9.40 ____________________

c. 7.06 ____________________

d. 12.15 ____________________

4. Write the matching decimal fraction and mixed number.

a. six and seventeen hundredths

b. six and seventy hundredths

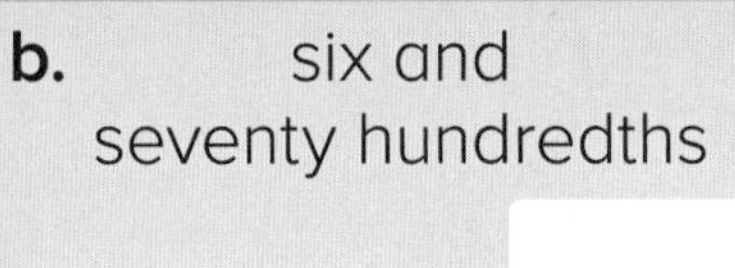

c. six and seven hundredths

Step Ahead Loop the numbers that are the same as 705 hundredths.

0.705 $7\frac{5}{10}$ 7.05 $7\frac{5}{100}$ 0.75

Step In Writing Decimal Fractions Using Expanded Notation

Read the number on the expander.

What is the value of each 4 on the expander?

What is the value of the 6?

Just like whole numbers, decimal fractions can be recorded using expanded notation.

Write the missing numbers.

(____ × 1) + (____ × 0.1) + (____ × 0.01)

____ (1) + ____ (0.1) + ____ (0.01)

Which of these methods do you prefer?

Sofia wrote a different decimal fraction using expanded notation. She wrote the places in an incorrect order.

(1 × 0.1) + (7 × 1) + (9 × 0.01)

What decimal fraction did she expand?

Write the decimal fraction on the expander.

Step Up

1. Write the missing numbers to match the expander.

a. 3 ones 7 2 — (____ × 1) + (____ × 0.1) + (____ × 0.01)

b. 5 ones 1 6 — (____ × 1) + (____ × 0.1) + (____ × 0.01)

c. 7 ones 0 5 — (____ × 1) + (____ × 0.1) + (____ × 0.01)

2. Write each decimal fraction using expanded notation.

a. 6.85	
b. 8.18	
c. 6.03	
d. 1.80	
e. 0.75	

3. Write the decimal fraction that has been expanded.

a. $(2 \times 1) + (5 \times 0.1) + (2 \times 0.01)$

b. $8(1) + 4(0.1) + 1(0.01)$

c. $5(1) + 6(0.1) + 7(0.01)$

d. $(6 \times 0.1) + (7 \times 0.01)$

Step Ahead Look carefully at the decimal fraction that has been expanded. Then write the decimal fraction on the expander.

a. $(9 \times 0.01) + (4 \times 1) + (7 \times 0.1)$

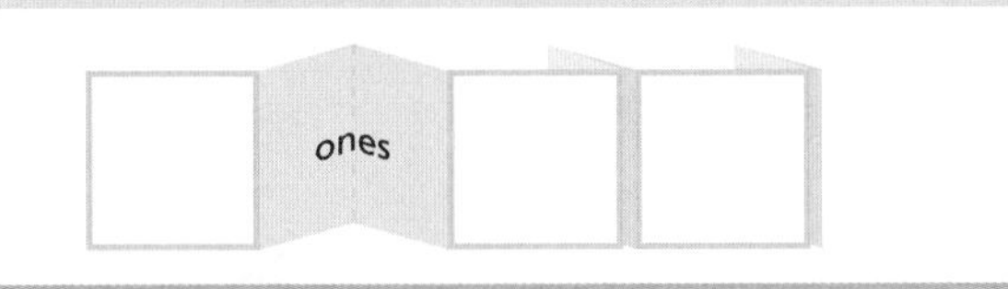

b. $(6 \times 0.1) + (1 \times 0.01) + (5 \times 1)$

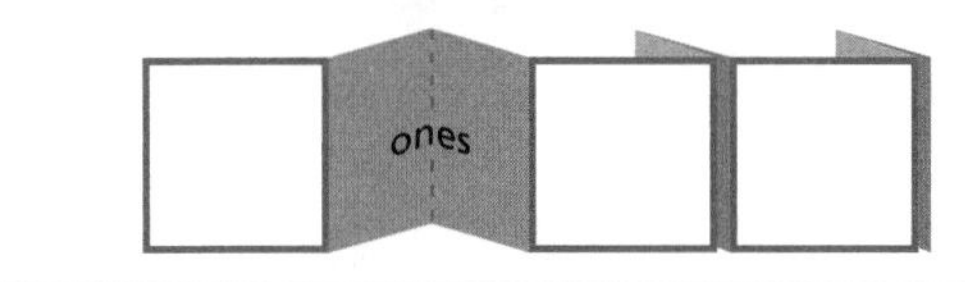

c. $4(0.1) + 7(1) + 2(0.01)$

ones

d. $9(0.01) + 2(1)$

ones

Step In Locating Decimal Fractions on a Number Line

The distance between each whole number on these number lines is one whole.

What number is the blue arrow pointing to? What helped you figure it out?

What other decimal fraction describes that position? How do you know?

Look where the red arrow is pointing. Which two decimal fractions describe that position?

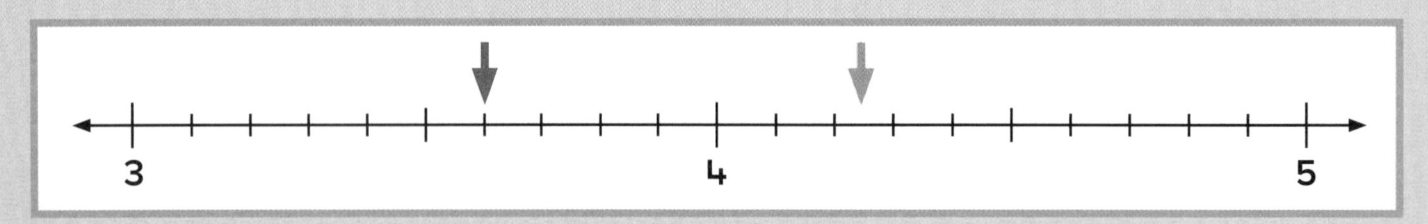

What number do you think the green arrow is pointing to? How could you figure it out?

Step Up

The distance between each whole number is one whole. Write the decimal fraction that is shown by each arrow. Think carefully before you write.

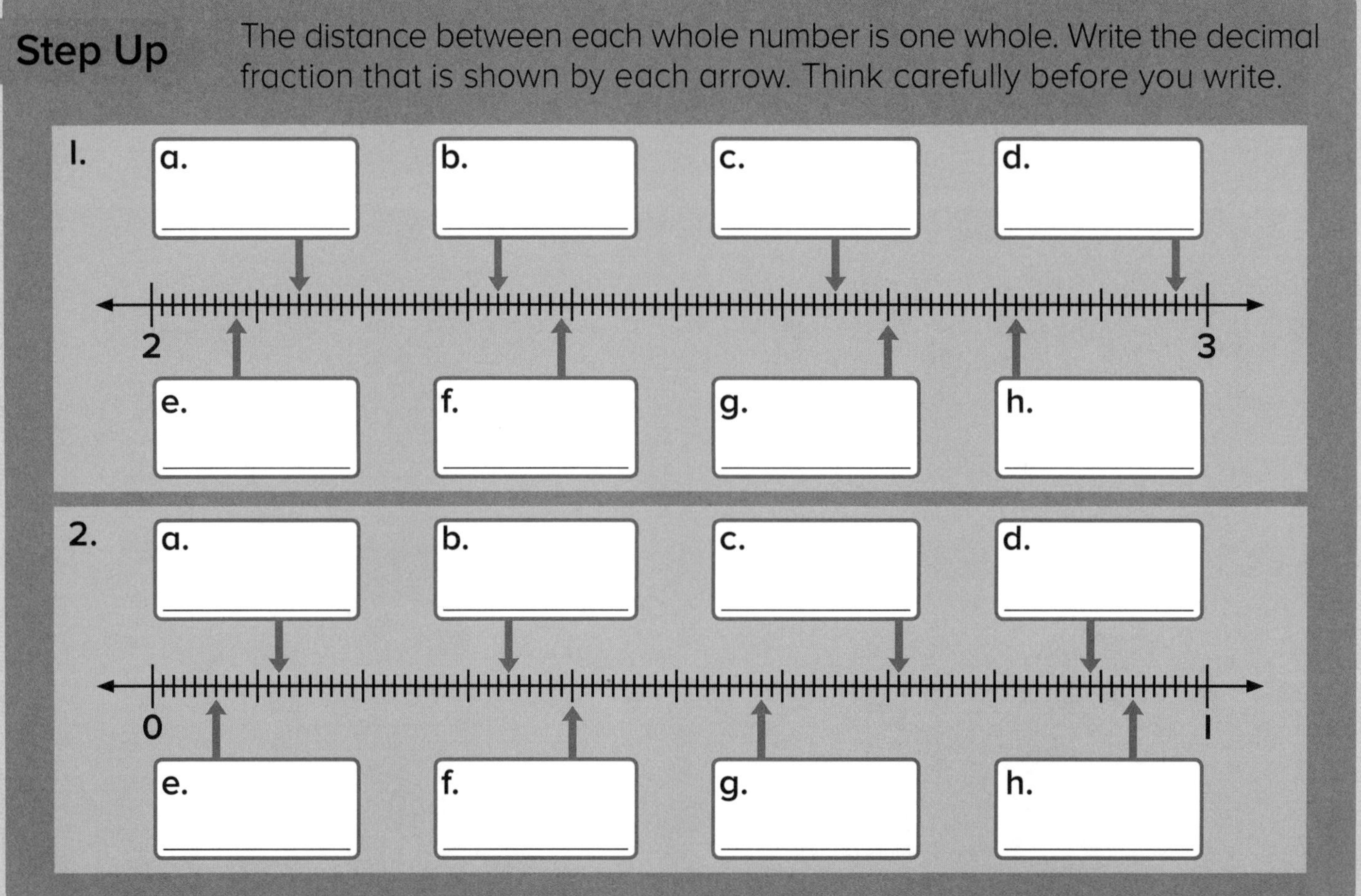

3. The distance between each whole number is one whole. Draw a line to join each numeral to its approximate position on the number line. Be as accurate as possible.

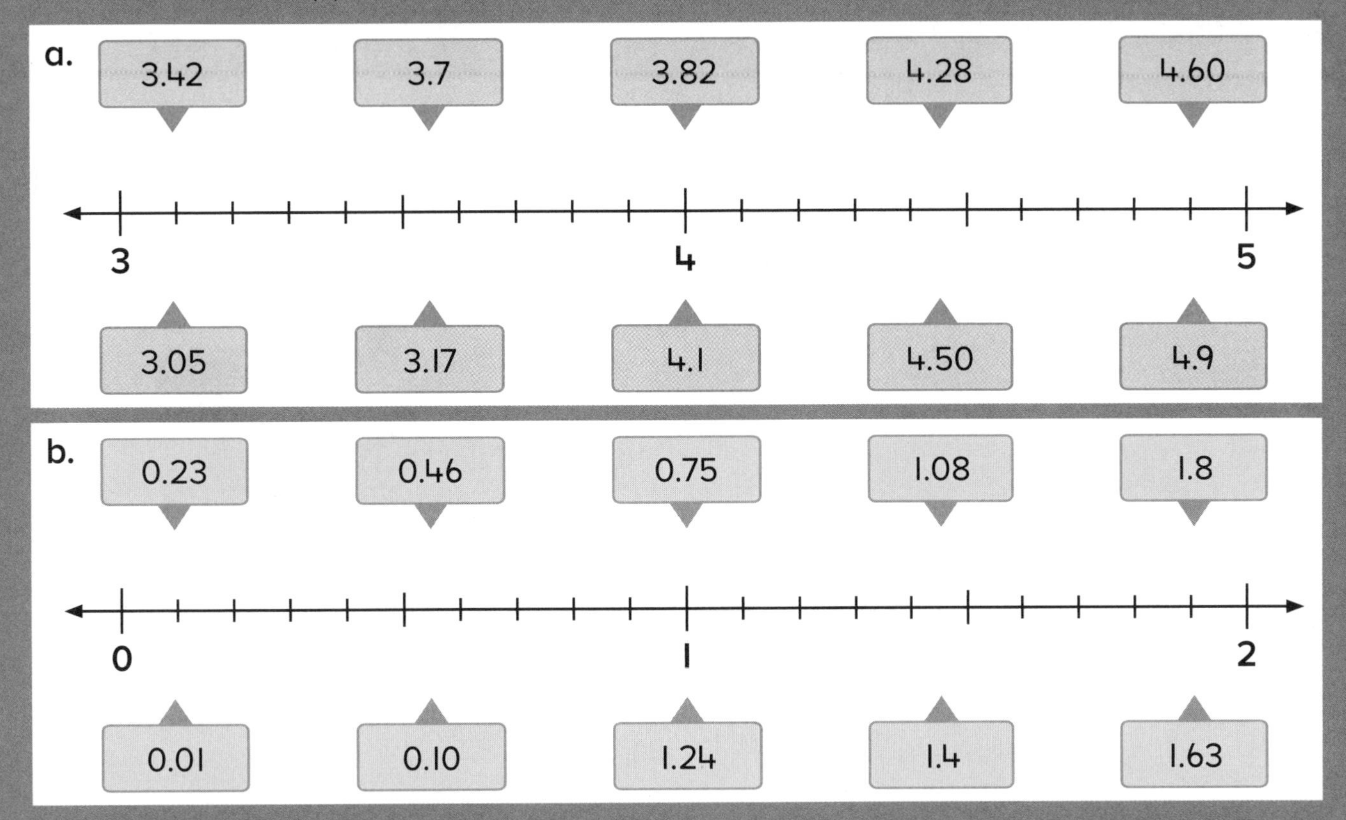

Step Ahead

Race times can be recorded in whole seconds, tenths, and hundredths of a second. Draw arrows and write initials to show the approximate position of each athlete's time. Write above or below the number line. The first one has been done for you.

2012 Olympic Games Men's 200 Meters

Athlete	Time (s)
Usain Bolt	19.32
Yohan Blake	19.44
Warren Weir	19.84
Wallace Spearmon	19.90

Athlete	Time (s)
Churandy Martina	20.00
Christophe Lemaitre	20.19
Alex Quiñónez	20.57
Anaso Jobodwana	20.69

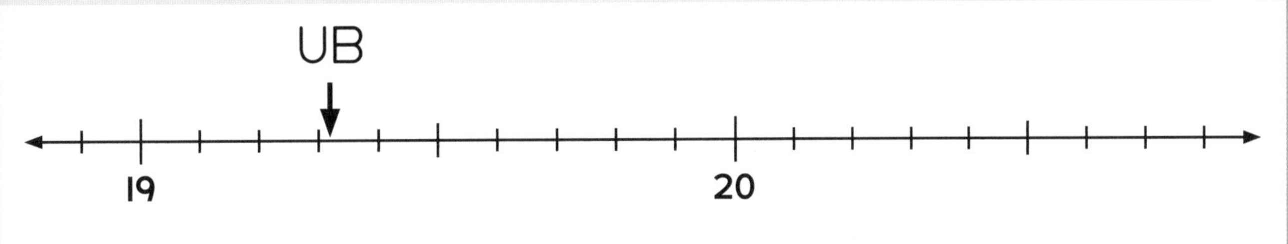

Step In Comparing and Ordering Decimal Fractions

Look at these six decimal fractions.
Which number is greater, C or F?
How could you figure it out?

A	B	C	D	E	F
3.41	3.38	2.6	3.8	3.04	2.43

Noah thought it would be easier to compare the numbers if they had the same denominator. How should he change the numbers? Do you need to change only one number or both numbers?

I would think about where the numbers would be on a number line.

Between which two whole numbers are the numbers C and F?
How could you show the locations of the numbers on this number line?

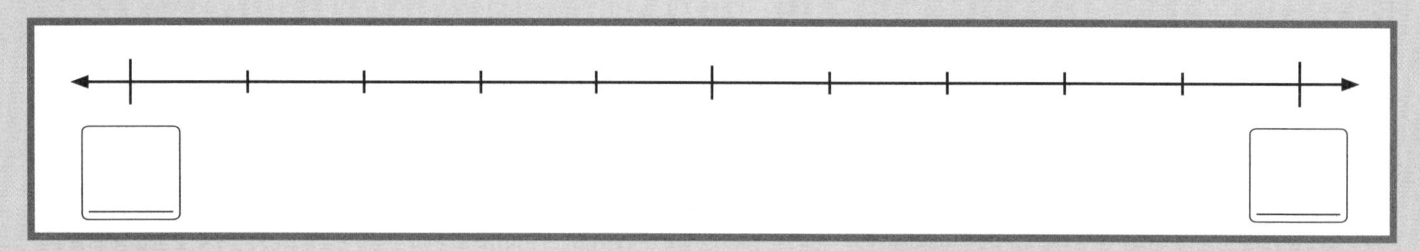

I would think about the place value of each number.

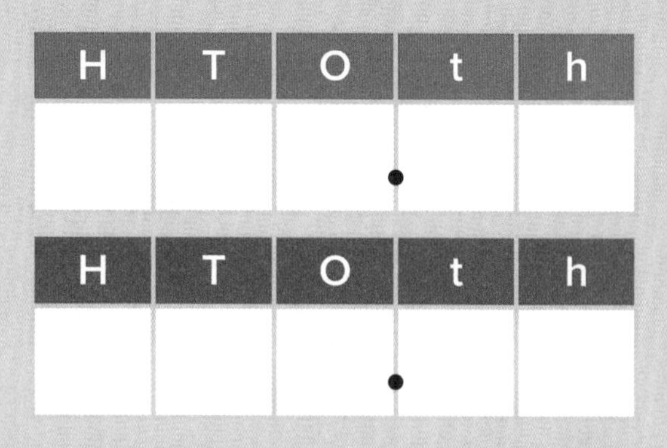

Write each number in these place-value charts.
How do the charts help you figure out the greater number?

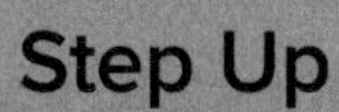

1. Write **<**, **>**, or **=** to make each sentence true. Use what you know about equivalence to help you.

a. $\frac{5}{10}$ ◯ $\frac{8}{100}$	**b.** $\frac{7}{10}$ ◯ $\frac{70}{100}$	**c.** $\frac{125}{100}$ ◯ $\frac{14}{10}$	**d.** $\frac{275}{100}$ ◯ $\frac{275}{10}$
e. $1\frac{75}{100}$ ◯ $1\frac{7}{10}$	**f.** $4\frac{1}{10}$ ◯ $4\frac{1}{100}$	**g.** $2\frac{3}{10}$ ◯ $2\frac{30}{100}$	**h.** $2\frac{10}{100}$ ◯ $5\frac{9}{10}$

These eight decimal fractions are between 1 and 4. Use the data in the table to answer Questions 2 and 3. Use the number line or what you know about equivalence to help you.

P	Q	R	S	T	U	V	W
1.96	2.91	3.4	3.12	2.19	2.03	3.2	2.3

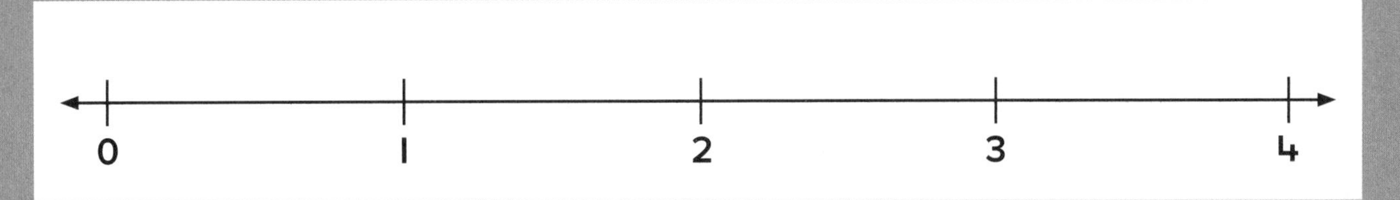

2. Write the fraction from the table. Then write < or > to complete each sentence.

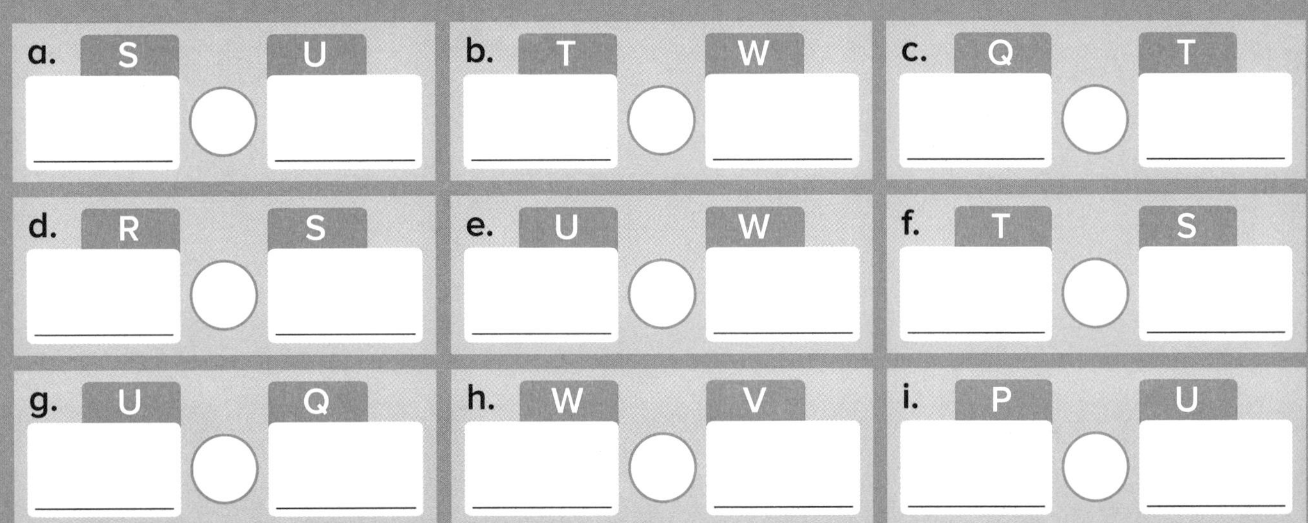

3. Write the decimal fractions in order from **least** to **greatest**.

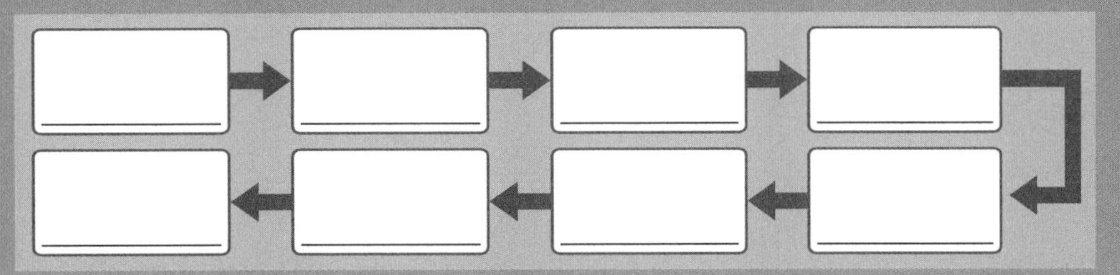

Step Ahead Write these numbers in order from **greatest** to **least**.

0.2	0.58	0.6	1.4	1.07	2.00	0.09

greatest						least

Step In Developing a Rule to Calculate the Area of Rectangles

Each small square in this large rectangle measures 1 yard by 1 yard.

What are the dimensions of the large rectangle?

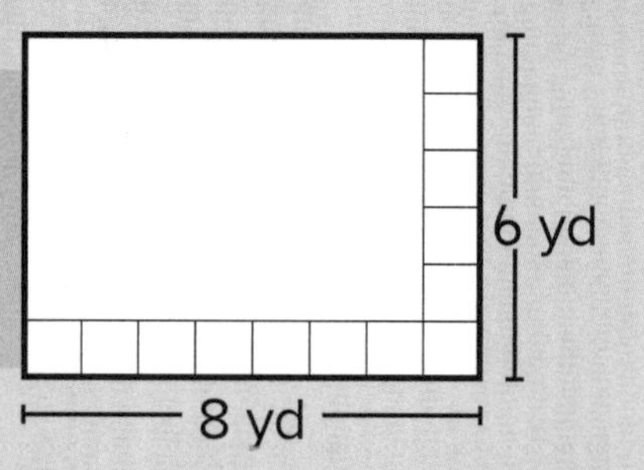

A short way to write square units is to use a small numeral 2. So, 370 square yards can be written as 370 yd^2.

How could you use the dimensions to figure out the area of the rectangle?

Does the order in which you multiply matter? Explain.

What rule could you write to calculate the area of any rectangle?

____

Use your rule to calculate the area of a rectangle that is 7 yards wide and 9 yards long.

Step Up

1. Imagine that each small square inside these large rectangles measures 1 yd by 1 yd. Write the dimensions of the whole rectangle. Then write how you will use the dimensions to calculate the area.

a.

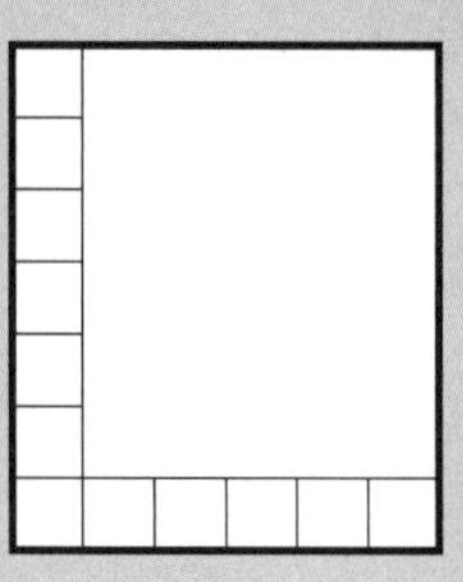

Length _______ yd Width _____ yd

____

____

Area __________ yd^2

b.

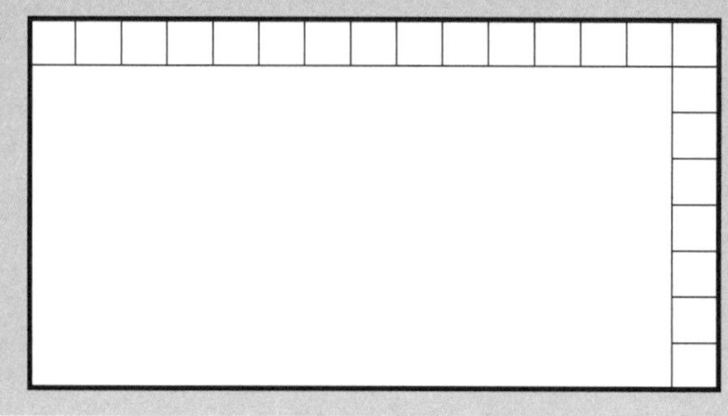

Length _______ yd Width _____ yd

____

____

Area __________ yd^2

2. Calculate the area of each rectangle. Show your thinking.

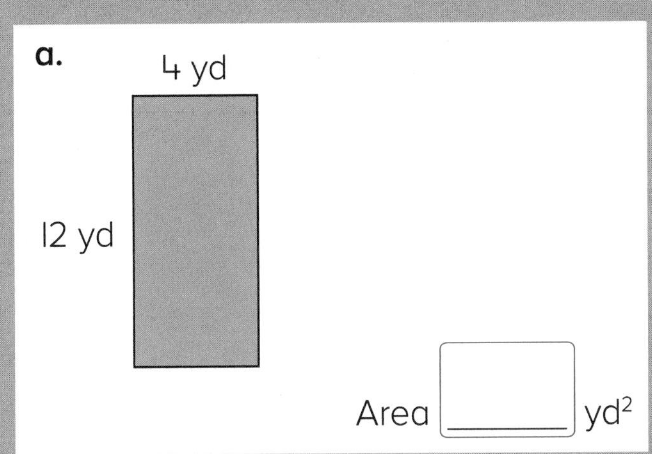

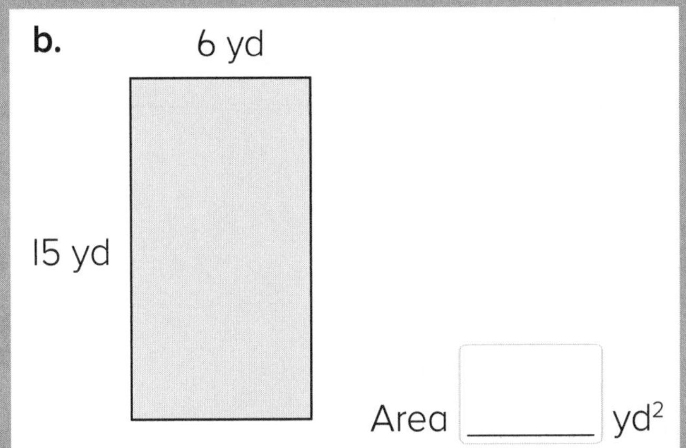

3. Write possible dimensions for each rectangle.

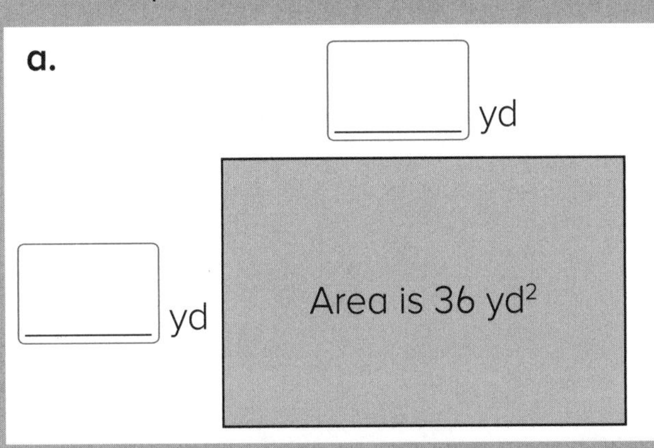

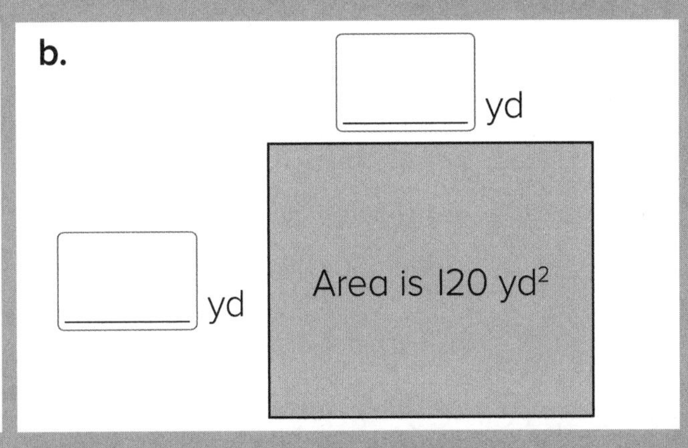

4. Write how you figured out each dimension in Question 3.

____

____

Step Ahead Figure out the area of this rectangle.

Area ______ yd²

8 yd

9 yd

15 yd

Working Space

Step In Working with the Area of Rectangles

This diagram shows the floor area of a room that will be covered with tiles and carpet. The shaded area will be tiled.

6 m
5 m
Tiles
Carpet
7 m
14 m

How can you figure out the area of floor that will be covered with carpet?

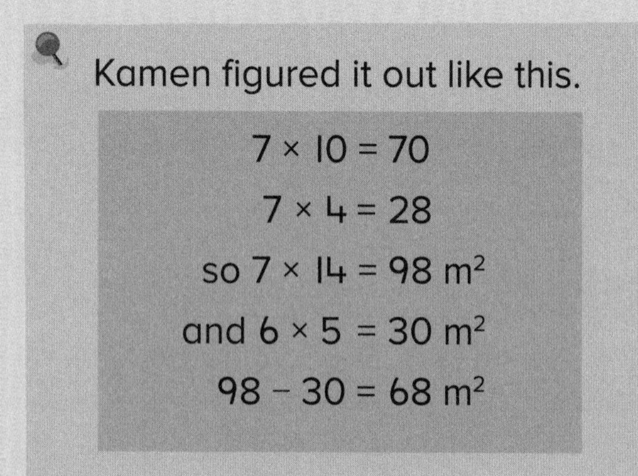

Kamen figured it out like this.

$7 \times 10 = 70$
$7 \times 4 = 28$
so $7 \times 14 = 98$ m²
and $6 \times 5 = 30$ m²
$98 - 30 = 68$ m²

Oscar figured it out like this.

$14 - 6 = 8$ m
$8 \times 7 = 56$ m²
$7 - 5 = 2$ m
$2 \times 6 = 12$ m²
$56 + 12 = 68$ m²

What steps did Kamen use?
What steps did Oscar use?

Is there another way you could figure out the area?

Which way do you like best? Why?

Step Up

1. Imagine you wanted to lay turf in this barnyard. Write how you would calculate the area.

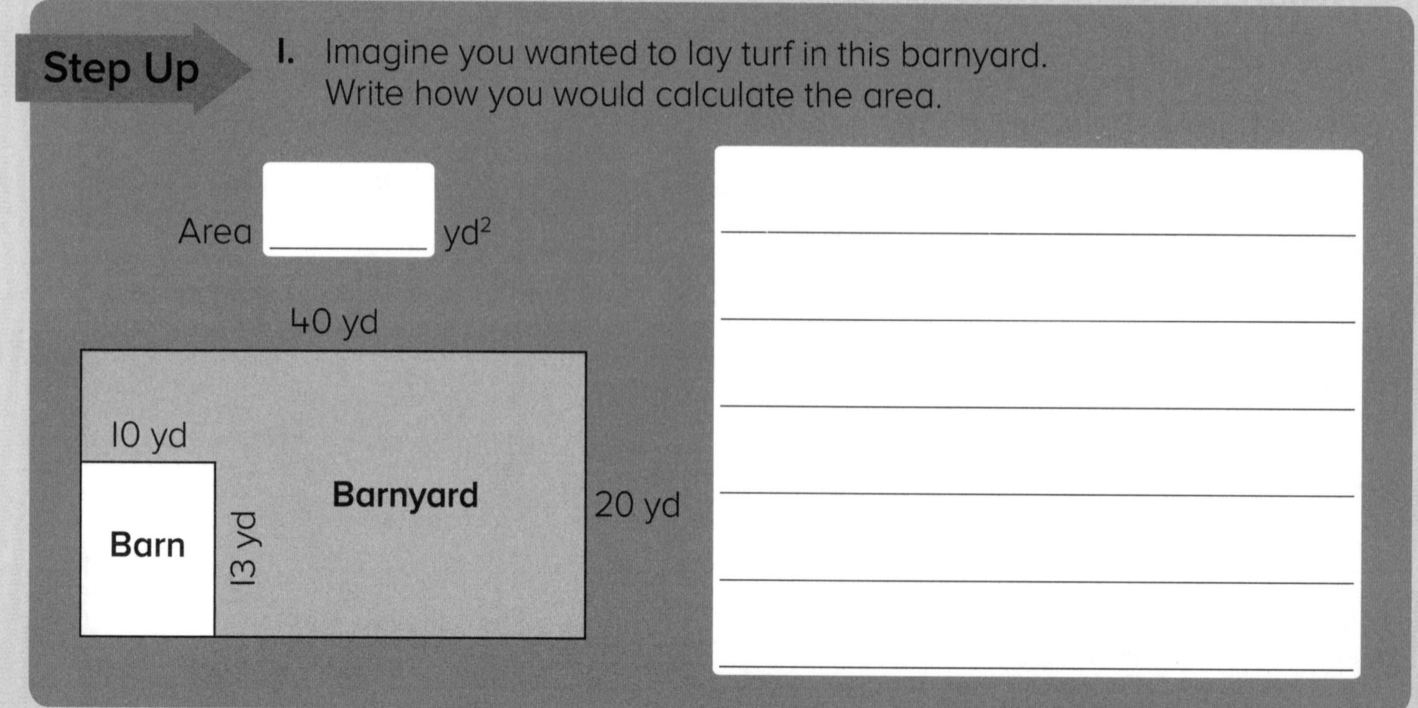

2. Calculate the area of each shaded part. Use the working space below.

a.

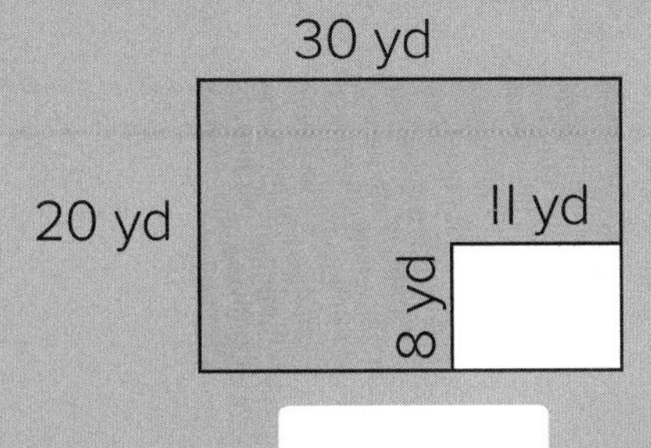

Area ________ yd²

b.

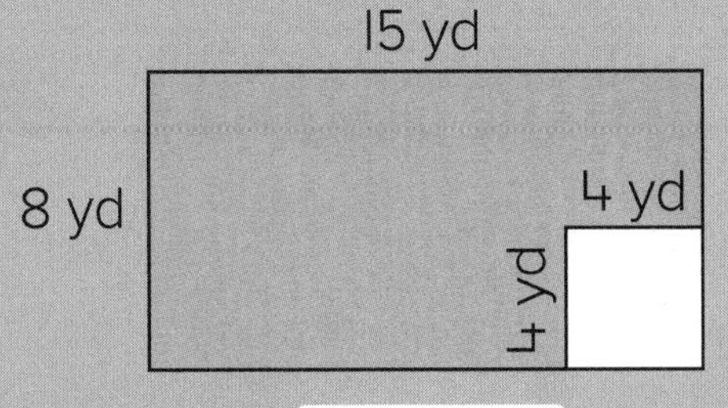

Area ________ yd²

c.

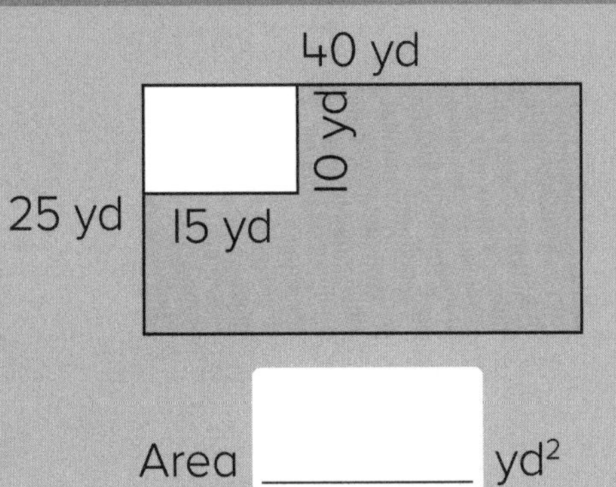

Area ________ yd²

d.

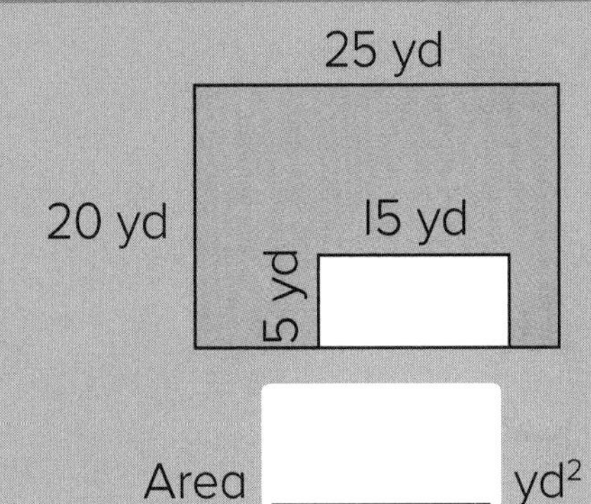

Area ________ yd²

Working Space

Step Ahead Calculate the area of the shaded part.

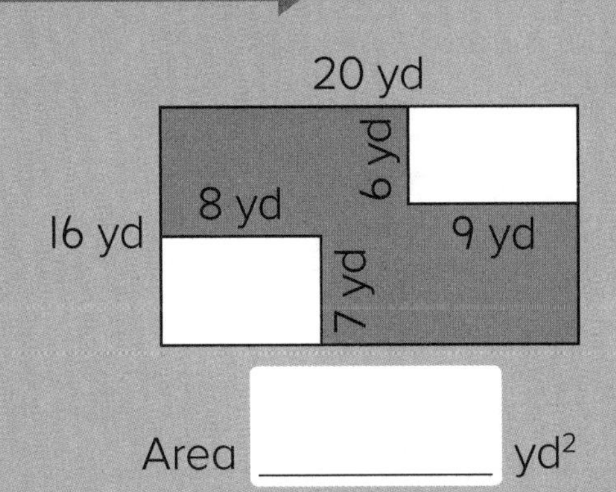

Area ________ yd²

Working Space

Step In — Developing a Rule to Calculate the Perimeter of Rectangles

What are the dimensions of this mirror frame?

What do you call the distance around a rectangle?

How could you figure out the perimeter of this mirror frame?

12 in

6 in

12 + 12 + 6 + 6 = 36 inches

What is another way you could figure out the perimeter?

You could multiply the length and width by 2. Then add them together. That's 2 × 12 + 2 × 6.

What rule could you write to figure out the perimeter of a rectangle?

____

Step Up

1. Calculate the perimeter of each frame.

a.

18 in

9 in

2 × 18 = ______

2 × 9 = ______

Perimeter ______ in

b.

7 in

15 in

2 × 7 = ______

2 × 15 = ______

Perimeter ______ in

2. Calculate the perimeter of these. Show your thinking.

a.

12 in

18 in

Perimeter ______ in

b.

15 in

21 in

Perimeter ______ in

3. Calculate the perimeter of each rectangle. Show your thinking.

a. **Length is 15 in. Width is 8 in.**

Perimeter ______ in

a. **Length is 25 in. Width is 16 in.**

Perimeter ______ in

Step Ahead Figure out the perimeter of each polygon. For each shape, all sides are the same length.

a.

6 in

Perimeter ______ in

b.

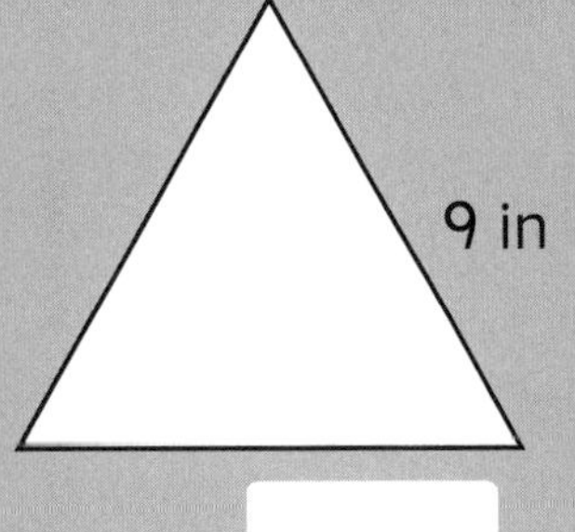

9 in

Perimeter ______ in

c.

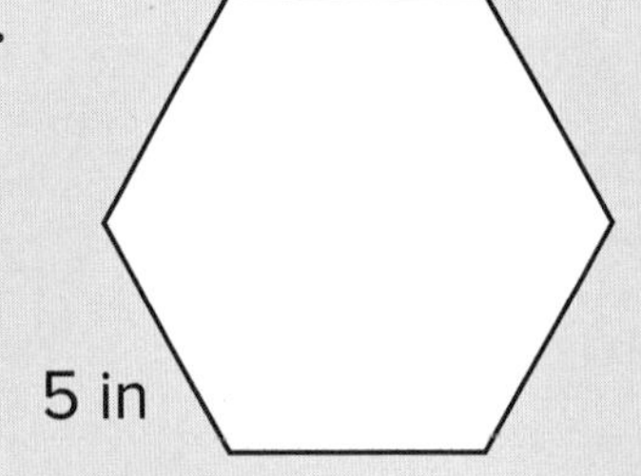

5 in

Perimeter ______ in

Step In Solving Problems Involving Perimeter and Area

This rectangular backyard has an area of 90 yd².

What is the length of each unknown side?

How do you know?

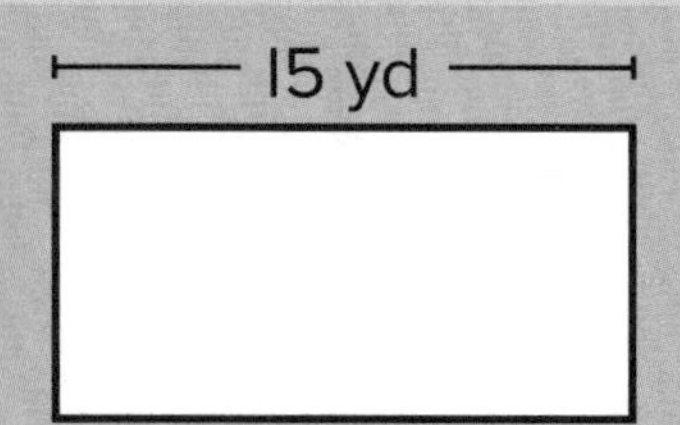

The length of the short side is the only length that remains unknown. I'll call this length **S**.
S = 90 ÷ 15 or 15 x **S** = 90

Ruben has 20 yards of fencing wire.

How much more wire would he need to fence the backyard?

How did you figure out the perimeter of the backyard?

Step Up

1. Measure each side length in centimeters. Then calculate the perimeter and area.

a.

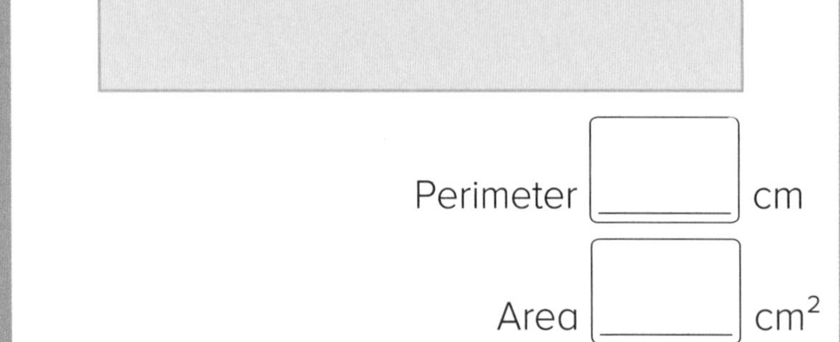

Perimeter ______ cm

Area ______ cm²

b.

Perimeter ______ cm

Area ______ cm²

c.

Perimeter ______ cm

Area ______ cm²

2. Solve each problem. Show your thinking.

a. A pyramid has a square base. The perimeter of the base is 60 yards. What is the length of each side of the base?

_______ yd

b. Cathy's backyard is a rectangle. The short sides are 6 yards long. The long sides are twice as long. What is the area of her backyard?

_______ yd^2

c. Pamela's desk is 24 inches wide and 48 inches long. Her teacher's is 30 inches wide and 60 inches long. What is the difference in area?

_______ in^2

d. A rectangular poster has an area of 320 square inches. One longer side is 20 inches. What is the length of one shorter side?

_______ in

Step Ahead Solve this problem. Draw a picture to help your thinking.

Anoki buys 150 yards of fencing wire to build a rectangular enclosure. He needs 10 yards of wire left over. Write possible side lengths for the enclosure.

Short side _______ yd

Long side _______ yd

Step In Adding Tenths

Alfredo and Emma are going on a 5-km fun run.

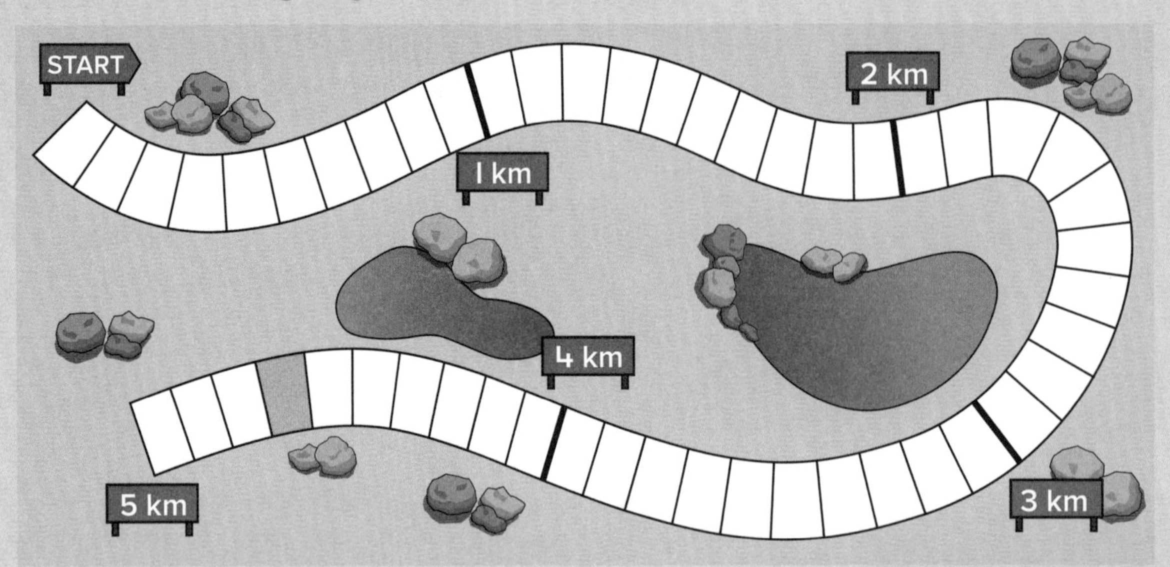

How has each kilometer been divided?

What fraction of one kilometer does the orange part show?

> A short way to write kilometer is km.

Shade 1.3 km of the track from the start.

What is two-tenths of a kilometer more? How can you figure it out?

What equation with decimal fractions could you write to show what is happening?

____ + ____ = ____

What equation with mixed numbers and common fractions could you write?

____ + ____ = ____

On another fun run, the total distance is 10 km.

If you were at the mark for 5.3 km, where will you be after you run 2.4 km farther along the track? How can you figure it out?

I would add the ones together, then add the tenths together, then add the totals. I use the same strategy for adding two-digit whole numbers.

It's like adding mixed numbers. I would add the whole numbers and fractions separately then add the totals together.

I could start with 5.3, then add 2, then add 0.4.

Can you think of another method?

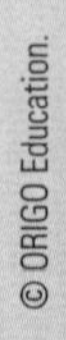

Step Up

1. Calculate the total distance for each of these.

a. 3.4 km + 2.3 km = ______ km

b. 2.1 km + 3.5 km = ______ km

c. 2.7 km + 4.2 km = ______ km

d. 6.3 km + 1.4 km = ______ km

e. 6.1 km + 2.3 km = ______ km

f. 3.2 km + 3.5 km = ______ km

g. 1.6 km + 4.2 km = ______ km

h. 4.5 km + 1.4 km = ______ km

i. 5.3 km + 2.3 km = ______ km

j. 5.4 km + 3.5 km = ______ km

2. There are checkpoints located every 3.1 km along a fun run.

a. Write how far each checkpoint is from the start.

START	Checkpoint 1	Checkpoint 2	Checkpoint 3	Checkpoint 4	Checkpoint 5	FINISH
	______	______	______	______	______	

b. The finish is located 1.5 km after the last checkpoint.

How long is the fun run? ______ km

Step Ahead

Madison and Noel ran a relay. Madison ran the first 3.1 kilometers then Noel ran the last 3.3 kilometers.

a. Did they run more than or less than 6.05 kilometers in total? ______

b. Write how you know. ______

______

______

Step In Adding Hundredths

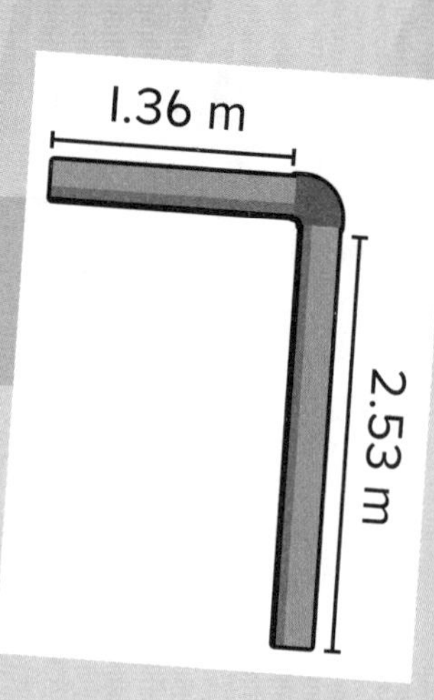

A new downspout is being made to attach to the side of a building. This sketch shows the pipes that are needed.

How could you figure out the total length of pipe?

I would add the ones together, then the tenths, then the hundredths.

These two items are needed for the downspout.
What is their total cost? How could you figure it out?

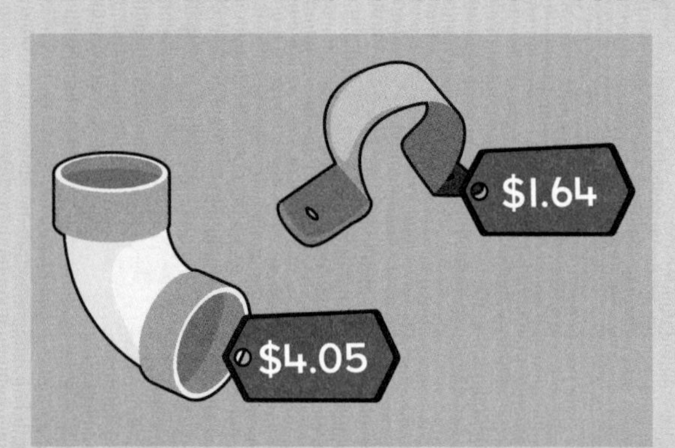

It's easy to think about this. The whole numbers are dollars and the fractions are cents.

Step Up

1. Add the lengths and write the total. Show your thinking.

a. 4.32 m + 3.65 m = ______ m

b. 3.72 m + 3.15 m = ______ m

c. 1.65 m + 0.23 m = ______ m

d. 2.84 m + 5.03 m = ______ m

2. Write the total cost. Show your thinking.

a. $3.56 $1.42

$ ______

b.  $5.24 $3.45

$ ______

c. $2.06 $2.31

$ ______

d. $4.20 $1.50

$ ______

e. $3.71 $5.00

$ ______

f. $0.65 $1.24

$ ______

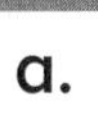

Step Ahead Write each decimal fraction as a mixed number or common fraction then write the total. The first numbers have been done for you.

a. 4.35 + 1.62	b. 2.17 + 3.41	c. 1.62 + 1.05
$4\frac{35}{100} + 1\frac{62}{100} =$ ☐		
d. 0.02 + 0.07	e. 1.40 + 0.08	f. 0.04 + 0.60

Step In Adding Tenths and Hundredths

Norton drew these pictures to help figure out the total of 0.4 and 0.23.

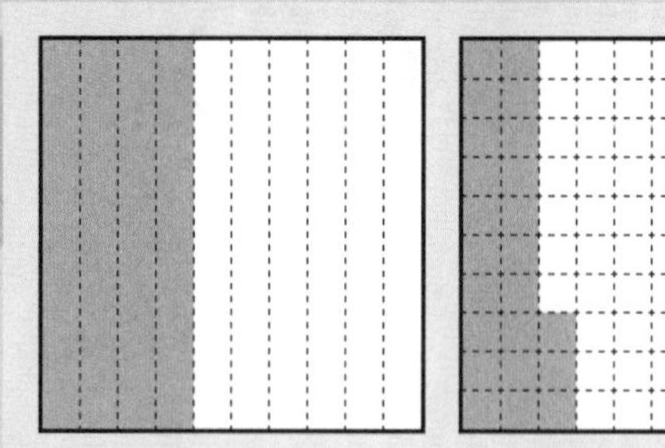

How could you use the pictures to help you?

Chloe wrote the numbers as common fractions to help her think about the problem.

She realized the denominators were different and knew that adding fractions was easier when they had the same denominator.

How could she change the fractions?

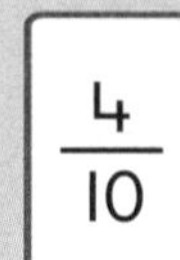

Steven thought about the value of each place and knew if he added like places he would find the total.

What helps him identify the places correctly?

The decimal point tells me where the ones place is. Then it's easy.

How would you use each of these methods to figure out the total of 2.05 and 0.8?

Step Up

1. Complete each equation. You can use the pictures to help you. Each large square is one whole.

a. 0.5 + 0.34 = ____________

b. 0.3 + 0.25 = ____________

c. 1.0 + 0.43 = ____________

d. 0.1 + 0.11 = ____________

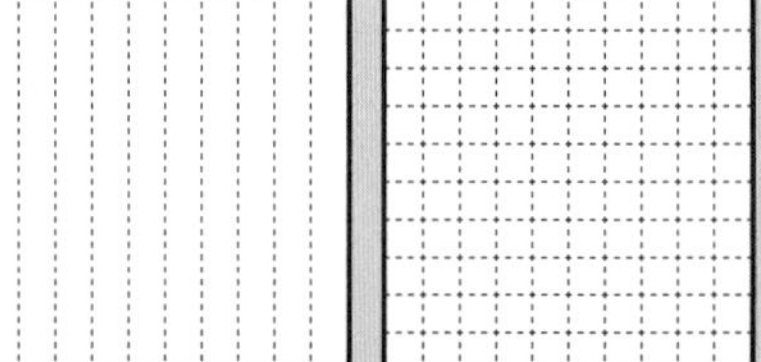

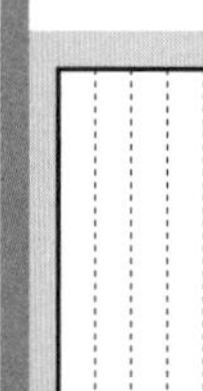

e. 0.6 + 0.20 = ____________

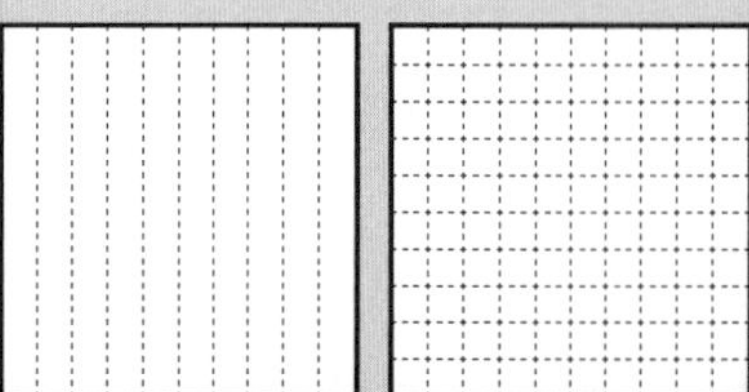

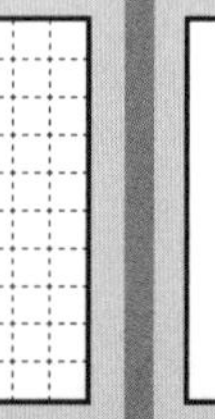

f. 0.4 + 0.03 = ____________

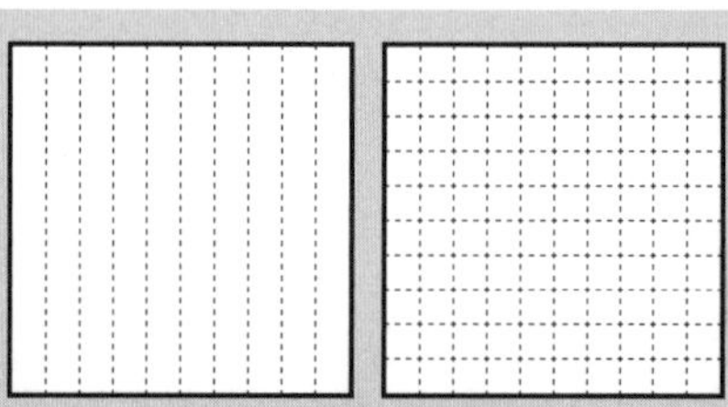

2. Use what you know about equivalence to calculate each total.

a. $\frac{6}{10} + \frac{15}{100} =$	**b.** $\frac{5}{10} + \frac{5}{100} =$	**c.** $\frac{2}{10} + \frac{45}{100} =$
d. $\frac{8}{10} + \frac{12}{100} =$	**e.** $2\frac{1}{10} + \frac{30}{100} =$	**f.** $\frac{1}{10} + 2\frac{7}{100} =$
g. $1\frac{14}{100} + \frac{6}{10} =$	**h.** $\frac{2}{100} + \frac{9}{10} =$	**i.** $3\frac{33}{100} + \frac{4}{10} =$

3. Choose six totals from Question 2. Write each as a decimal fraction.

a.	b.	c.	d.	e.	f.
______	______	______	______	______	______

4. Show each decimal fraction as the sum of three numbers.

a. 1.34 = 1 + 0.3 + 0.04 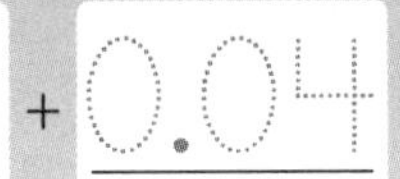	**b.** 2.47 = 1 + 1.2 + 0.27
c. 1.45 = ______ + ______ + ______	**d.** 2.96 = ______ + ______ + ______
e. 0.67 = ______ + ______ + ______	**f.** 1.50 = ______ + ______ + ______
g. 1.0 = ______ + ______ + ______	**h.** 0.1 = ______ + ______ + ______

Step Ahead

Figure out which pairs of numbers add to a total that is a whole number. Use the same color to show matching pairs. Some numbers have no match.

0.95 0.6 0.90 2.0

0.1 0.09 1.2 0.50 2.40

0.8 3.5 1.05 0.01

Step In Adding Decimal Fractions

This table shows the amount of protein in some fast foods.

How could you figure out the total protein for one lean burger and one serving of fries?

Selena used a number line to figure out the total.

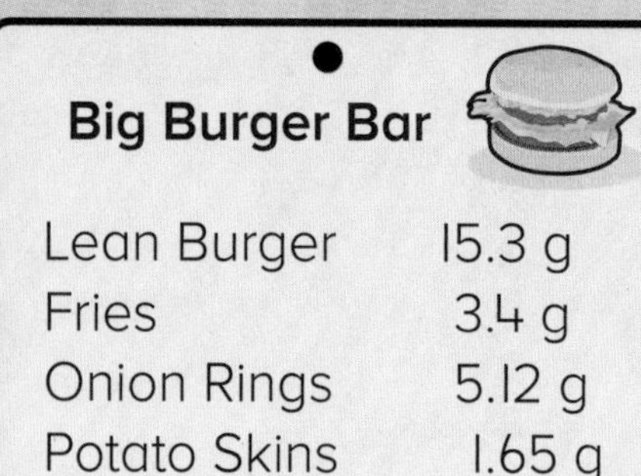

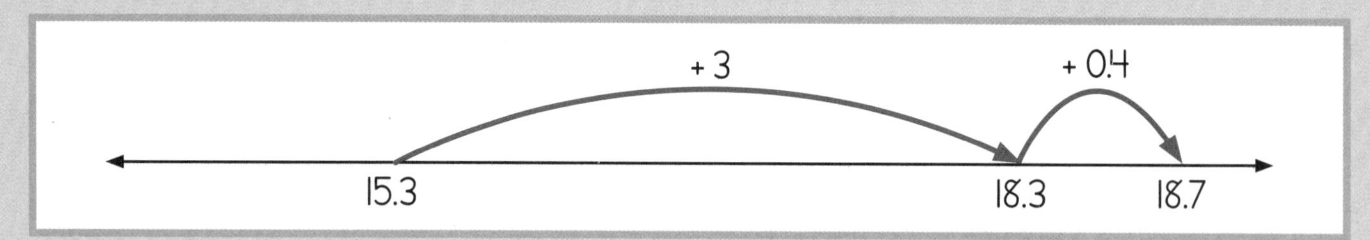

What steps did she follow? What is another way to figure out the total?

How would you figure out the total protein for one serving of fries and one serving of onion rings?

Felipe used common fractions.

$3\frac{4}{10} + 5\frac{12}{100} =$

$3\frac{40}{100} + 5\frac{12}{100} =$

$8\frac{52}{100}$

Lomasi used place value.

$3 + 5 = 8$

$0.4 + 0.1 = 0.5$

$0.00 + 0.02 = 0.02$

$8 + 0.5 + 0.02 = 8.52$

Describe each strategy. Which strategy do you prefer? Why?

Step Up

1. Draw jumps on the number line to figure out each total.

a. $2.3 + 5.4 =$ ______

b. $4.5 + 3.1 =$ ______

2. Figure out each total. Draw jumps to show your thinking.

a. 6.2 + 1.37 = ____

b. 2.05 + 5.6 = ____

3. Figure out each total. Show your thinking.

a. 2.45 + 1.32 = ____

b. 7.3 + 2.53 = ____

c. 12.09 + 5.3 = ____

d. 10.71 + 11.06 = ____

Step Ahead Write the value of each coin as a decimal fraction of one dollar.

Step In Adding Decimal Fractions (with Regrouping)

Three students threw a shot put twice and added the distances.

	1st Throw	2nd Throw	Total
Harry	3.5 m	3.7 m	m
Maria	3.09 m	3.45 m	m
Nathan	4.2 m	3.92 m	m

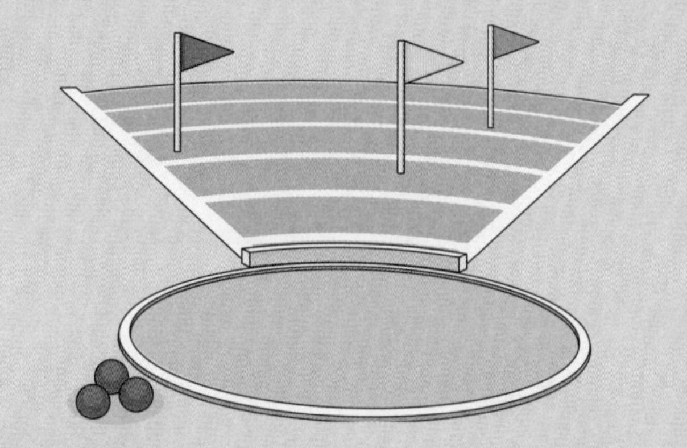

How could you figure out the total distance of Harry's throws?

How could you figure out the total distance of Maria's throws?

Hugo figured out the total like this.

3.09 + 3.45

3 + 3 = 6
0.0 + 0.4 = 0.4
0.09 + 0.05 = 0.14
6.54

Akeema figured it out like this.

3.09 + 3.45

$3\frac{9}{100} + 3\frac{45}{100} = 6\frac{54}{100}$

Toby figured out 3.10 + 3.44.
He knew it would give the same total.

What steps does each person follow? Which strategy do you prefer? Why?

Use the strategy you like best to figure out the total length of Nathan's throws.

Who threw the greatest total distance?

Step Up

1. Figure out each total. Show your thinking.

a. 3.6 + 4.8 = ______

b. 2.65 + 3.18 = ______

c. 5.2 + 3.85 = ______

2. Figure out each total. Show your thinking.

a. $3.80 $4.30

$ ________

b. $1.90 $5.60

$ ________

c. $2.38 $2.45

$ ________

d. $7.62 $1.09

$ ________

e. $5.40 $1.70

$ ________

f. $3.85 $2.90

$ ________

Step Ahead Figure out and write the missing lengths.

	1st Throw	2nd Throw	Total
Charlie	3.5 m	m	7.02 m
Mikita	m	4.25 m	9.2 m
Tomas	m	m	8.05 m

Step In: Using the Standard Algorithm to Add Decimal Fractions

These two packages were weighed in kilograms.

Estimate the mass of the two packages together.

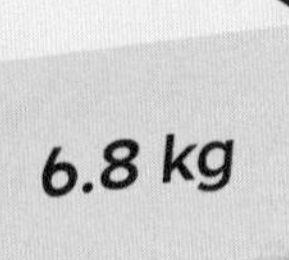

How could you figure out the exact mass of the two packages?

Amber used the standard addition algorithm to figure out the total. What steps does she follow?

Step 1

	T	O	t	h
		6.	8	
+		5.	7	2
		.		2

Step 2

	T	O	t	h
		1 6.	8	
+		5.	7	2
		.	5	2

Step 3

	T	O	t	h
		1 6.	8	
+		5.	7	2
	1	2.	5	2

Amber wrote 6.8 in the top row. Does the total change if she writes 6.80?

What does the 1 above the 6 represent?

Step Up

1. Calculate the total mass of each pair of packages.

a.

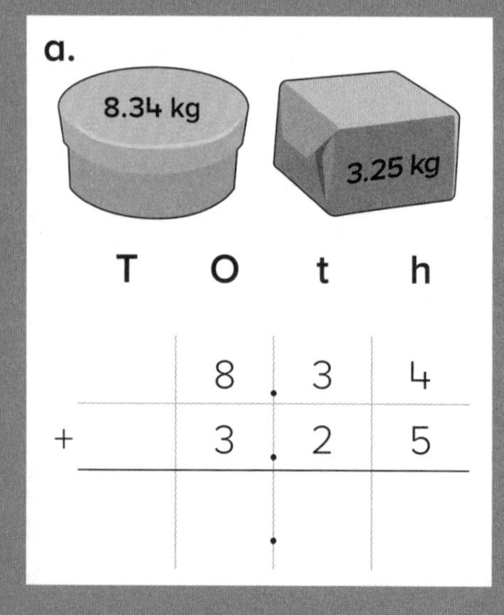

	T	O	t	h
		8.	3	4
+		3.	2	5
		.		

b.

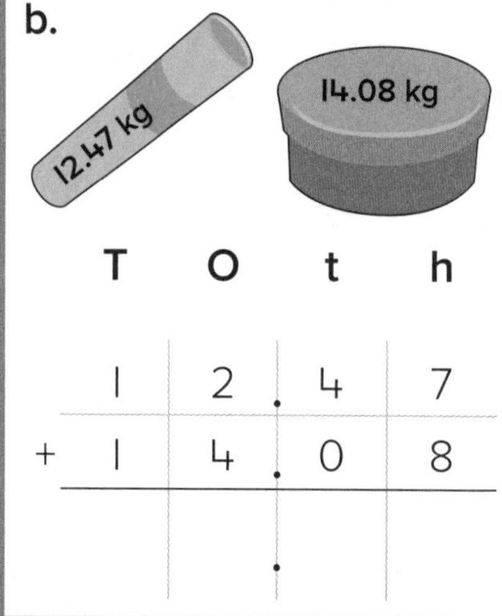

	T	O	t	h
	1	2.	4	7
+	1	4.	0	8
		.		

c.

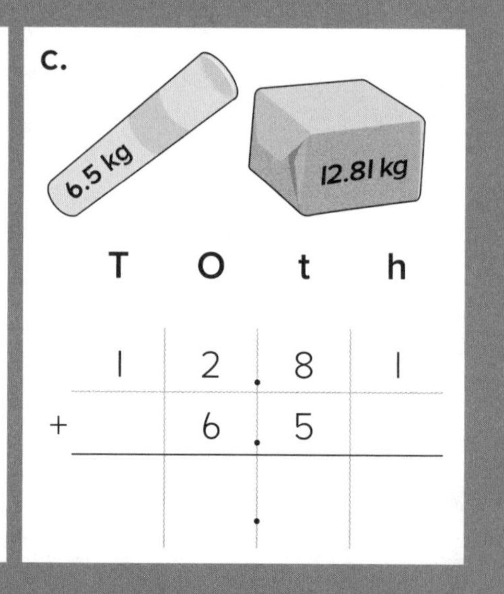

	T	O	t	h
	1	2.	8	1
+		6.	5	
		.		

2. Calculate the total mass of these packages.

a.

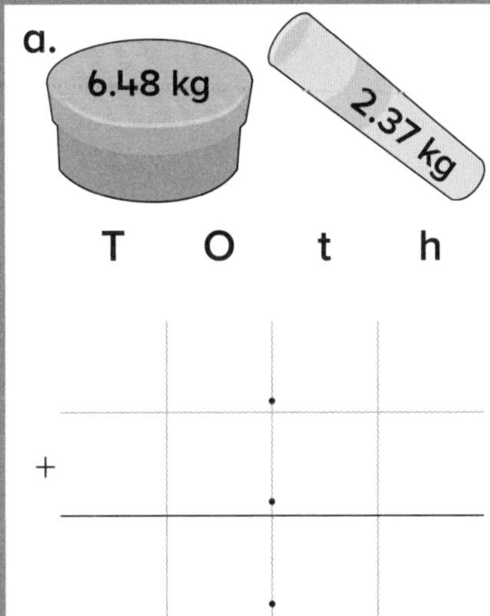

b.

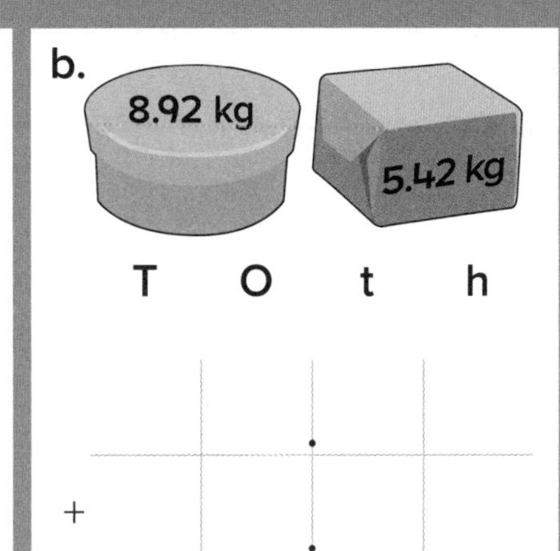

c.

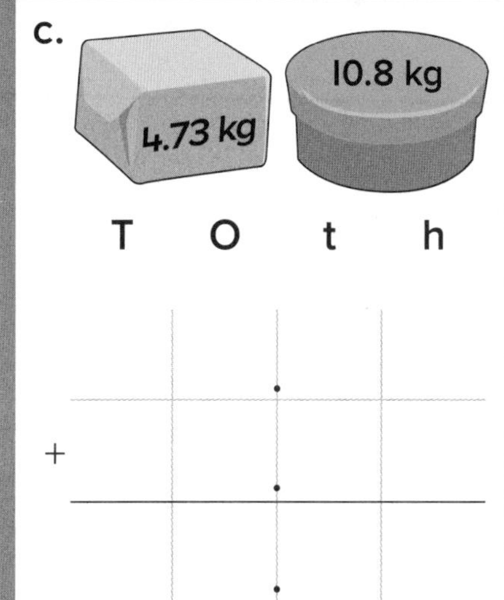

d.

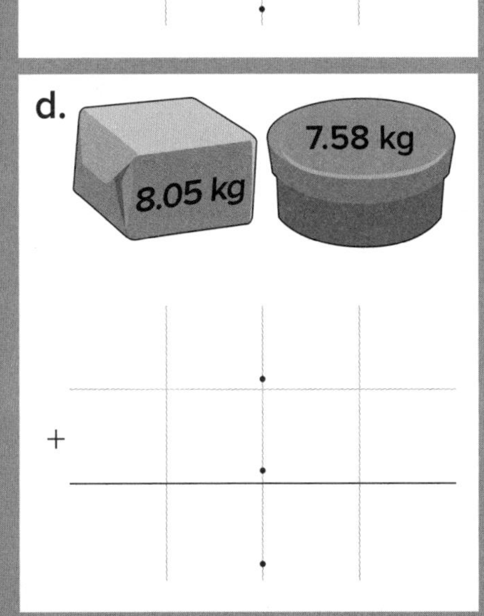

e.

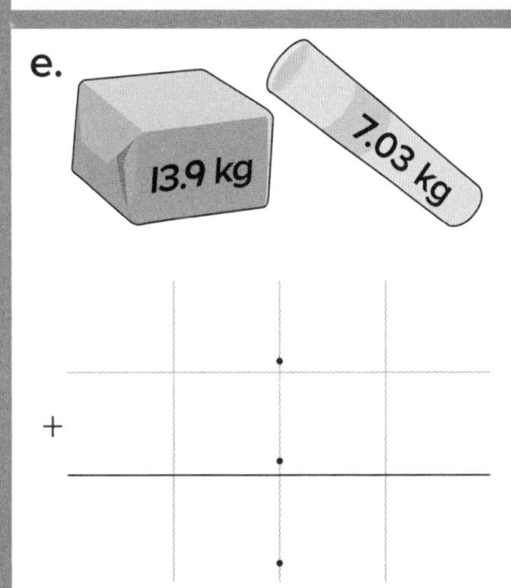

f.

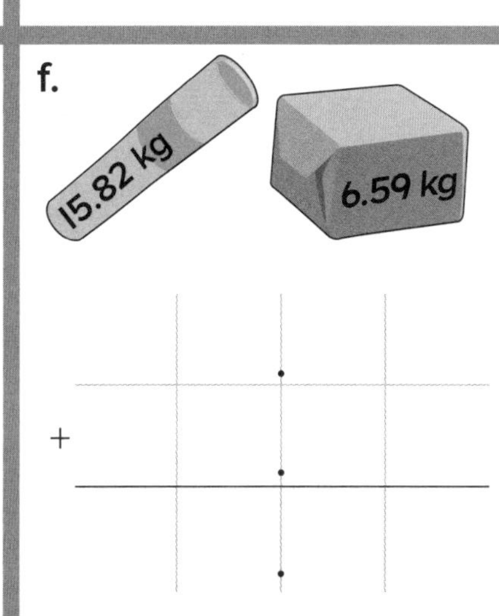

Step Ahead This student seems to repeat the same error on a test. Describe the mistake in words.

	2 .	3
+	4 .	6
	6 .	9

	4 .	7
+	3 .	8
	7 .	15

	5 .	2
+	3 .	5
	8 .	7

	7 .	3
+	7 .	9
	14 .	12

Step In Using the Standard Algorithm to Add More Than Two Decimal Fractions

Estimate the perimeter of this triangle.

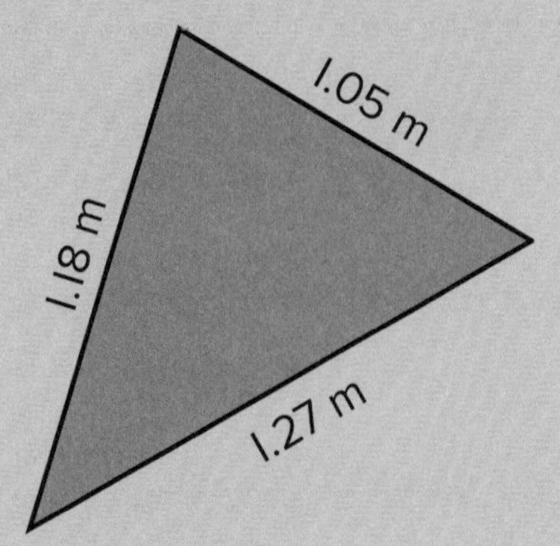

Each side is just over one meter, so the perimeter is between 3 and 4 meters.

How could you figure out the exact perimeter?

Tama and Violeta both used a written method.

Tama added the hundredths first.

```
    2
  1.18
  1.27
+ 1.05
  3.50
```

Violeta used partial sums. She added the ones first.

```
  1.18
  1.27
+ 1.05
  3.00
  0.30
  0.20
  3.50
```

Describe the steps that they followed.

Does it matter in what order the side lengths are recorded?

Is there another way you could do it?

Step Up

1. Calculate the perimeter of each triangle. Record the steps you use.

a.

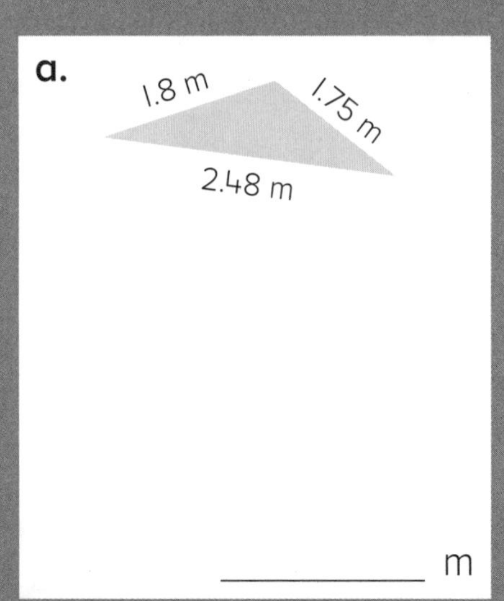

_______ m

b.

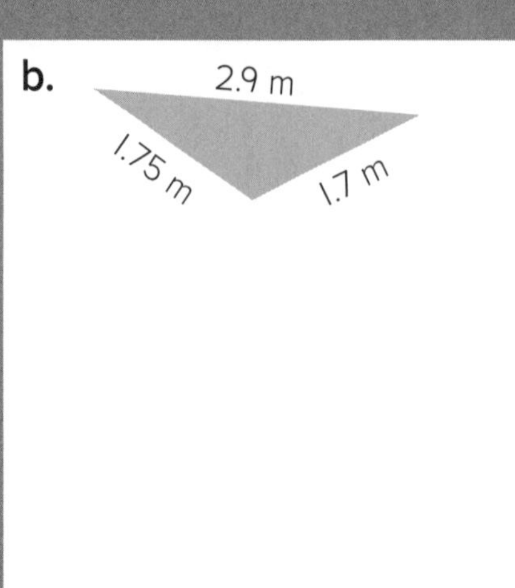

_______ m

c.

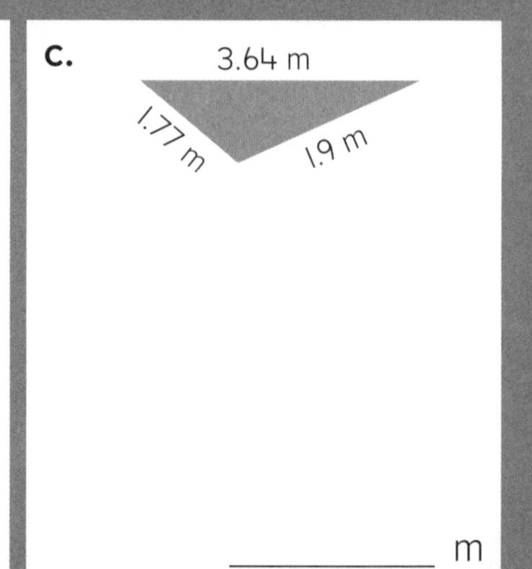

_______ m

2. Calculate these perimeters. Record the steps you use.

a.

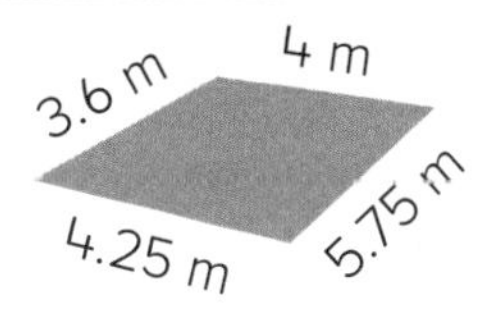

__________ m

b.

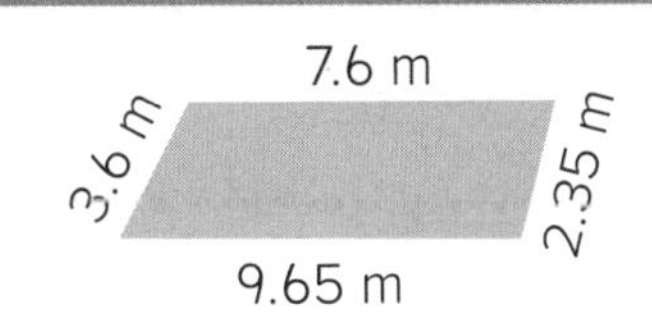

__________ m

c.

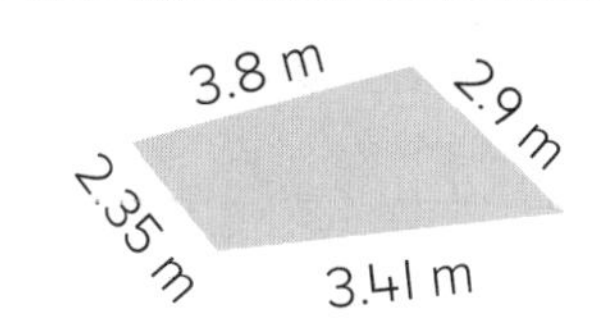

__________ m

d.

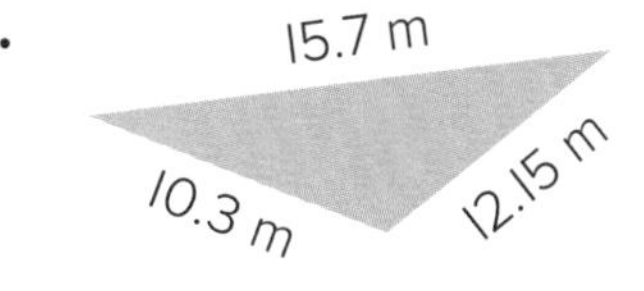

__________ m

e.

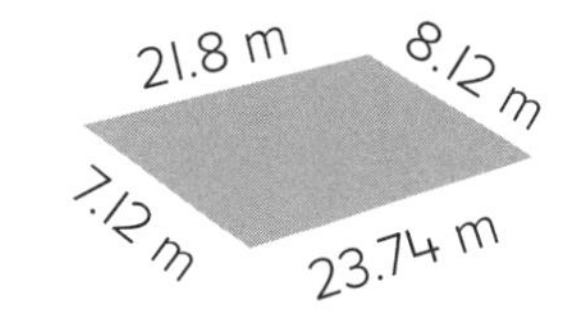

__________ m

f.

14.35 m

7 m

11.2 m

__________ m

Step Ahead

Draw and label a shape that has sides of different length and a perimeter of 10 meters. Show each side measure as a decimal fraction involving hundredths.

Step In — Converting Meters and Centimeters

Miles has to cut paper streamers for a party.
Each streamer has to be about 70 centimeters long.
The whole roll is 4 meters long.

Will there be enough on the roll for 10 streamers?
How do you know?

In the word **centimeter**, **centi** means one-hundredth. A related word is **cent**, because one cent is one-hundredth of a dollar.

This picture shows the length of Ella's arm span in centimeters.

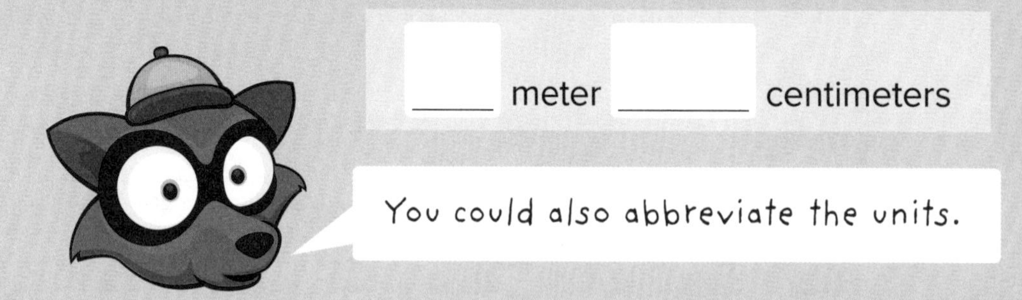

How could you **say** the length of Ella's arm span?

How could you **write** the length of Ella's arm span?

_____ meter _______ centimeters

You could also abbreviate the units.

Step Up

1. Write each distance using centimeters.

a. 5 m is _______ cm

b. 50 m is _______ cm

c. 13 m is _______ cm

d. 130 m is _______ cm

e. 280 m is _______ cm

f. 4,300 m is _______ cm

2. Write the missing lengths in meters and centimeters. Then draw lines to show where the other lengths are located on the measuring tape.

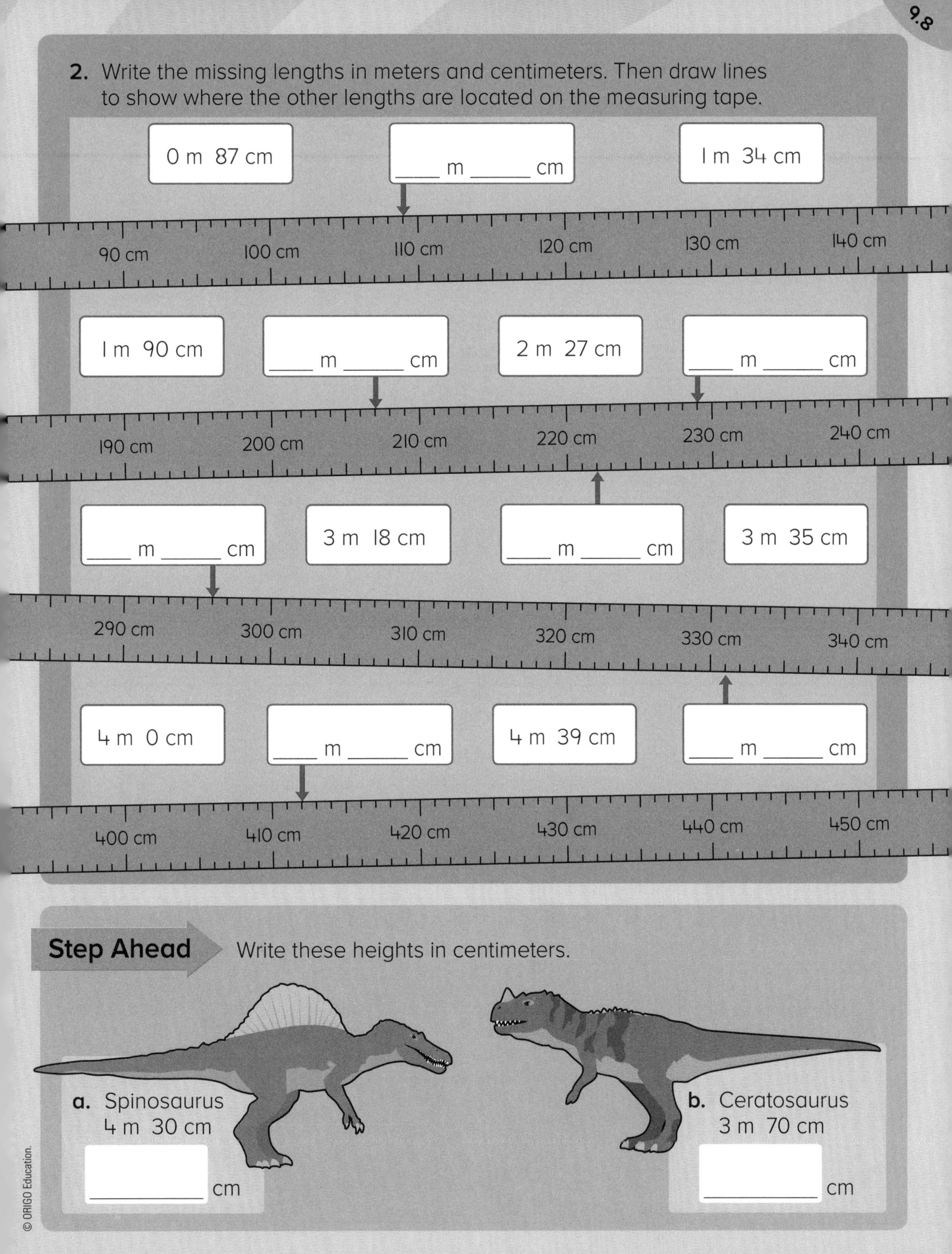

Step Ahead Write these heights in centimeters.

a. Spinosaurus
4 m 30 cm
__________ cm

b. Ceratosaurus
3 m 70 cm
__________ cm

Step In Working with Millimeters

Some types of ants are shorter than one centimeter.

One millimeter is one-tenth of the length of a centimeter.

How many millimeters are the same length as one centimeter?
How many millimeters are the same length as five centimeters?

How long is each ant from head to tail? How do you know?

A short way to write millimeter is mm.

Step Up

1. List things in your classroom that are a little **less than** one millimeter thick and a little **more than** one millimeter thick.

A little less than one millimeter thick	A little more than one millimeter thick
________	________
________	________
________	________

2. Measure and label the dimensions of these stickers in millimeters.

a. ______ mm ______ mm

b. ______ mm ______ mm

c. ______ mm

d. ______ mm ______ mm

e. ______ mm ______ mm

f. ______ mm ______ mm ______ mm

3. Complete these.

a. I centimeter is the same length as ________ millimeters.

b. 100 centimeters is the same length as ________ millimeters.

c. I meter is the same length as ________ millimeters.

4. Use the information in Question 3 to help you complete these.

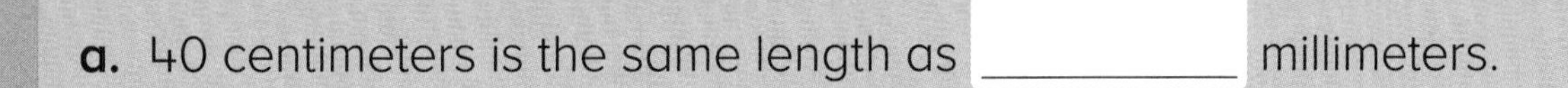

a. 40 centimeters is the same length as ________ millimeters.

b. 85 centimeters is the same length as ________ millimeters.

c. 125 centimeters is the same length as ________ millimeters.

5. Write these lengths in millimeters.

a. 5 cm 4 mm is ________ mm

b. 13 cm 8 mm is ________ mm

Step Ahead

Complete the missing numbers in this machine.

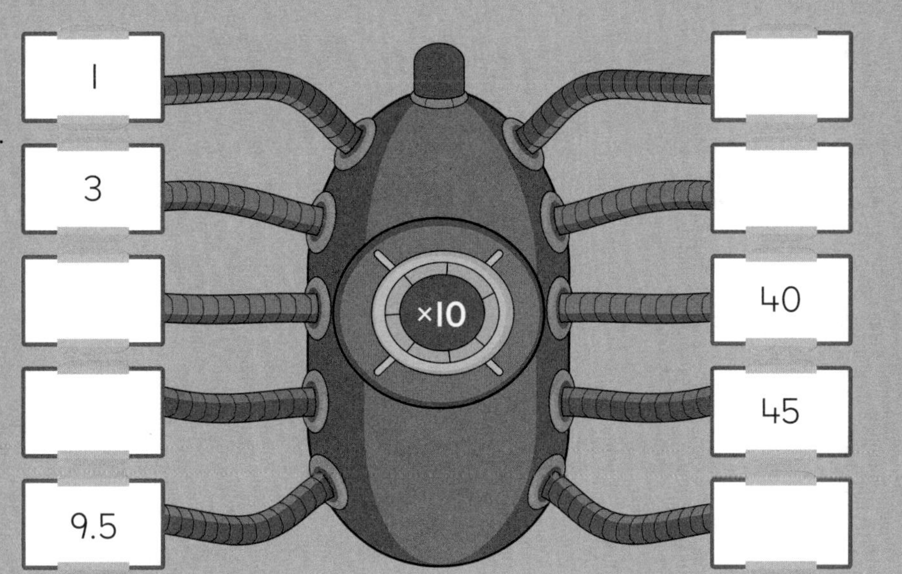

Step In Exploring the Relationship between Meters, Centimeters, and Millimeters

This block measures 10 cm.

How many millimeters are in 10 cm?
How do you know?

How many centimeters are in one meter? How can you check?

You could check by placing 10 tens blocks along one side of a meter stick.

In the word **millimeter**, milli means one-thousandth. A related word is **millipede**, a creature with so many legs it was guessed that they have about 1,000.

How many millimeters are in one meter?
How did you figure it out?

How would you change these? 3,500 mm to meters | 12 meters to millimeters

Step Up

1. Complete each of these.

a. 6 meters is the same length as ________ cm	**b.** 9 meters is the same length as ________ cm	**c.** 4 meters is the same length as ________ cm
d. 11 centimeters is the same length as ________ mm	**e.** 15 centimeters is the same length as ________ mm	**f.** 7.5 centimeters is the same length as ________ mm
g. 8.5 meters is the same length as ________ mm	**h.** 23.5 meters is the same length as ________ mm	**i.** 46.5 meters is the same length as ________ mm

2. Look at this floor plan. Write each dimension in millimeters.

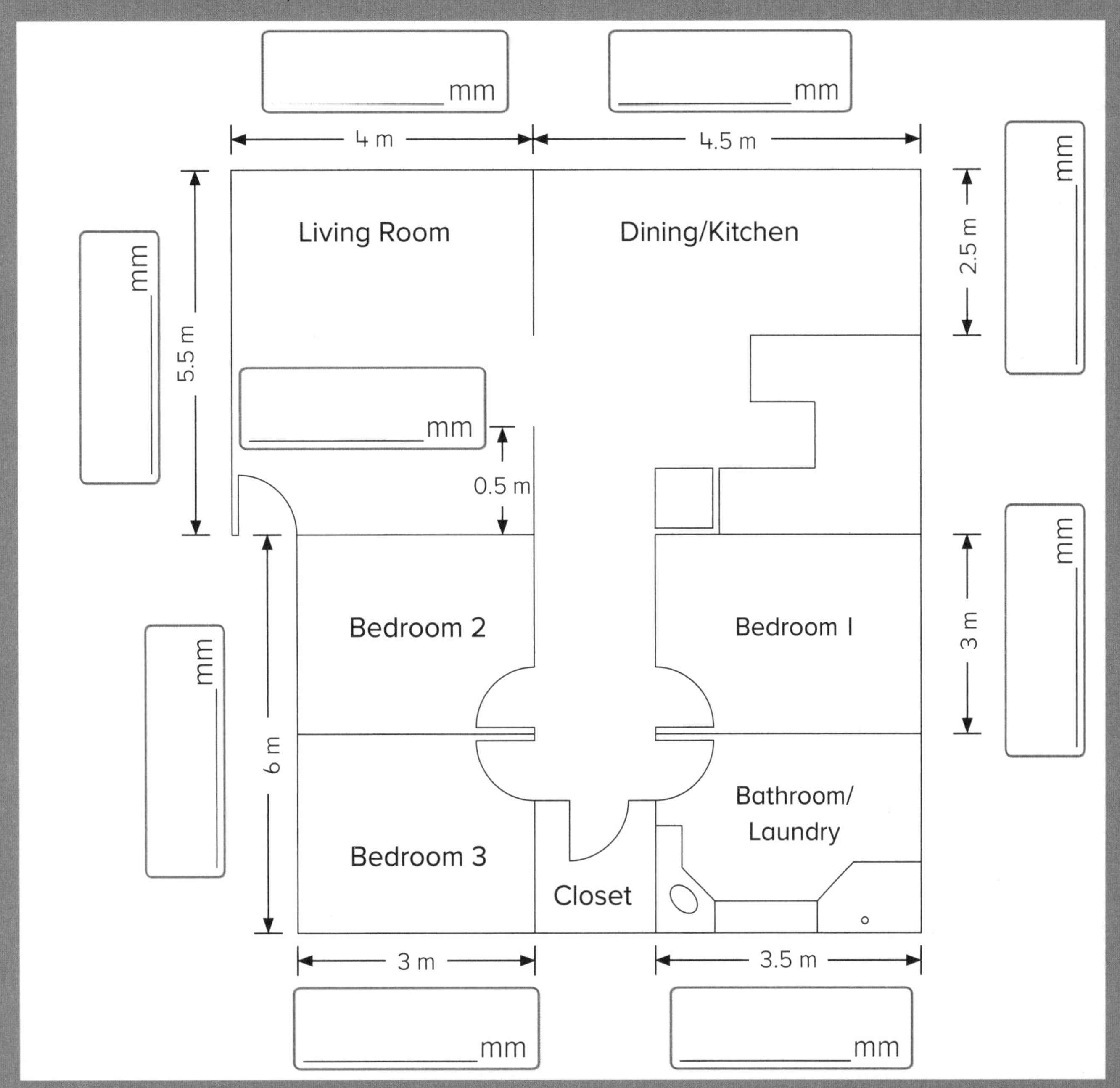

Step Ahead Complete the missing numbers in this table to show equivalent lengths.

Millimeters (mm)	Centimeters (cm)	Meters (m)
		2.5
	400	
4,500		

Step In Working with Kilometers

Where have you heard of kilometers before?

Rapid City
II miles
18 km

I have seen kilometers as **km** on some road signs.

My mom and dad do a 5-kilometer fun run every year.

Kilometers are used to measure long distances. How is "kilo" different from "milli"?

Look at a meter stick.

How many meter sticks would you need to make one kilometer?

In the word **kilometer**, kilo means one thousand. A related word is **kilogram**, which is equal to 1,000 grams. A short way to write kilometer is km.

Some other metric units of length are not used often but help show the relationship between metric units of length.

Look at this diagram.
What do you notice?

A **dekameter** is equal to 10 meters.
A short way to write dekameter is dam.
A **hectometer** is equal to 100 meters.
A short way to write hectometer is hm.

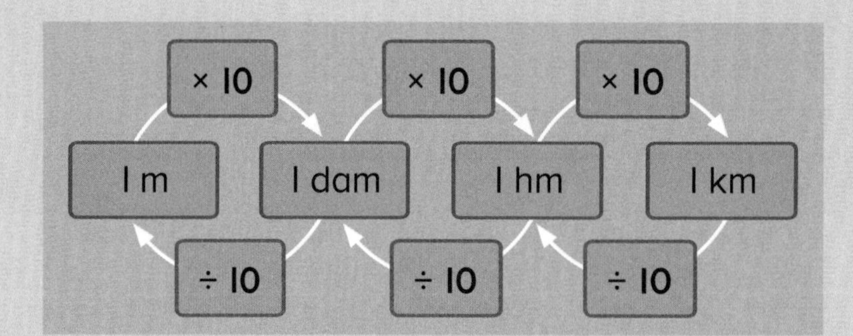

How is the relationship between kilometers and meters the same as the relationship between meters and millimeters?

Step Up

1. Complete these.

a. 1 kilometer is the same length as ______ m	b. 10 kilometers is the same length as ______ m	c. 100 kilometers is the same length as ______ m

2. a. These hiking trails are in Yellowstone National Park. Loop the trails that are between 1,000 and 6,000 meters long. Use the information above to help you.

b. Lucy's family hiked about 15,000 m. Which trails might they have walked? Write two different combinations.

____

____

3. Write these lengths in meters.

a. 16 km 8 m is ______ m

b. 5 km 40 m is ______ m

Step Ahead

Complete the table below to show equivalent distances.

mm	cm	dm	m	dam	hm	km
			600			0.6

Step In Solving Word Problems Involving Metric Length

Two friends live at opposite ends of the same straight street. They arranged to meet at a store on their street. Marcos lives 34 meters from the store and Stella lives half a kilometer from the store.

How many meters is it from Marcos' home to Stella's home?

What do you need to find out?

What information will help you?

How could you figure out the distance?

I need to think about how many meters make 1 kilometer. Then I can figure out how many meters make half a kilometer.

Step Up

1. Figure out the answer to each problem. Show your thinking and be sure to use the correct units in your answer.

a. Denton has two pet lizards, Apollo and Dino. Apollo is half a meter long from head to tail and Dino is 38 cm long. Which lizard is longer?

b. Ribbon A is 500 mm long. Ribbon B is taped to the end of Ribbon A so that the total length is 63 cm. How long is Ribbon B?

mm

c. Evan rode 450 meters to Theo's house. Together they rode 3 km to the mall. How many meters did Evan ride in total?

m

d. Mana's grandparents live 60 km away. If she visits them twice in one month how far will she travel in total?

km

2. Solve each problem. Show your thinking.

a. There were three alligators at a zoo. The smallest was 1.5 meters long. The second was 68 cm longer than the smallest one. The largest was 2 meters 10 cm longer than the second one. How long was the largest alligator?

_______ cm

b. A carpenter is cutting a piece of lumber for some shelves. The piece of lumber is 2 meters long. Each shelf needs to be 645 mm long and there are two shelves. How much lumber will be left over after the shelves are cut?

_______ mm

c. Emilio jumped forward 3 times and measured the length of each jump. The first jump was 1 m 34 cm, the second was 1 m 46 cm, and the third was 1 m 15 cm. How far did he jump in total?

_______ cm

d. Monique ran three times around a 400-m track. Olivia ran 1.5 km.

Who ran farther, Monique or Olivia? 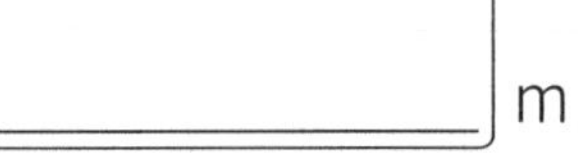

How far did she run?

_______ m

Step Ahead Complete each equation. Use scrap paper to make notes. Check your answers.

a. _______ km + 540 m = 10,540 m

b. 3,000 cm + _______ m = 3,200 cm

c. 10 cm + _______ cm = 170 mm

d. _______ mm + 3 m = 4,863 mm

Step In — Subtracting Decimal Fractions (Tenths or Hundredths)

Cristina is planning a hike. How much farther is Springwood Falls than Big Rock Valley?

Springwood Falls is more than double the distance.

Michael drew jumps on this number line to figure out the exact difference.

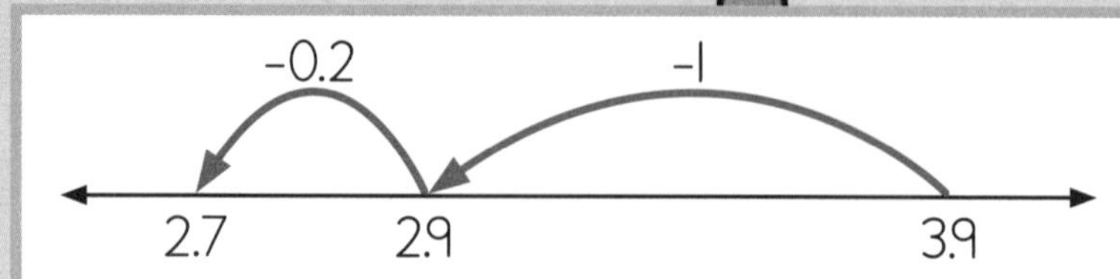

What steps did he follow? What is another way to find the difference?

Cristina decides to buy some supplies.
How would you figure out the difference in cost between these two items?

Jacob figured it out like this.

$7.99 – $2.45

$7.99 – $2 = $5.99
$5.99 – 40¢ = $5.59
$5.59 – 5¢ = $5.54

What steps did Jacob follow? What is another way to find the difference?

Step Up

1. Draw jumps on the number line to figure out each difference.

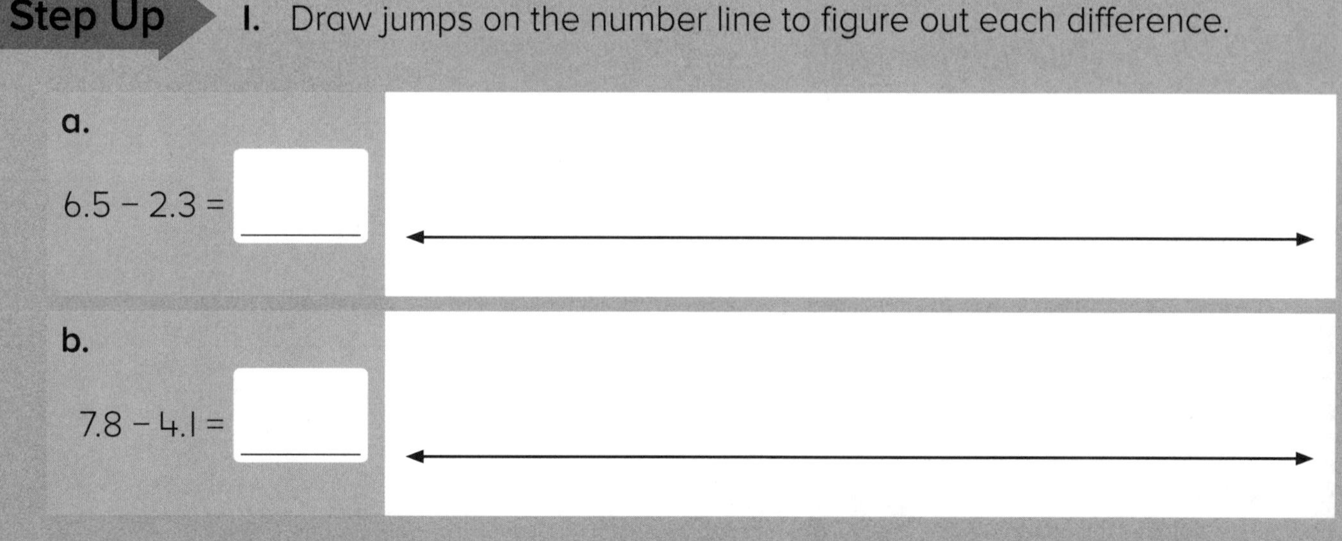

a. 6.5 – 2.3 = ____

b. 7.8 – 4.1 = ____

2. Figure out the difference between these prices. Show your thinking.

a. 
$3.50 $1.20

$ ______

b. $6.70 $5.30

$ ______

c. 
$8.40 $3.30

$ ______

d. $4.88 $1.32

$ ______

e. $5.75 $2.52

$ ______

f. 
$6.99 $3.47

$ ______

Step Ahead A student used this number line to figure out 7.81 − 2.41. Write the correct difference. Then explain the mistake that was made.

7.81 − 2.41 = 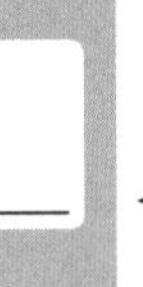 ______

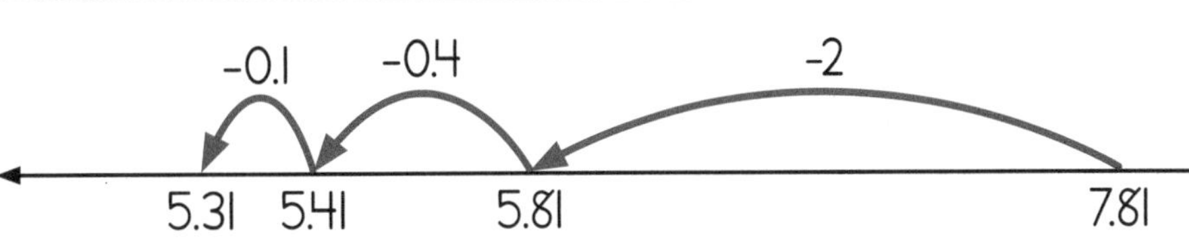

____

____

Step In — Subtracting Decimal Fractions (Tenths and Hundredths)

Look at these performance scores.

How could you figure out the difference between Ramon's score and Allison's score?

TALENT QUEST

LEADER BOARD	
Ramon	12.4
Allison	15.92
Sakeema	18.51
Isabel	7.2

I know that 12.4 is the same as 12.40.

Breyann used this written method to figure out the difference.

What steps did she follow?

$$\begin{array}{r} 15.92 \\ -\ 0.40 \\ \hline 15.52 \\ -\ 12.00 \\ \hline 3.52 \end{array}$$

What are some other differences that you can figure out? Record your thinking in the working space.

Working Space

Step Up

1. Figure out these differences. Show your thinking.

a. 8.60 − 5.1 = ______

b. 13.6 − 10.02 = ______

c. 14.92 − 10.3 = ______

2. Figure out the amount that is left in the wallet after each purchase.

a. Wallet: $7.60 Price tag: $3.50 $____	**b.** Wallet: $15.95 Price tag: $4.20 $____	**c.** Wallet: $16.35 Price tag: $5.20 $____
d. Wallet: $9.75 Price tag: $4.03 $____	**e.** Wallet: $13.59 Price tag: $2.47 $____	**f.** Wallet: $19.55 Price tag: $12.25 $____

Step Ahead Aaron has $20 in his wallet. He buys two of these meal deals. How much money does he have left over? $____

Working Space

Step In: Using the Standard Algorithm to Subtract Decimal Fractions

How could you figure out the difference in mass between these two dogs?

It must be about 3 kg because the difference between 17 and 14 is 3.

14.2 kg

17.65 kg

These students figured it out like this.

Laura

```
  17.65
-  0.20
  17.45
- 14.00
   3.45
```

Carlos

17.65 – 14.2

17 – 14 = 3

$\frac{65}{100} - \frac{20}{100} = \frac{45}{100}$

Difference is $3\frac{45}{100}$

Dorothy

```
  17.65
- 14.2
   3.45
```

What are the steps in each method? Whose method do you prefer? Why?

What other way could you calculate the difference?

How could you figure out the difference in cost between these two items?

The numbers are a bit "messy" so I would use a written method.

Step Up

1. Use Dorothy's method to figure out each difference.

a.

	T	O	t	h
		7 .	8	6
–		3 .	4	0
		.		

b.

	T	O	t	h
	1	8 .	9	3
–		6 .	5	1
		.		

c.

	T	O	t	h
	2	4 .	0	7
–	1	2 .	0	3
		.		

2. Figure out the difference between each pair of weights. Show your thinking.

a.

kg

b.

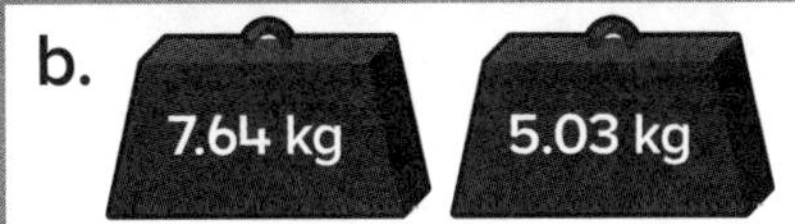

kg

c.

kg

d.

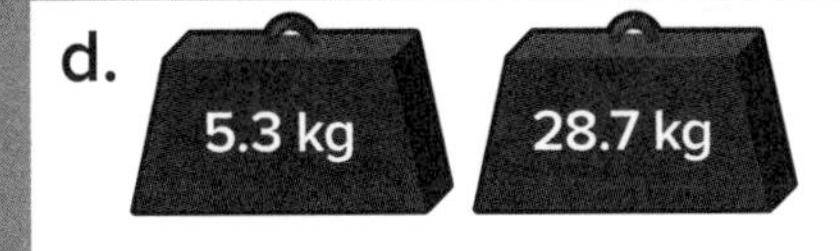

kg

e.

8.07 kg 19.17 kg

kg

f.

34.55 kg 13.05 kg

kg

Step Ahead

A student used the standard subtraction algorithm to figure out 16.45 − 3.2. Write the correct answer. Then explain the mistake that was made.

```
   1 6 . 4 5
 −       3 . 2
 -------------
   1 6   1 . 3
```

Step In Subtracting Decimal Fractions Involving Tenths (Decomposing Ones)

What do you know about tides? Do tides occur at the same time each day? Look at this table.

Tide Chart

Day	1st high	2nd high	1st low	2nd low
Monday	9.2 ft	8.4 ft	1.8 ft	0.9 ft
Wednesday	9.3 ft	8.1 ft	1.6 ft	0.8 ft

How could you figure out the difference between the first and second high tides on Monday?

Sandra knows the difference is small, so she decides to start at 8.4 and count on to 9.2. She shows her thinking by drawing jumps on this number line.

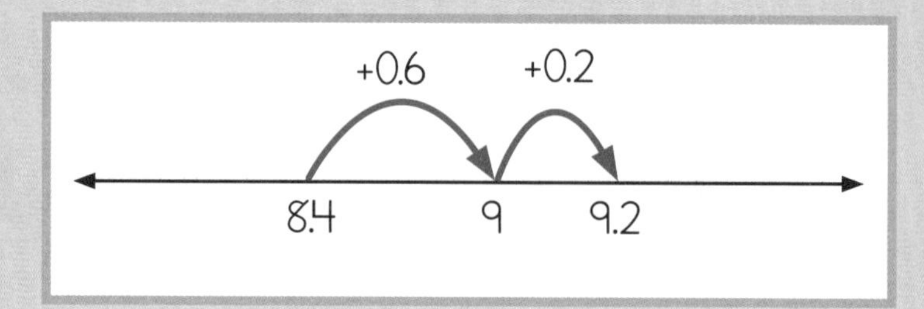

What steps did Sandra follow?

What is the difference? How is the difference shown on the number line?

Eddison used the standard subtraction algorithm to figure out the difference between the second high tide and the second low tide on Wednesday.

$$\begin{array}{r} {}^{7}\not{8}\,.\,{}^{11}\not{1} \\ -\;0\,.\,8 \\ \hline 7\,.\,3 \end{array}$$

What steps did he follow? What does each red digit represent?

Step Up

1. Draw jumps on the number line to figure out each difference.

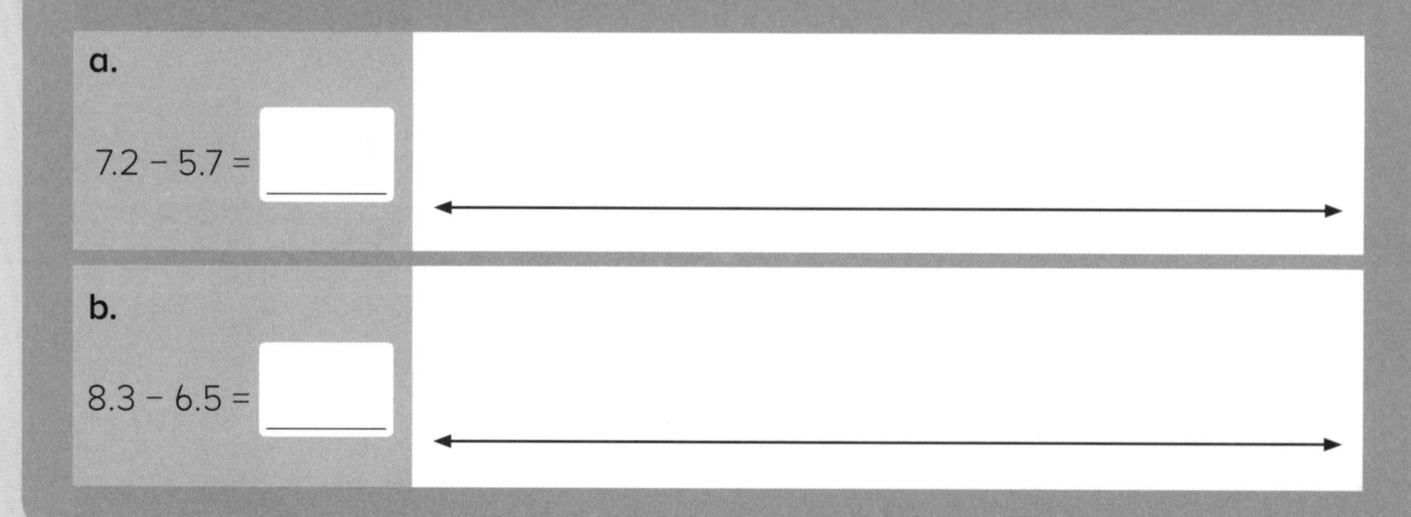

2. Figure out the difference between the tides. Show your thinking

a. High tide 7.3 ft	Low tide 1.6 ft
	_____ ft

b. High tide 8.2 ft	Low tide 1.9 ft
	_____ ft

c. High tide 9.4 ft	Low tide 2.5 ft
	_____ ft

d. High tide 8.5 ft	Low tide 3.7 ft
	_____ ft

Step Ahead

High tide on Monday was 0.4 ft more than on Tuesday. Thursday's tide was 9.1 ft. This was 0.3 ft more than on Monday but 0.2 ft less than on Sunday.

Figure out the height of the tide on each day.

Monday _____ ft

Tuesday _____ ft

Thursday _____ ft

Sunday _____ ft

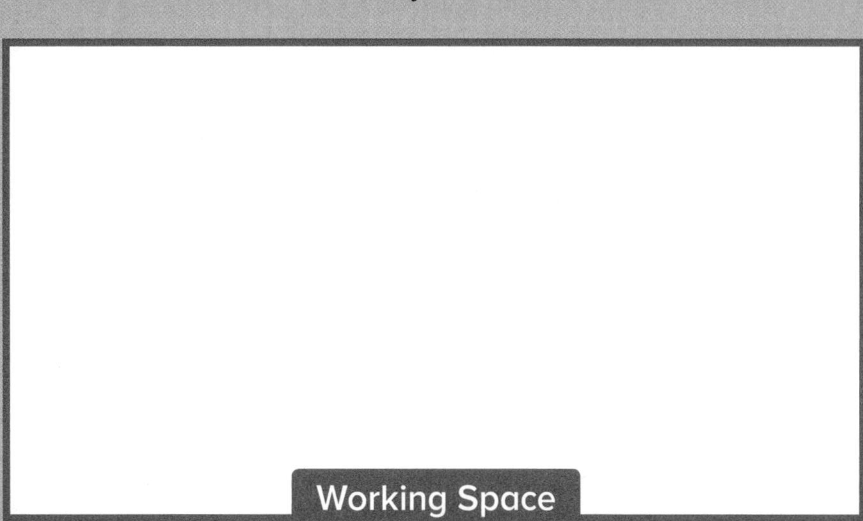

Step In Subtracting Decimal Fractions Involving Hundredths (Decomposing Tenths)

Angela jumped 4.85 meters in the long jump event at school.
Ryan jumped 0.97 meters less than Angela. Mika jumped 0.29 meters less than Angela.

How could you figure out the length of Ryan's jump?

I would count back and adjust my answer like this.

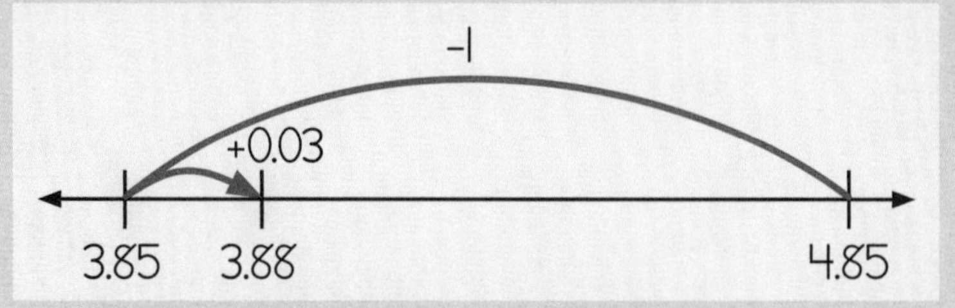

Draw jumps on this number line to show how you could figure out the length of Mika's jump.

These three written methods were used to figure out the length of Mika's jump.

What are the steps for each method? Complete the calculations.

4.85 − 0.09 = 4.76

4.76 − 0.20 = ____

Difference is ____

4.85 − 0.29

4 − 0 = 4

$\frac{85}{100} - \frac{\square}{100} = \frac{\square}{100}$

Difference is ____

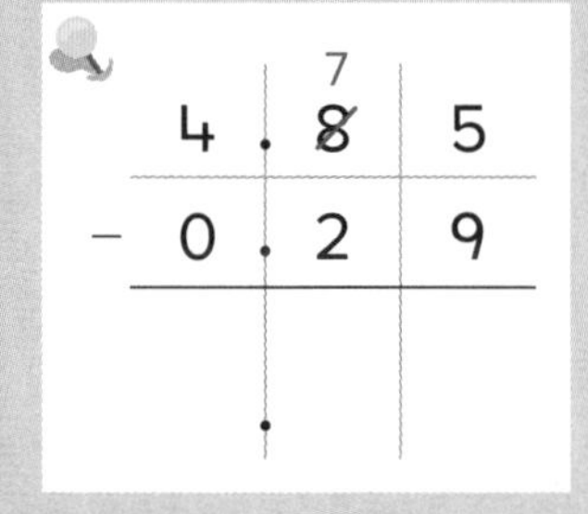

Which method do you prefer? Why?

Step Up

1. Elias jumped 1.80 meters short of this long-jump record.

Write a number sentence to show how far Elias jumped.
Then draw jumps on the number line to show how you figured it out.

____ − ____ = ____

2. Draw jumps on the number line to figure out each difference.

a. 7.65 − 3.26 = ______

b. 9.20 − 7.85 = ______

3. Figure out each difference. Show your thinking.

a. 8.46 − 3.18 = ______

b. 9.35 − 5.72 = ______

c. 15.82 − 12.09 = ______

d. 18.03 − 10.85 = ______

e. 10.72 − 4.27 = ______

f. 21.58 − 17.53 = ______

Step Ahead Imagine you have this money and you buy both items. How much money will you have left?

$______

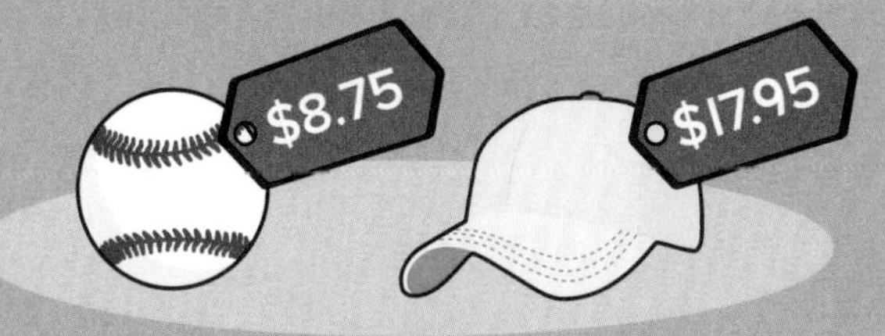

Step In Subtracting Decimal Fractions (Decomposing Multiple Places)

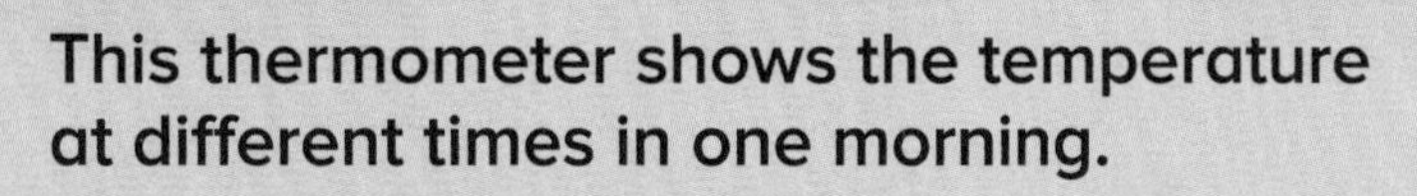

This thermometer shows the temperature at different times in one morning.

How does the temperature change?

What are some temperature changes that you could figure out in your head?

60
12 noon 55.7°F
11 a.m. 53.09°F
50
10 a.m. 49.32°F
8 a.m. 44.7°F
7 a.m. 42.3°F
40
30
20
10
0

I can easily figure out the difference between 44.7 and 55.7.

What was the change in temperature between 10 a.m. and 8 a.m.? How do you know?

Nadia decided to use the standard subtraction algorithm to calculate the difference. Complete her calculation below.

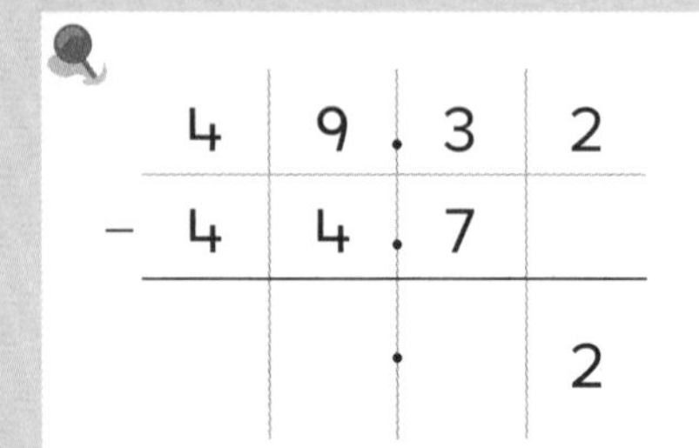

Step Up

1. Use the thermometer above to figure out the temperature change between these times.

a. 11 a.m. to 12 noon	b. 10 a.m. to 11 a.m.
______ °F	______ °F

2. Figure out each difference. Show your thinking.

a. $32.30 - 19.8 =$ ______	b. $18.37 - 12.9 =$ ______	c. $25.02 - 10.4 =$ ______
d. $14.5 - 9.07 =$ ______	e. $28.3 - 15.72 =$ ______	f. $16.04 - 0.9 =$ ______
g. $24.3 - 17.24 =$ ______	h. $16.79 - 5.73 =$ ______	i. $12.88 - 10.99 =$ ______

Step Ahead Solve these word problems.

a. It is 45.03°F in Tacoma, WA. The temperature in Olympia is 0.2°F less. What is the temperature in Olympia?

______ °F

b. It was 48.50°F outside. The temperature dropped 0.8°F over the next hour. What is the new temperature?

______ °F

Step In — Consolidating Strategies to Subtract Decimal Fractions

Which package is heavier? How do you know?

About how much is the difference?

17.25 kg

5.6 kg

The difference between 17 and 5 is 12, so the first package is about 12 kg heavier.

How could you figure out the exact difference?

Mark followed these steps.

What steps did he follow?

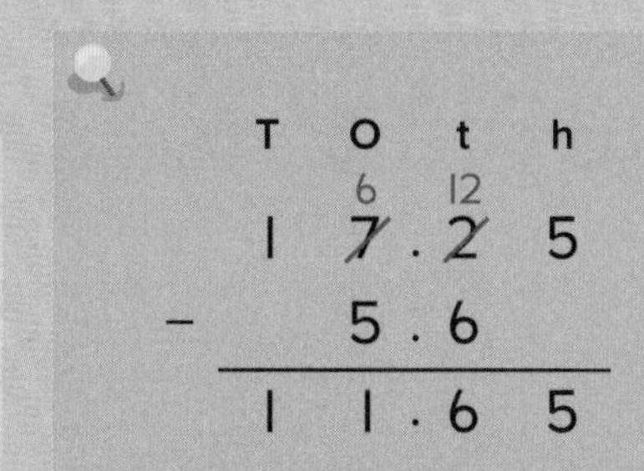

Step Up

1. For each of these, use Mark's method to figure out the difference in mass.

a.

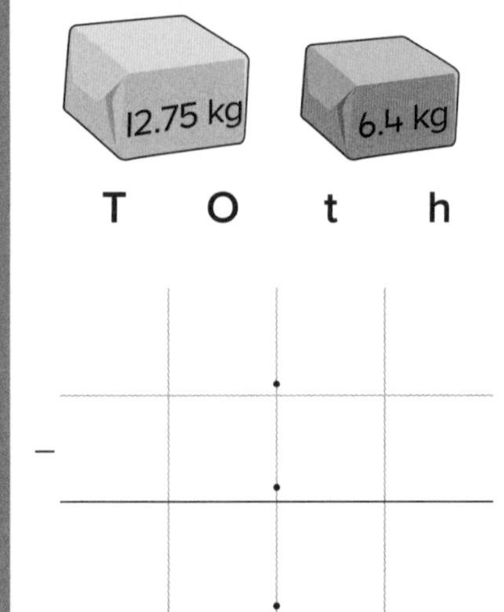

b.

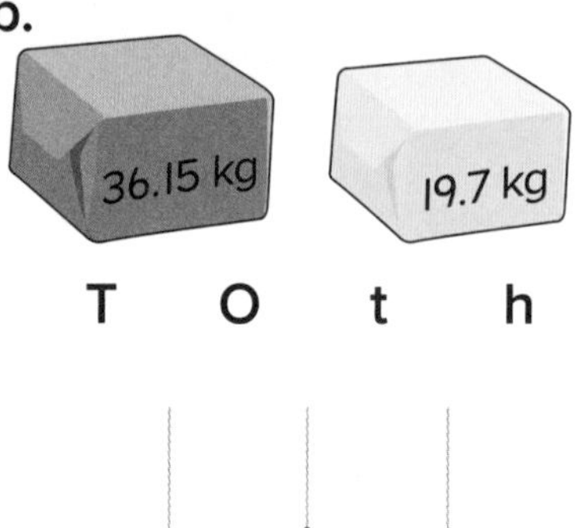

c.

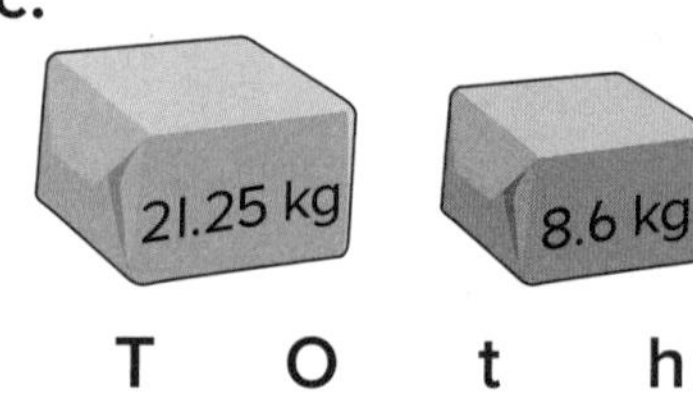

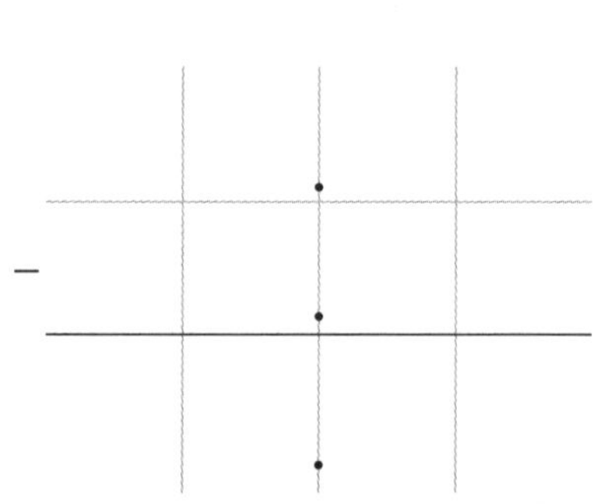

2. Calculate the difference in mass between these sacks of grain. Record the steps you use.

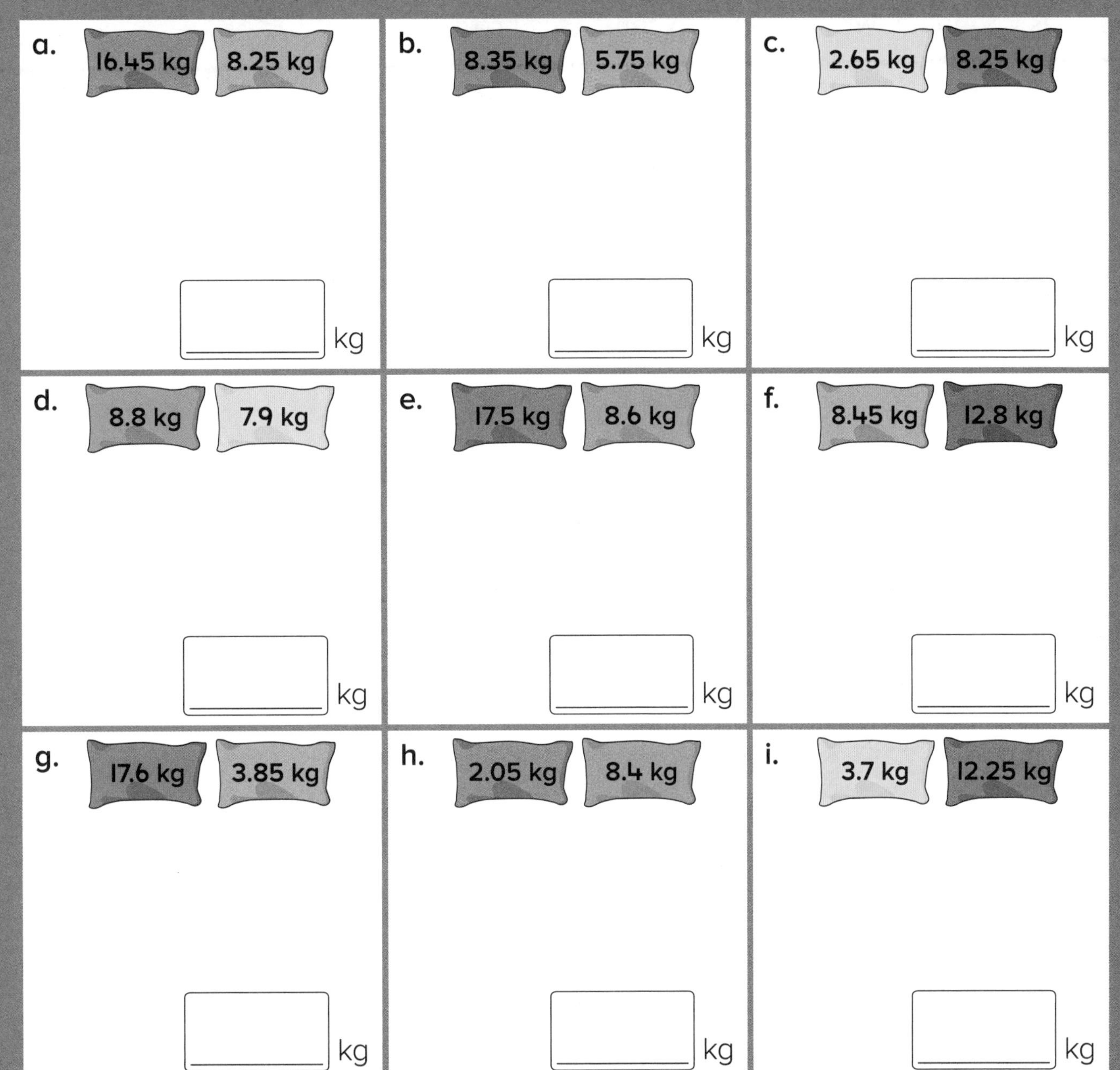

Step Ahead Write a mass in each box to make the balance pictures true.

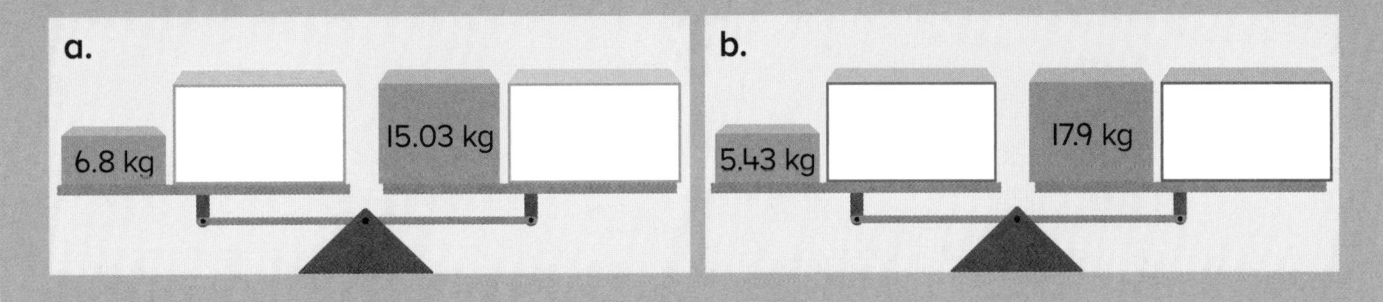

Step In Solving Word Problems Involving Decimal Fractions

Dylan is wrapping two packages to send. He knows that the store closes in half an hour. One package weighs 5.2 lb and the other weighs a quarter of a pound.

What is the total weight of the packages? ________ lb

What information in the story is necessary to help you answer the question?

What steps will you follow to figure it out?

First I will need to make sure I am adding the same type of fractions.

How could you figure out the **difference** in weight between the two packages?

Step Up

1. Figure out the answer to each problem. Show your thinking.

a. There are 3 bags of dog biscuits. Each bag weighs 1.25 kg. What is the total weight?

________ kg

b. It is 8.3 miles to the beach. Mark drove 4.6 miles before lunch. How much farther is it to the beach?

________ mi

c. Kettle A holds 1.7 liters. Kettle B holds 2.2 liters. What is the difference in the amounts of water they hold?

________ L

d. There is $2.48 in a money box. If you put in three more dimes, how much money will there be inside?

$________

2. Solve each problem. Show your thinking.

a. On Monday, Giselle ran $3\frac{1}{4}$ km. On Tuesday, she ran 2.3 km. On Wednesday, she ran 4.1 km. How far did she run in total on Monday and Wednesday?

________ km

b. The record time for the 100 m sprint was 12.5 seconds. Toby beat this time by 1.09 seconds. What is the new record time for the 100 m sprint?

________ s

c. If you put 2.5 gallons of water into an empty 3.5-gallon bucket then add a quarter gallon of liquid fertilizer, how much liquid will be in the bucket?

________ gal

d. Jack has $2 to buy stickers. A red sticker costs $0.57, a blue sticker is $1.62, and a green sticker costs $1.20. Which two stickers can he buy?

____

What is the total cost? $________

Step Ahead

a. Which ice cream is the better buy?

____

b. Write how you know.

____

____

____

Step In Exploring Points, Lines, Line Segments, and Rays

A straight line continues in both directions forever.

When you draw a straight line, it is just a part of a longer continuous line. This part is called a **line segment**.

Look at the line below. The arrows show that it continues in both directions forever. Points A, B, and C are all on the same line.

A **line segment** has a start point and an end point.

All the points beginning at Point A and ending at Point B form one line segment $\overline{AB}$.

What other line segments are part of this line?

Point B splits the line into two parts. Each part is called a half line or a ray. A ray is named with its start point written first, followed by another point that the ray goes through.

A **ray** is part of a line that begins at a point and continues on forever.

Look at the line above.
If Point B is the start point, the two rays $\overrightarrow{BC}$ and $\overrightarrow{BA}$ go in opposite directions.

Polygons can be described by naming the line segments that make their sides or the points that are the vertices. This can help identify shapes.

Use a color pencil to trace over the polygon made by joining the points A, C, G, and F.
What shape is it?

What other polygons can you see and describe?

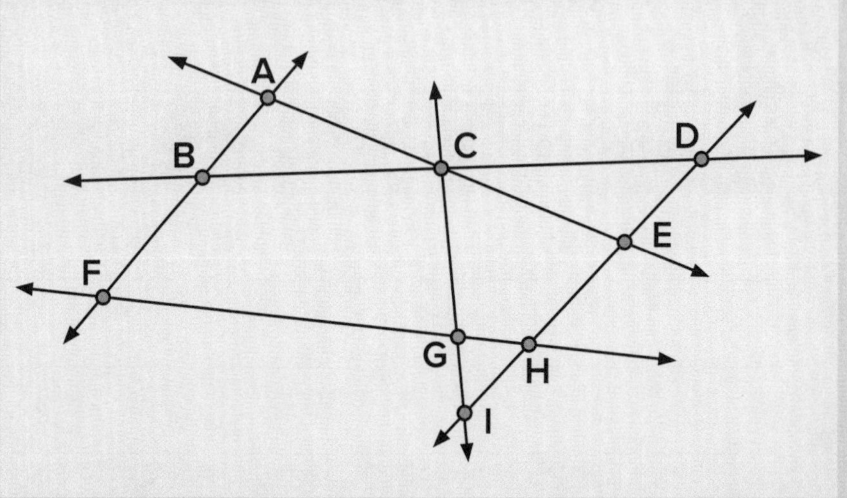

Step Up

1. Name five unique line segments you can see on the line below.

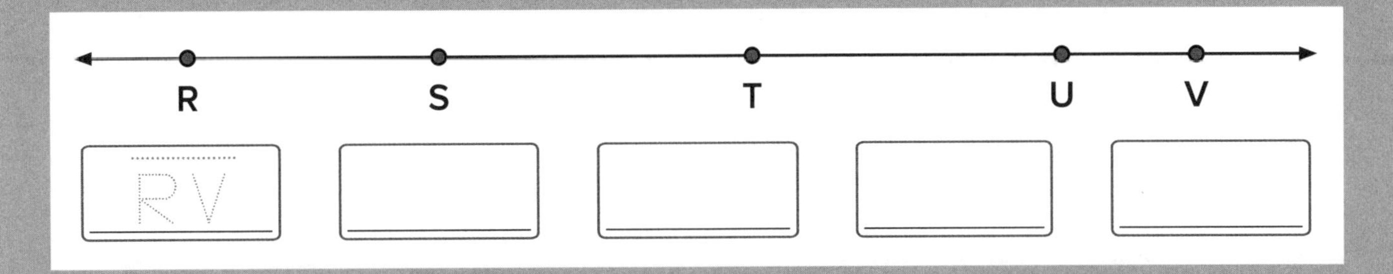

2. Look at the line above. Name a pair of rays that start at each of these end points.

Point S	Point T	Point U
________ and ________	________ and ________	________ and ________

3. Look at the picture below.

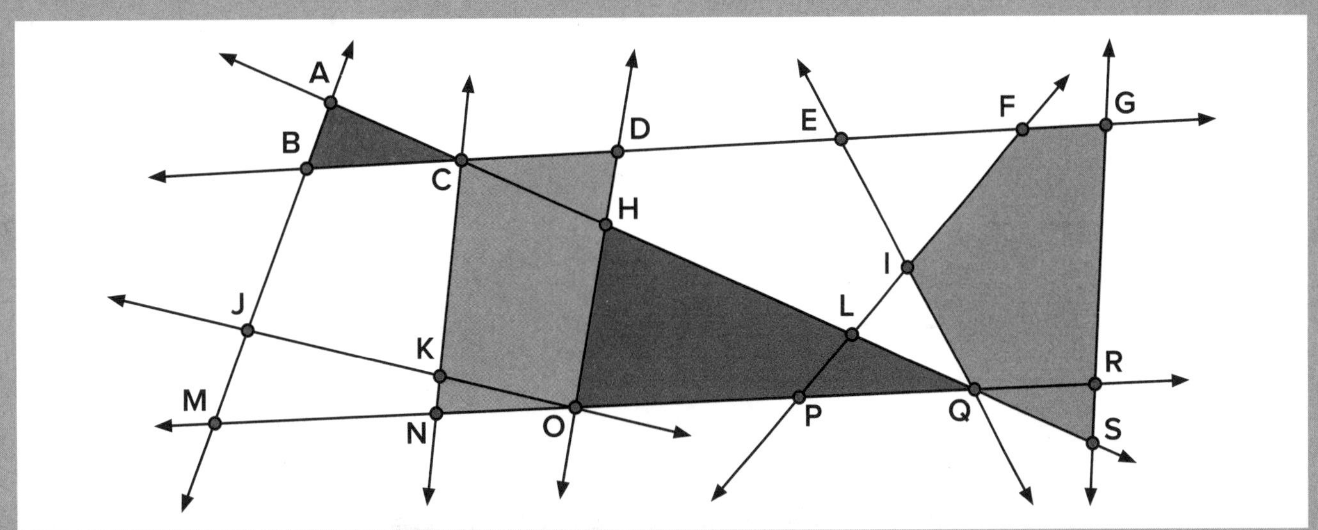

Write the points that make up the **vertices** of each shaded polygon.

Blue ________ Green ________ Red ________ Orange ________

Step Ahead

Look at the picture in Question 3. Find other examples of each polygon below. Write the points that are the vertices of each shape.

a. triangle ________

b. quadrilateral ________

c. pentagon ________

d. hexagon ________

Step In Identifying Parallel and Perpendicular Lines

What do you know about parallel lines?
Where might you see parallel lines?

Which two line segments below are parallel?
How do you know?

When two lines are the same distance apart for their entire lengths, they are **parallel**.

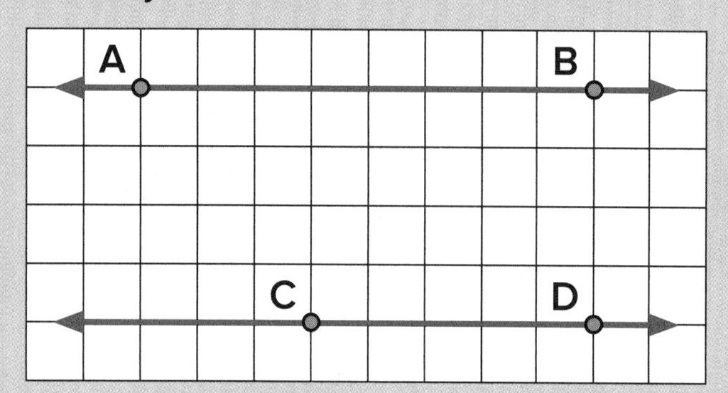

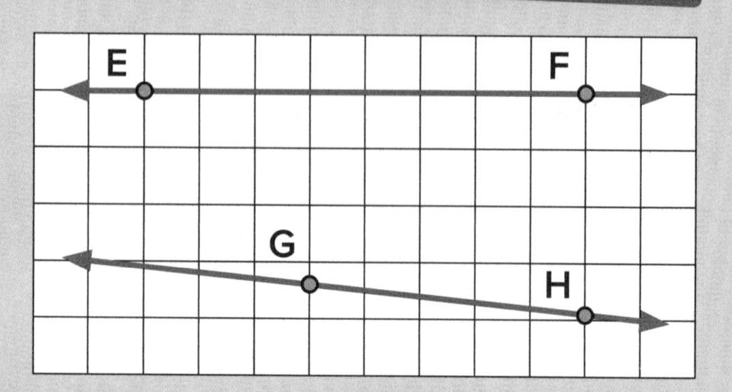

Parallel line segments do not have to be directly opposite each other or the same length. If the lines that they are part of are parallel, then the line segments will be parallel too.

The line segment $\overline{JK}$ below is parallel to line segment $\overline{ST}$ and also to line segment $\overline{TU}$.

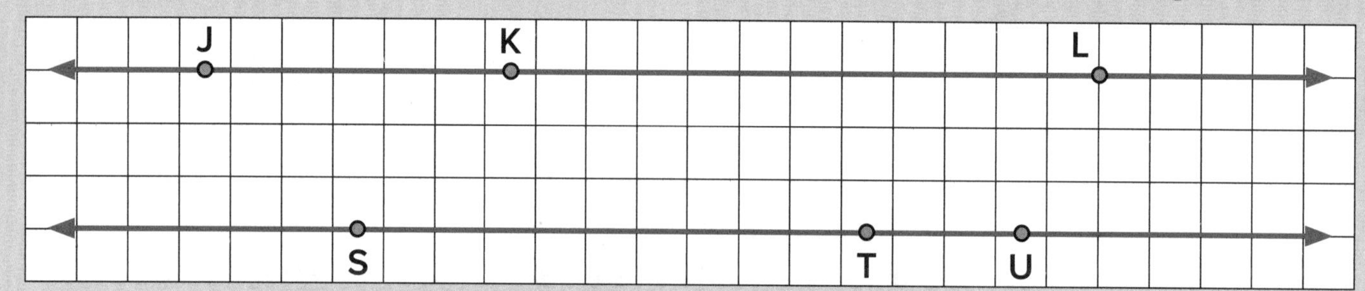

Which other line segments are parallel?

Perpendicular lines make a right angle with each other. The blue line is perpendicular to the purple line.

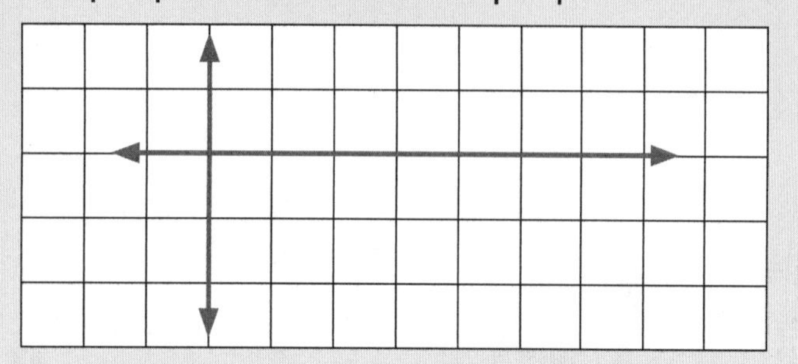

Perpendicular lines do not have to be vertical or horizontal. These lines are also perpendicular to each other.

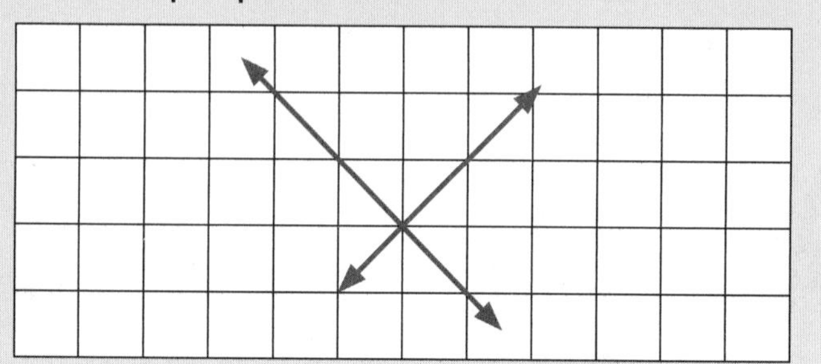

Perpendicular line segments do not need to intersect one another.

However, the lines that they are part of must intersect.

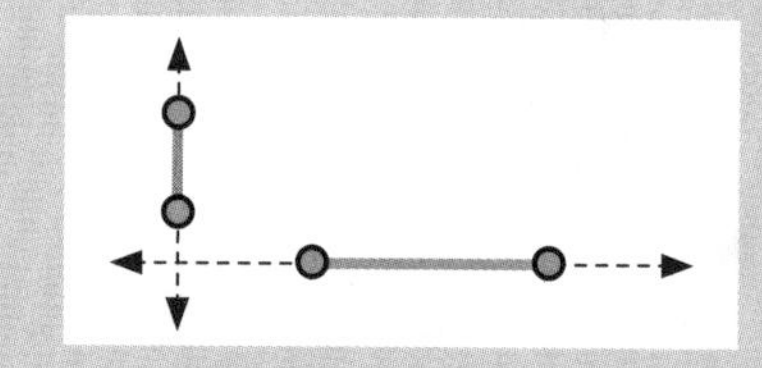

Step Up

Cut out the shapes from the support page and paste them in the correct spaces below. Some shapes do not belong in any of the spaces.

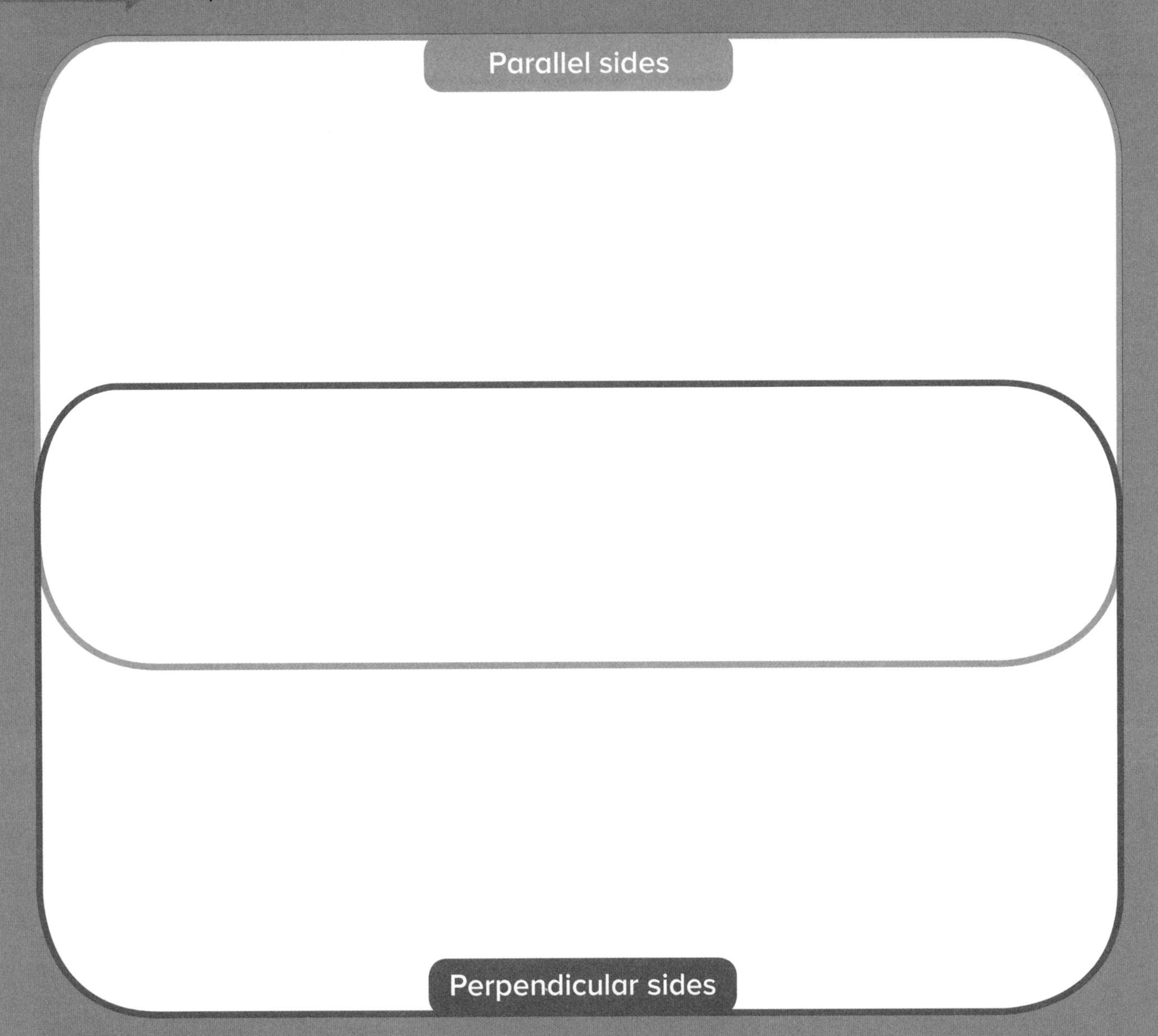

Step Ahead

Draw a square and a non-square rectangle. One side of each has been drawn for you. Use a protractor to check your drawings.

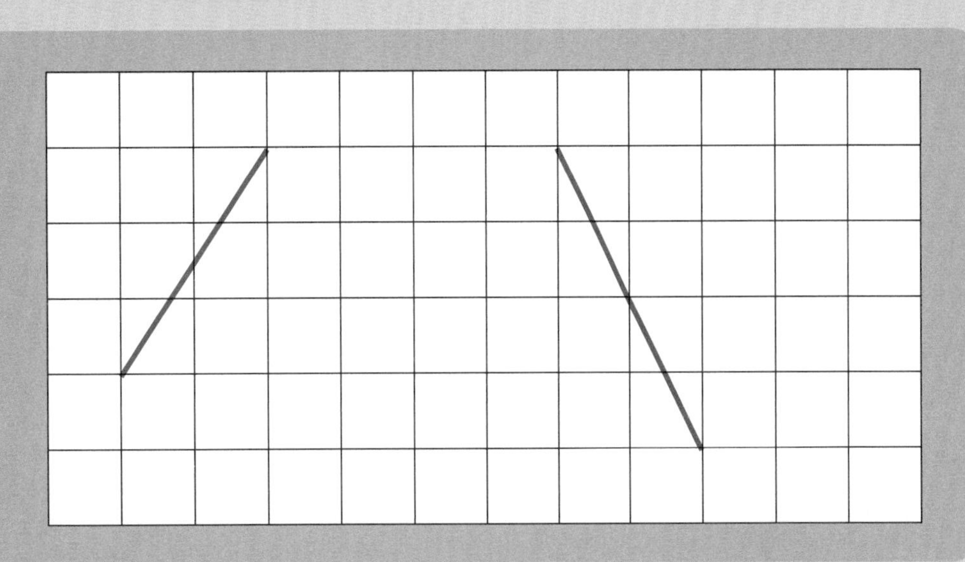

Step In Analyzing 2D Shapes

What do you know about this shape?
What do you think the arrows mean?
What does the ⊾ symbol tell you?

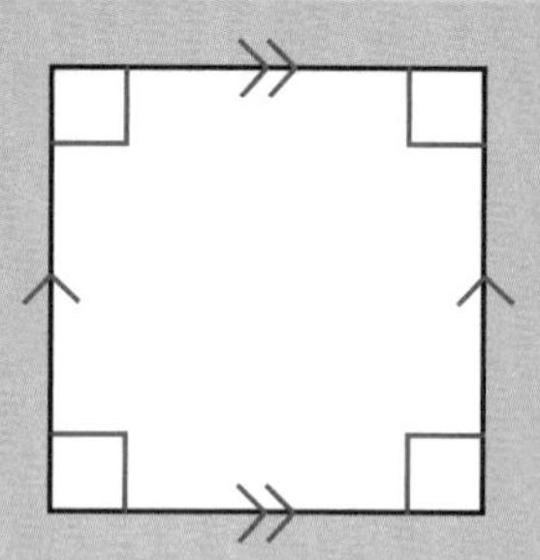

What do you know about this shape?
What does each symbol tell you about the shape?

Right angles can be shown using this symbol.

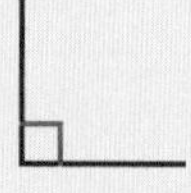

Congruent sides can be shown using the same number of lines.

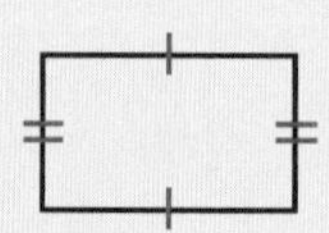

Congruent angles can be shown using the same number of arcs.

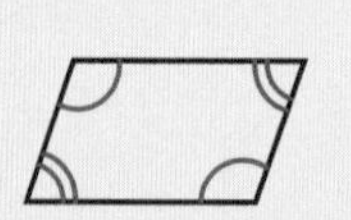

Can a triangle have a pair of parallel sides?

Step Up

1. Write the name of each shape. Then use the symbols on the shape to write the missing numbers.

a. ____________________

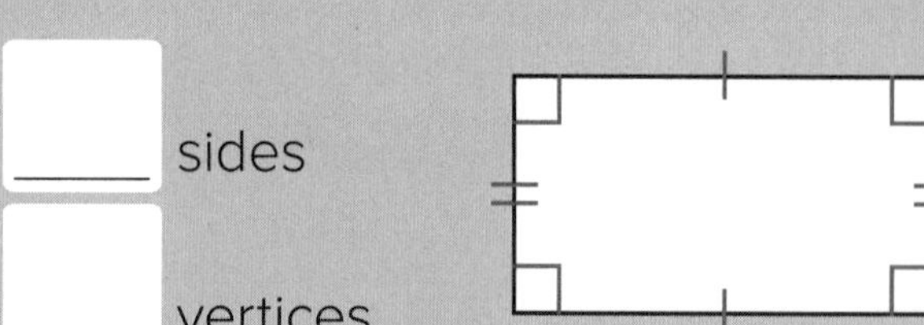

____ sides
____ vertices
____ pairs of congruent sides
____ pairs of parallel sides
____ right angles

b. ____________________

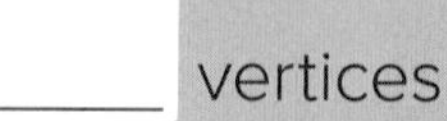

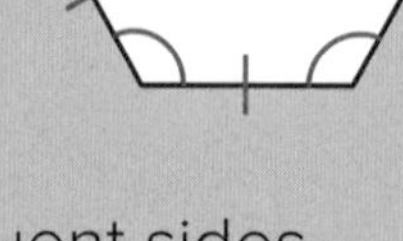

____ sides
____ vertices
____ pairs of congruent sides
____ pairs of parallel sides
____ right angles

2. Draw marks on each shape to show what you know about the **length of each side**.

a.

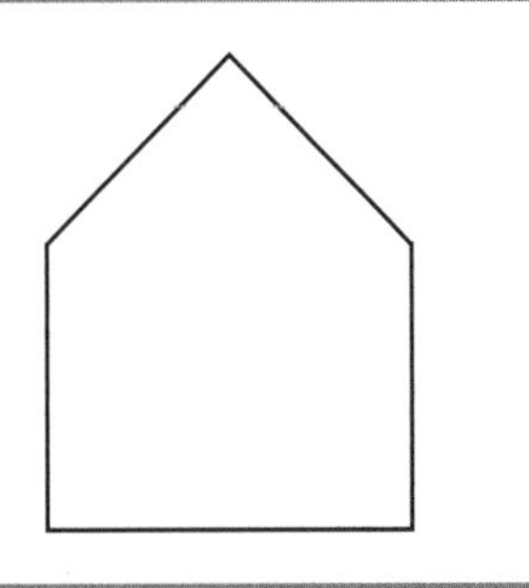

b.

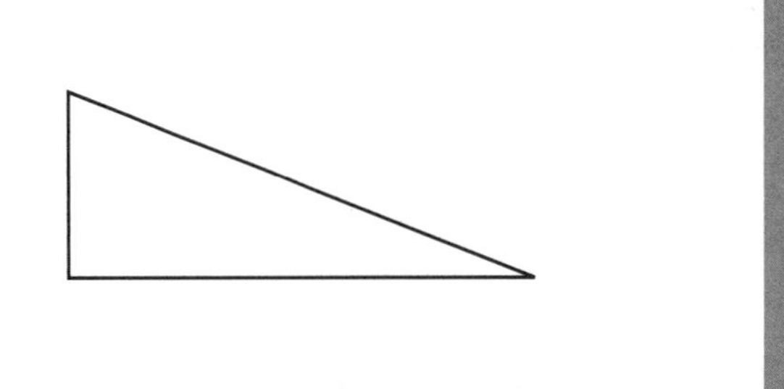

3. Draw marks inside each shape to show what you know about the **size of each angle**.

a.

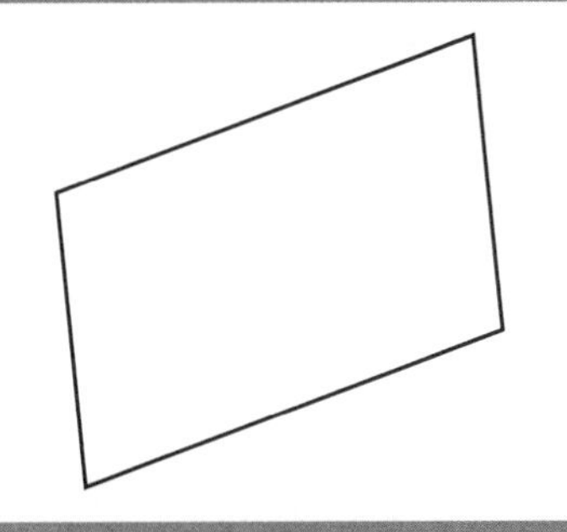

b.

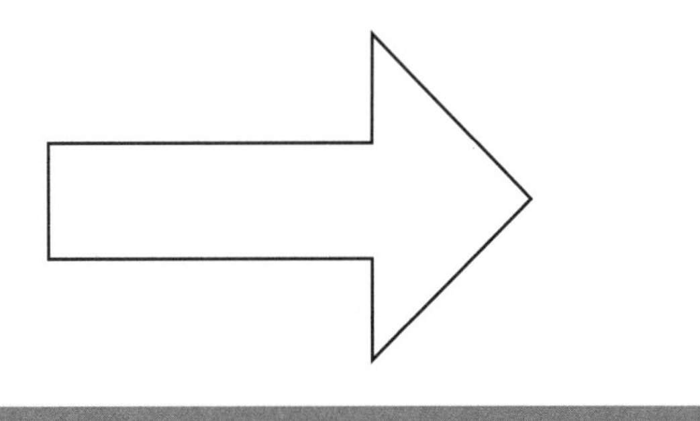

4. Draw marks on each shape to show what you know about **parallel sides**.

a.

b.

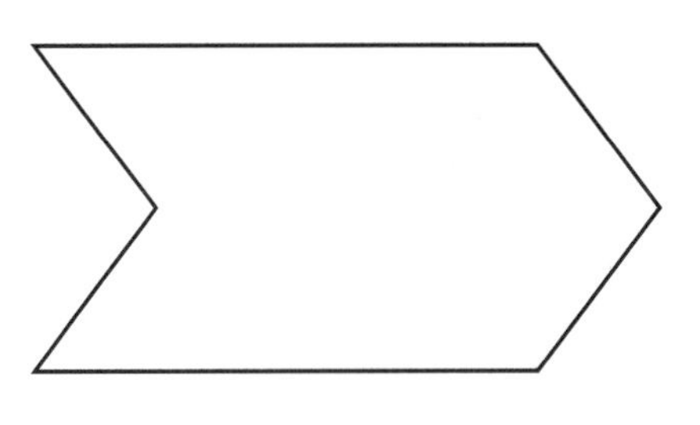

Step Ahead Draw and mark a shape to match the clues. Then write the name of the shape.

Clue 1 – My shape has four sides.

Clue 2 – My shape has two pairs of parallel sides.

Clue 3 – My shape has opposite angles that are equal.

My shape is a ______________________.

Step In Reflecting Shapes and Identifying Lines of Symmetry

Imagine you were wearing this shirt and looked in the mirror.
What would the shirt look like?

What words can you use to describe what mirrors do?

When I look in the mirror, I see my reflection.

Some shapes have parts that are a reflection of each other.
Draw the other half of the letter M on the other side of the dashed line. How will you know it is a reflection?

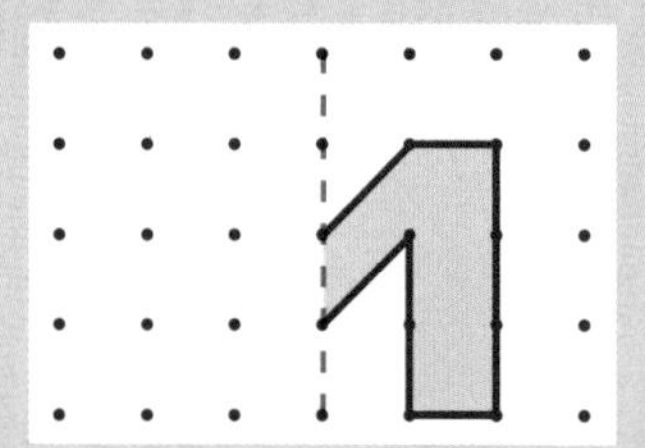

A **line of symmetry** splits a whole shape into two parts that are the same shape and the same size.

Draw a line of symmetry for each letter so that one side of the letter is a mirror image of the other. Not every letter has a line of symmetry.

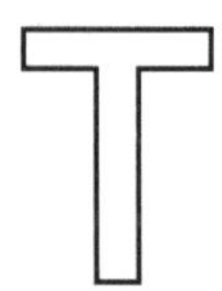

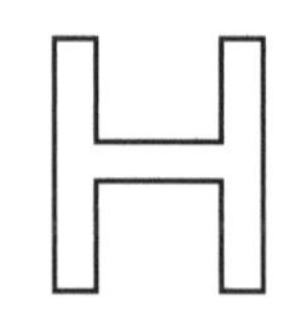

Z

What do you notice about the letters H and X?

Step Up

1. Draw the reflection of each shape on the other side of the dashed line.

a.

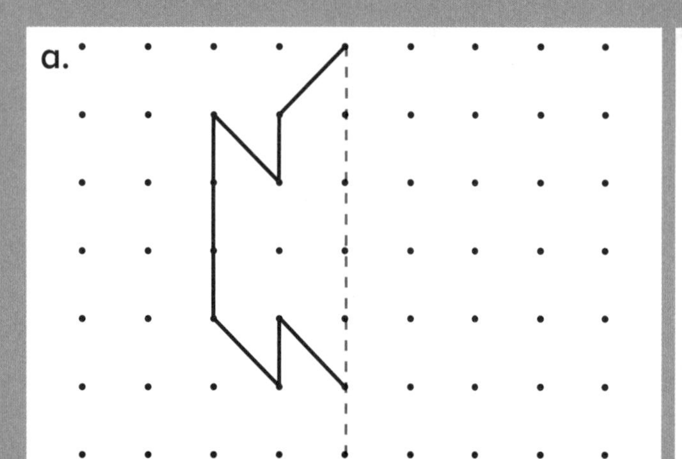

b.

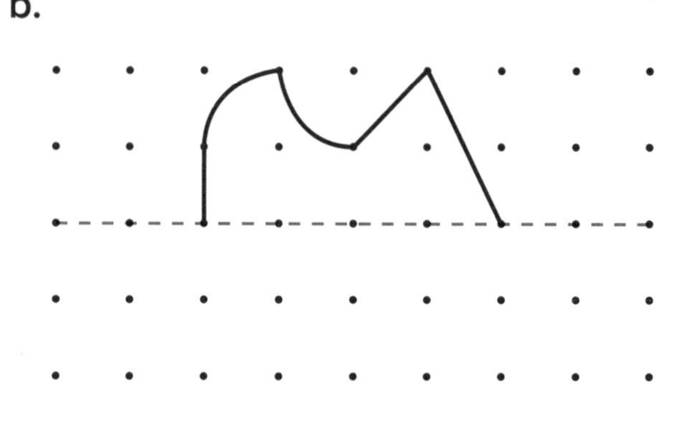

2. Find and draw the line of symmetry on each shape.

a.

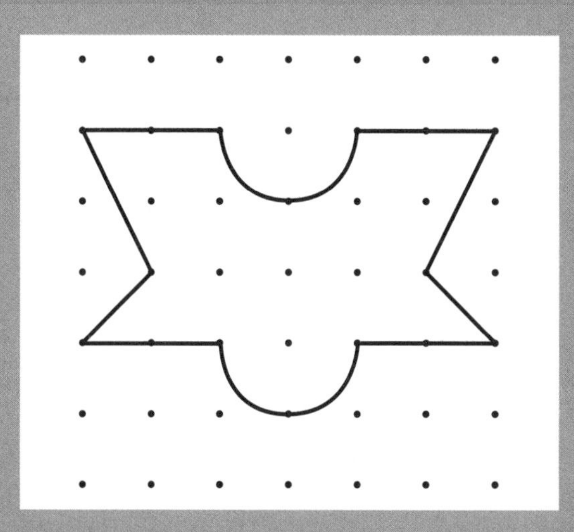

b.

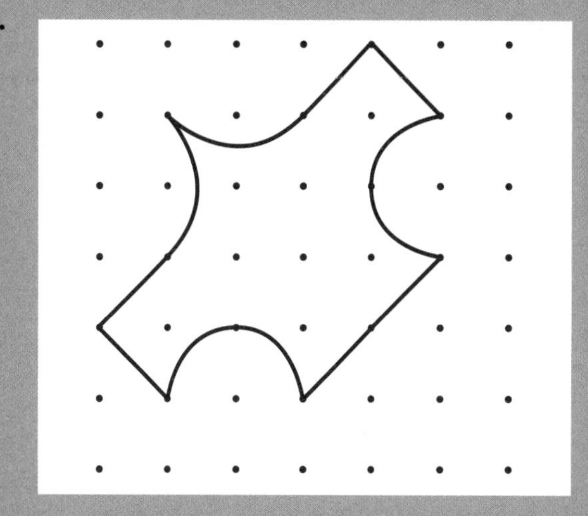

c.

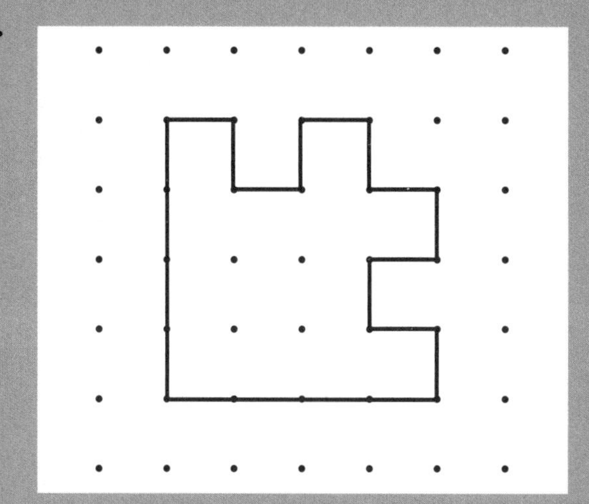

d.

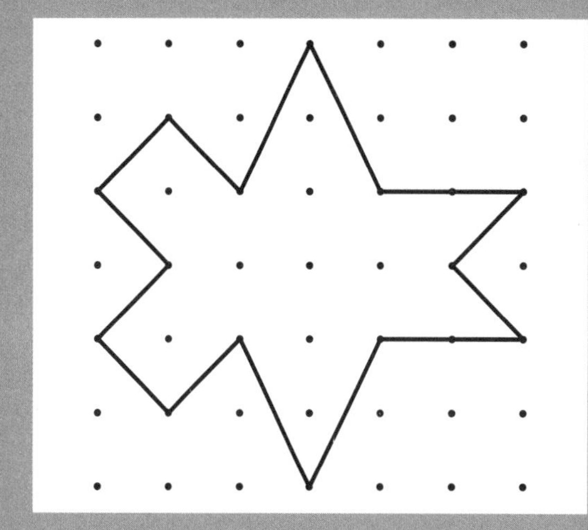

Step Ahead Draw one shape that has a line of symmetry. Show the line of symmetry on the shape. Then draw one shape that has no lines of symmetry.

a.

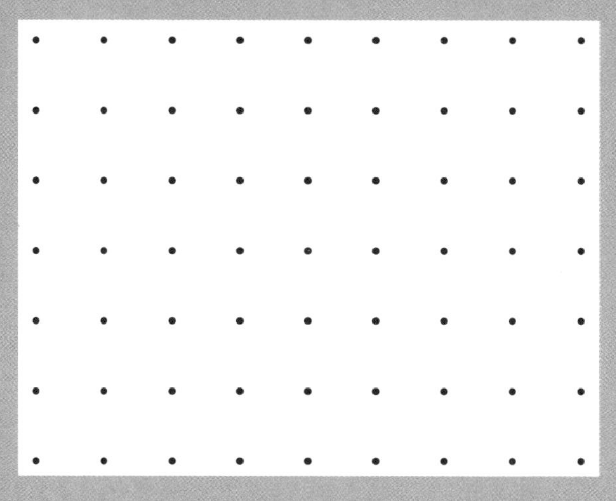

b.

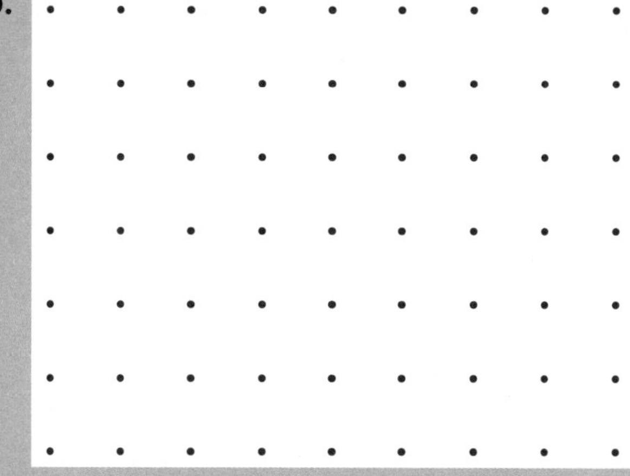

Step In Relating Multiplication and Division

What do you know about this rectangle?

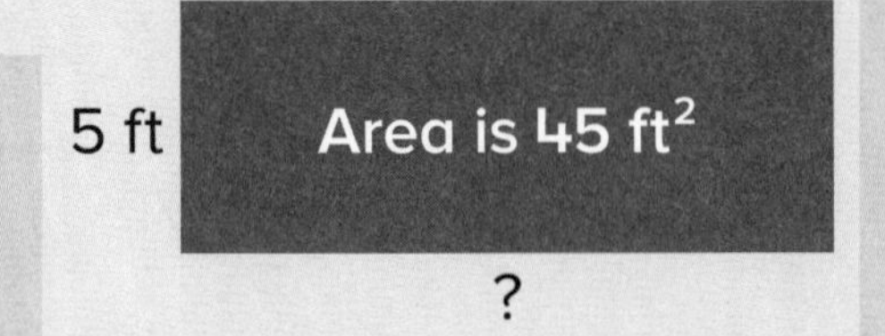

How can you figure out the length of the rectangle?

Write two number sentences that you could use to help you.

___ × ___ = ___   ___ ÷ ___ = ___

What do you know about this square rectangle?

What thinking would you use to figure out the length of the unknown side?

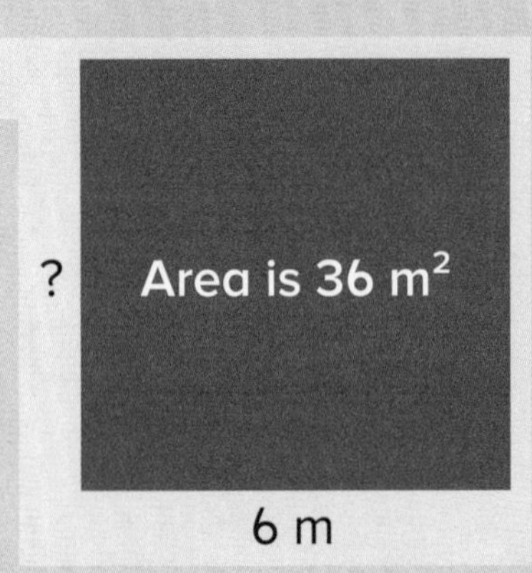

What number sentences could you write?

___   ___

Step Up

1. Complete the two number sentences that you could use to help figure out the unknown dimension. Then label the diagram.

a.

4 yd

Area is 28 yd²

yd

$4 \times$ ___ $= 28$

$28 \div 4 =$ ___

b.

Area is 48 ft²

ft

8 ft

$8 \times$ ___ $= 48$

$48 \div 8 =$ ___

2. Complete each of these.

a.

7 m

Area is 63 m^2

____ m

____ × ____ = ____

____ ÷ ____ = ____

b.

Area is 8 in^2

____ in

8 in

____ × ____ = ____

____ ÷ ____ = ____

c.

6 cm

Area is 42 cm^2

____ cm

____ × ____ = ____

____ ÷ ____ = ____

d.

Area is 27 yd^2

3 yd

____ yd

____ × ____ = ____

____ ÷ ____ = ____

3. Figure out the missing number in each fact.

a. 36 ÷ 9 = ____	**b.** 4 = ____ ÷ 8	**c.** 1 = ____ ÷ 9	**d.** 35 ÷ ____ = 7
e. 54 ÷ ____ = 9	**f.** ____ ÷ 9 = 9	**g.** 30 ÷ ____ = 5	**h.** 9 = ____ ÷ 2

Step Ahead

Write three pairs of possible dimensions for a rectangle that has an area of 600 ft^2.

____ × ____ = 600 ft^2

____ × ____ = 600 ft^2

____ × ____ = 600 ft^2

Step In Using the Partial-Quotients Strategy to Divide (Two-Digit Dividends)

Three friends share the cost of this gift.

How can you figure out the amount that each person will pay?

Marcelo used a sharing strategy.

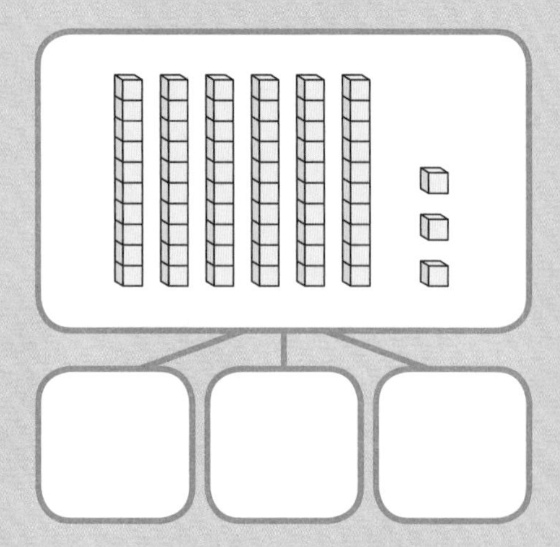

What do the blocks at the top of the chart represent?

What steps will he follow?

What amount will each person pay? How do you know?

What division sentence could you write?

Deana used a different strategy. She followed these steps.

Step 1	Step 2	Step 3
She drew a rectangle to show the problem. The length of one side becomes the unknown value.	She split the rectangle into two parts so that it was easier to divide by 3.	She thought: $3 \times 20 = 60$, $3 \times 1 = 3$, then $20 + 1 = 21$
3 [63] ?	3 [60 | 3]	3 [60 | 3] 20 + 1

Why did she split the rectangle into two parts?

Why did she choose the numbers 60 and 3?

Why did she add 20 and 1?

I'll call the amount that each person pays **A**.
To find the amount, Marcelo thinks $63 \div 3 = A$ and Deana thinks $3 \times A = 63$.

How could you use these strategies to figure out $96 \div 3$?

Step Up

1. These rectangles have been split into parts to make it easier to divide. Write the missing numbers. Then complete the equation.

a.

86 ÷ 2 = ______

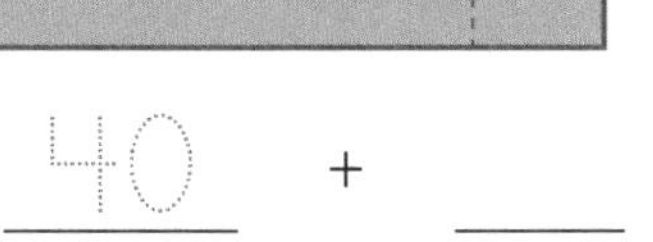

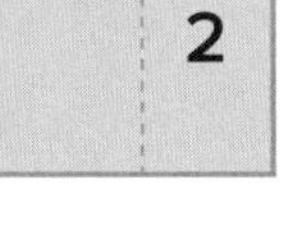

______ + ______

b.

69 ÷ 3 = ______

______ + ______

c.

62 ÷ 2 = ______

2 | 60 | 2

______ + ______

d.

48 ÷ 4 = ______

4 | 40 | 8

______ + ______

2. Inside each rectangle, write numbers that are easier to divide. Divide the two parts then complete the equation.

a.

93 ÷ 3 = ______

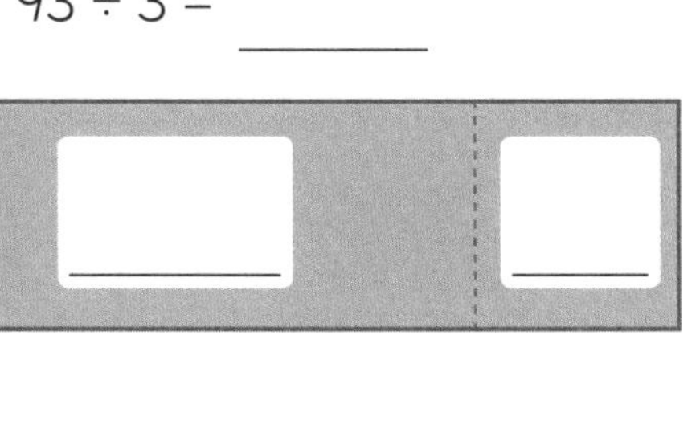

______ + ______

b.

77 ÷ 7 = ______

______ + ______

Step Ahead

Break each number into parts that you can easily **divide by 3.**

a.

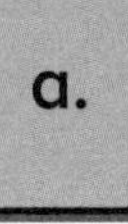
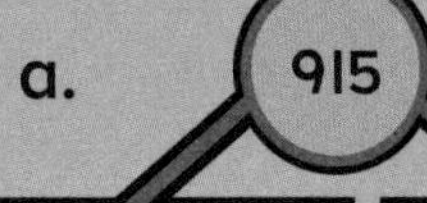

b.

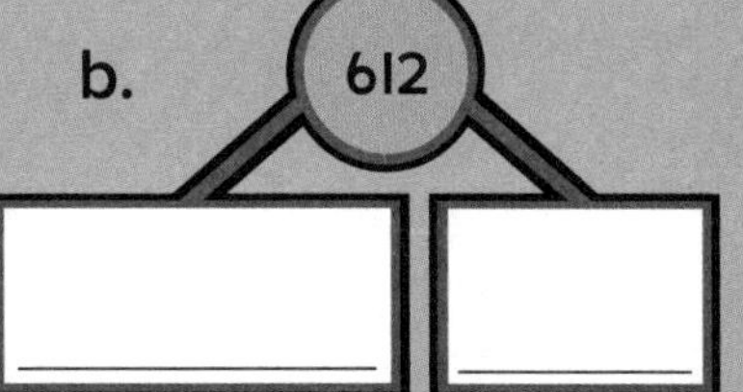

c.

Step In Reinforcing the Partial-Quotients Strategy for Division (Two-Digit Dividends)

How can you figure out the length of this rectangle?

I know that 5 x 10 = 50.
That leaves 25 left over.

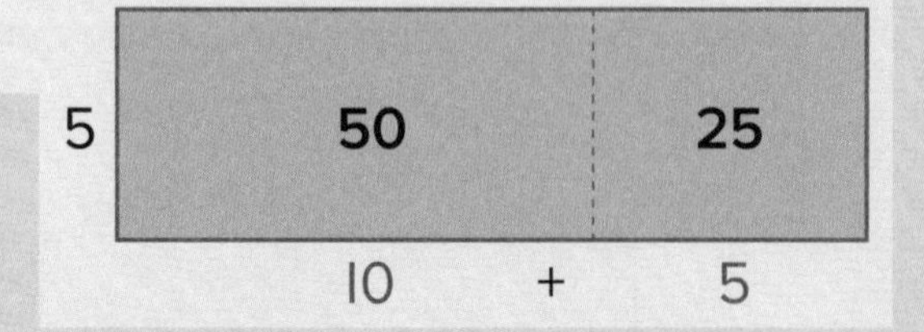

Victoria split the rectangle into two parts like this.

Why did she choose the numbers 50 and 25?

What is the length of the unknown side?

5 | 50 | 25
10 + 5

Split this rectangle into two parts so that it is easier to figure out 45 ÷ 3.

Write numbers inside the rectangle to show the parts.

How did you break 45 into two parts?

How could this help you figure out 45 ÷ 3?

Step Up

1. These rectangles have been split into two parts to make it easier to divide. Write the missing numbers. Then complete the equation.

a. 56 ÷ 4 = ______

4 | 40 | 16

______ + ______

b. 65 ÷ 5 = ______

5 | 50 | 15

______ + ______

c. 72 ÷ 6 = ______

6 | 60 | 12

______ + ______

d. 84 ÷ 7 = ______

7 | 70 | 14

______ + ______

2. Inside each rectangle, write numbers that are easier to divide.
Divide the two parts then complete the equation.

a.

90 ÷ 6 = ______

6

______ + ______

b.

51 ÷ 3 = ______

3

______ + ______

c.

60 ÷ 4 = ______

4

______ + ______

d.

91 ÷ 7 = ______

7

______ + ______

3. Break each starting number into parts that you can easily divide.
Then complete the equations.

a.

85 ÷ 5 = ______

is the same as

______ ÷ 5 **plus** ______ ÷ 5 = ______

b.

48 ÷ 3 = ______

is the same as

______ ÷ 3 **plus** ______ ÷ 3 = ______

c.

96 ÷ 8 = ______

is the same as

______ ÷ 8 **plus** ______ ÷ 8 = ______

d.

84 ÷ 6 = ______

is the same as

______ ÷ 6 **plus** ______ ÷ 6 = ______

Step Ahead Use the same thinking to complete these equations.

a. 42 ÷ 3 = ______

b. 95 ÷ 5 = ______

c. 84 ÷ 4 = ______

d. 102 ÷ 6 = ______

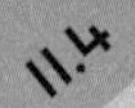

Step In Using the Partial-Quotients Strategy to Divide (Three-Digit Dividends)

Nam paid for this laptop in 3 monthly payments. He paid the same amount each month.

What amount did he pay each month? How do you know?

I would break 639 into parts that are easier to divide.

Describe how this rectangle has been split.

What is special about the numbers 600, 30, and 9?

What amount does Nam pay each month?

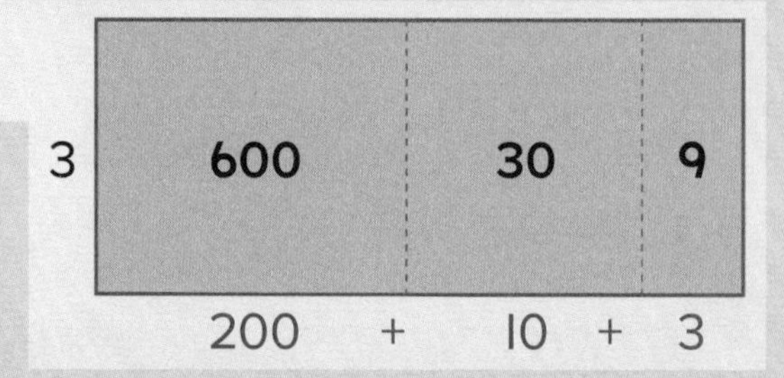

Miranda's laptop was $546. She paid the same amount each month for 6 months.

How can you figure out the amount that she paid each month?

It's easier to divide if you think of 546 as 54 tens and 6 ones.

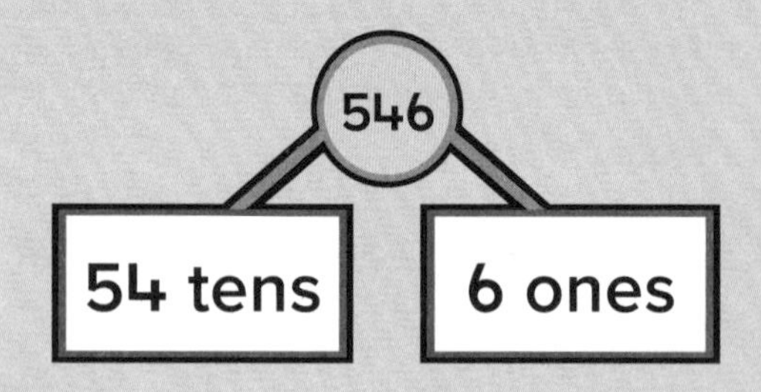

Complete the equations to figure out the amount that she paid each month.

540 ÷ 6 = ______

6 ÷ 6 = ______

546 ÷ 6 = ______

Use this strategy to figure out 279 ÷ 3.

Step Up

1. These rectangles have been split into parts to make it easier to divide. Divide each part then complete the equation.

a. 606 ÷ 6 = ________

6 | 600 | 6

________ + ______

b. 963 ÷ 3 = ________

3 | 900 | 60 | 3

________ + ______ + ______

c. 484 ÷ 4 = ________

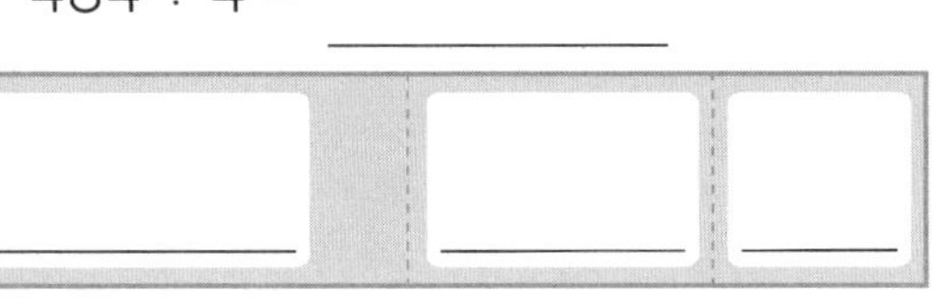

4

________ + ______ + ______

d. 530 ÷ 5 = ________

5

________ + ______

2. Estimate each answer in your head.
Then write number sentences to figure out the exact amount.

a. 742 ÷ 7 = ________

b. 693 ÷ 3 = ________

c. 630 ÷ 6 = ________

Step Ahead

Write the missing numbers.

a. ________ ÷ 4 = 132

b. ________ ÷ 6 = 104

Working Space

Step In Reinforcing the Partial-Quotients Strategy for Division (Three-Digit Dividends)

Donna paid $453 to buy 3 concert tickets.
Each ticket costs the same amount.
How could you estimate the price of each ticket?

I thought of a number that will give me 450 when multiplied by 3.

What numbers could you write in this diagram to help figure out the exact price of each ticket?

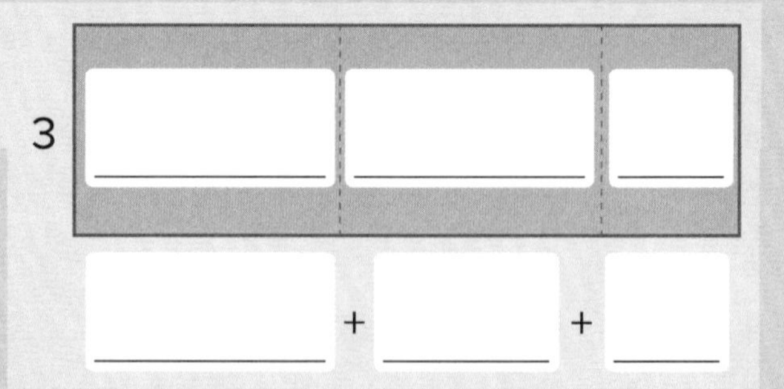

How do the parts in this diagram help you divide by 3?

Dwane paid $296 to buy 4 theme park tickets. Each ticket costs the same amount.
How could you figure out the price of each ticket?

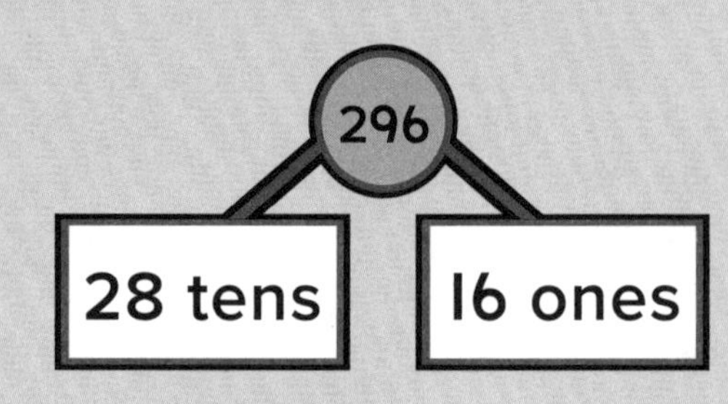

You could break 296 into parts that are easier to divide by 4.

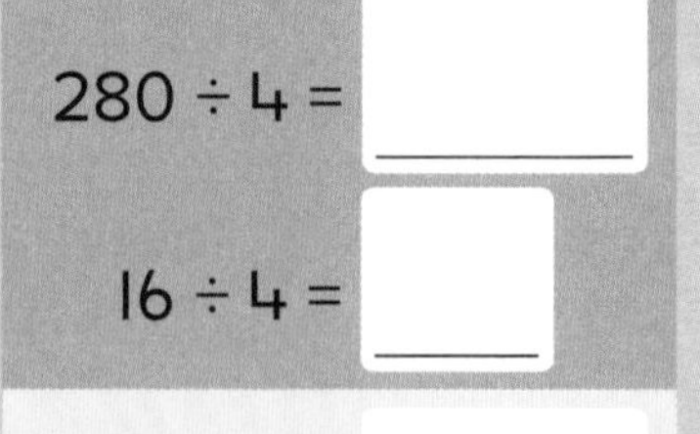

296 ÷ 4 = ______

What is the price of each ticket? How do you know?

How do the two parts help you divide by 4?

Use this strategy to figure out 258 ÷ 3.

Step Up

1. Break each number into parts that you can easily **divide by 4**.

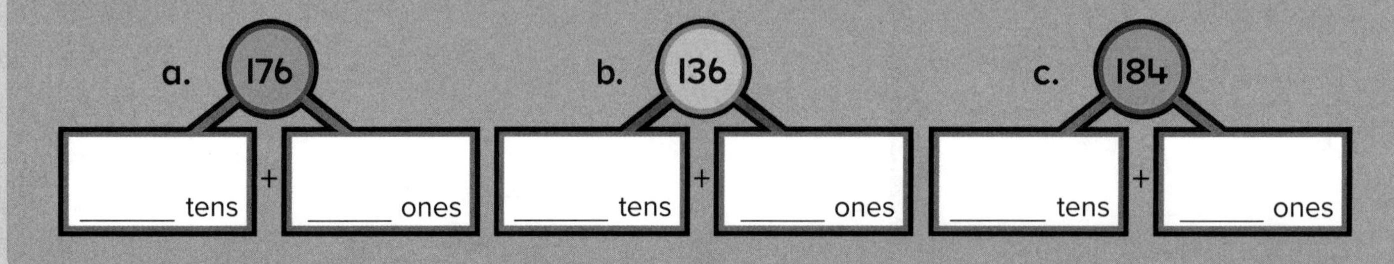

2. Write number sentences to figure out each answer.

a.
265 ÷ 5 = ______
250 ÷ 5 = ______
15 ÷ 5 = ______

b.
364 ÷ 4 = ______
320 ÷ 4 = ______
______ ÷ 4 = ______

c.
108 ÷ 3 = ______
90 ÷ 3 = ______
______ ÷ 3 = ______

d.
342 ÷ 6 = ______

e.
126 ÷ 3 = ______

f.
496 ÷ 8 = ______

g.
426 ÷ 3 = ______
300 ÷ 3 = ______
120 ÷ 3 = ______
6 ÷ 3 = ______

h.
786 ÷ 6 = ______
600 ÷ 6 = ______
180 ÷ 6 = ______
______ ÷ 6 = ______

i.
568 ÷ 4 = ______
400 ÷ 4 = ______
______ ÷ 4 = ______
______ ÷ 4 = ______

j.
489 ÷ 3 = ______

k.
847 ÷ 7 = ______

l.
524 ÷ 4 = ______

Step Ahead Figure out the cost of buying a two-day pass for each theme park. Then loop the theme park that is the least expensive.

2-DAY PASS GATOR TOWN
5 passes cost $480

2-DAY PASS Dream Land
4 passes cost $336

2-DAY PASS Ocean World
3 passes cost $324

Step In Using the Partial-Quotients Strategy to Divide (Four-Digit Dividends)

The Hornets have 6,936 members.
They have three times as many members as the Wild Cats.

How many members do the Wild Cats have?

There must be more than 2,000 members because 6,000 ÷ 3 = 2,000.

Hugo wrote these number sentences to figure out the answer.
Complete each of the sentences.

How did he break 6,936 into parts that are easier to divide by 3?

Can you think of another way to break 6,936 into parts?

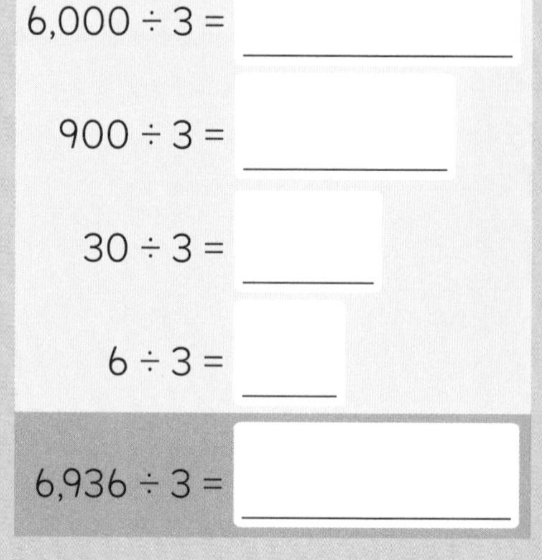

I would group the tens and ones together. 36 ÷ 3 is easy to figure out.

Step Up

1. Break each number into parts you can easily **divide by 4**.

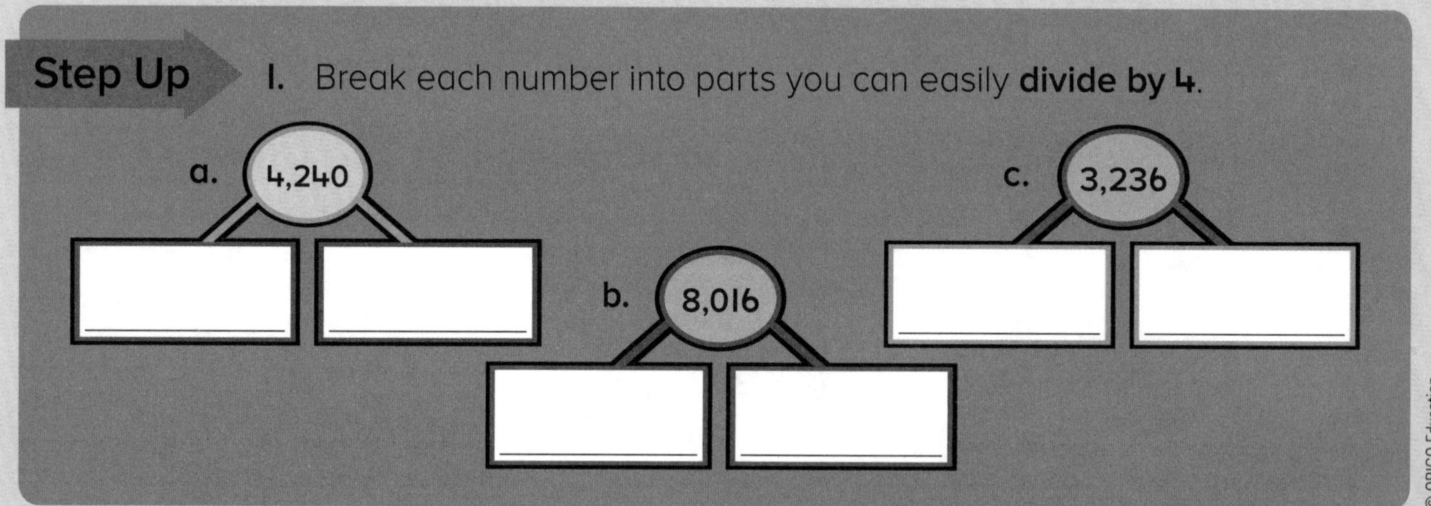

2. Write number sentences to figure out each of these.

a. $3,603 \div 3 =$ ____	**b.** $8,032 \div 4 =$ ____	**c.** $3,930 \div 3 =$ ____
$3,000 \div 3 =$ ____ $600 \div 3 =$ ____ $3 \div 3 =$ ____	$8,000 \div 4 =$ ____ $32 \div 4 =$ ____	$3,000 \div 3 =$ ____ $900 \div 3 =$ ____ $30 \div 3 =$ ____
d. $4,824 \div 4 =$ ____	**e.** $9,036 \div 3 =$ ____	**f.** $5,050 \div 5 =$ ____
g. $6,036 \div 6 =$ ____	**h.** $5,525 \div 5 =$ ____	**i.** $1,815 \div 3 =$ ____

Step Ahead Write the missing numbers.

a. ____ $\div 4 = 2,106$

b. ____ $\div 3 = 2,307$

Working Space

Step In — Reinforcing the Partial-Quotients Strategy for Division (Four-Digit Dividends)

A beachside apartment costs $5,236 to rent for 4 weeks.
What is the price of 1 week?

Would it cost more or less than $1,000 a week? How do you know?

Fatima wrote these number sentences to figure out the price.
Complete each of the sentences.

How did she break 5,236 into parts that are easier to divide by 4?

What is another way to break 5,236 into parts?

4,000 ÷ 4 = ______

1,200 ÷ 4 = ______

36 ÷ 4 = ______

5,236 ÷ 4 = ______

Another apartment costs $1,620 for 4 weeks rent.
What is the price of 1 week?

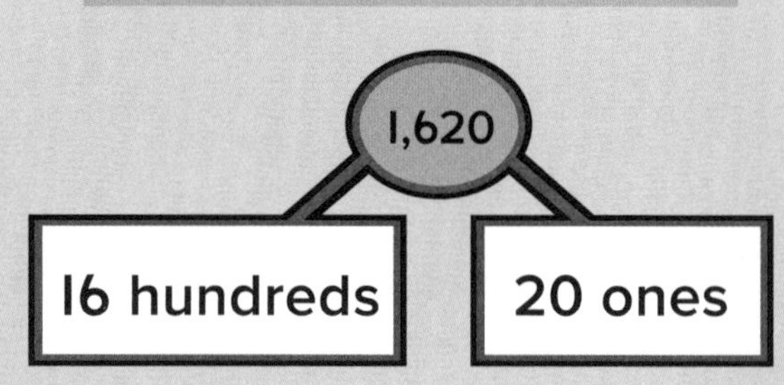

You could break 1,620 into parts that are easier to divide by 4. This diagram shows you how.

Complete the sentences.

1,600 ÷ 4 = ______

20 ÷ 4 = ______

1,620 ÷ 4 = ______

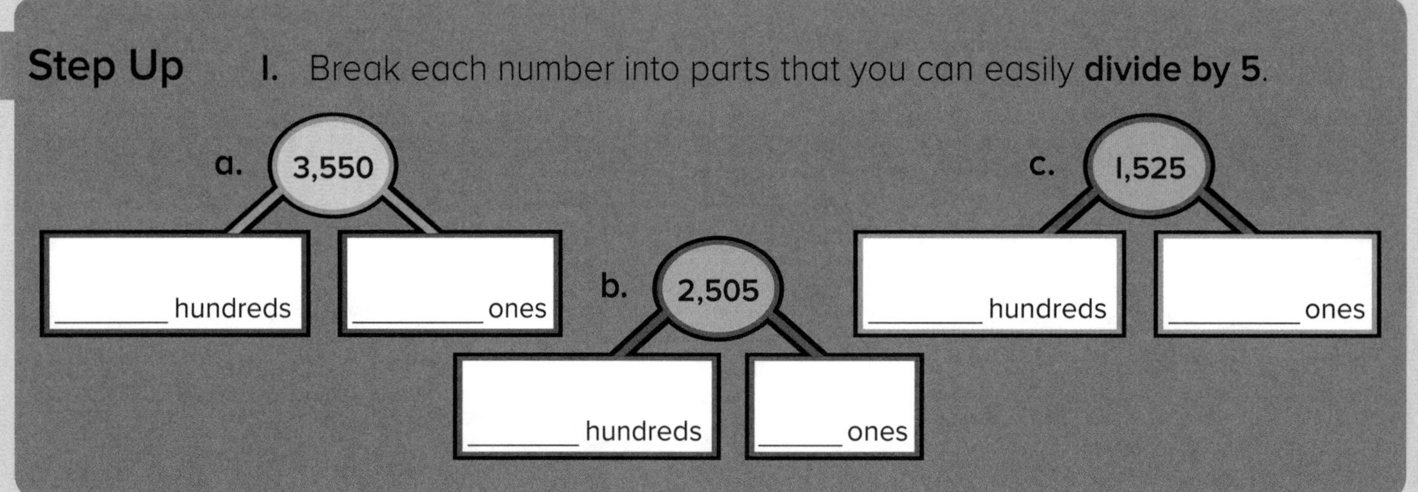

2. Write number sentences to figure out each of these.

a.	b.	c.
1,720 ÷ 4 = ______	1,659 ÷ 3 = ______	1,926 ÷ 6 = ______
1,600 ÷ 4 = ______	1,500 ÷ 3 = ______	1,800 ÷ 6 = ______
120 ÷ 4 = ______	______ ÷ 3 = ______	______ ÷ 6 = ______
	______ ÷ 3 = ______	______ ÷ 6 = ______

3. Estimate each answer in your head.
Then write number sentences to figure out the exact amount.

a.	b.	c.
5,612 ÷ 4 = ______	8,407 ÷ 7 = ______	7,830 ÷ 6 = ______

d.	e.	f.
4,650 ÷ 5 = ______	4,206 ÷ 3 = ______	9,640 ÷ 8 = ______

Step Ahead Loop the numbers that you can divide **equally** by 4.

3,216	4,810	1,720	5,204	5,642

Step In Solving Word Problems Involving Division

Imagine you buy one of these items and pay for it over several months.

How would the store figure out the amount you need to pay each month?

Imagine you buy the television and pay equal monthly amounts over six months.

How much would you pay each month?

How could you break $786 into parts that are easy to divide by 6?

Step Up

1. Refer to the prices above. Figure out the equal monthly payments for these items. Show your thinking.

a. 5 monthly payments

$______ each month

b. 6 monthly payments

$______ each month

2. Look at the prices on page 262. Solve these word problems. Show your thinking.

a. Ashley buys the cell phone. She pays $50 first then pays 4 equal monthly payments. How much does she pay each month?

$______

b. Toby buys the laptop and camera. He makes equal monthly payments over 7 months. What amount does he pay each month?

$______

c. David buys 6 cameras for his class. He makes equal payments over 5 months. What amount does he pay each month?

$______

d. Diana buys the cell phone and laptop. She makes equal monthly payments over 6 months. What amount does she pay each month?

$______

Step Ahead Calculate the monthly payments for each phone. Then draw a ✔ beside the plan that you would choose.

A

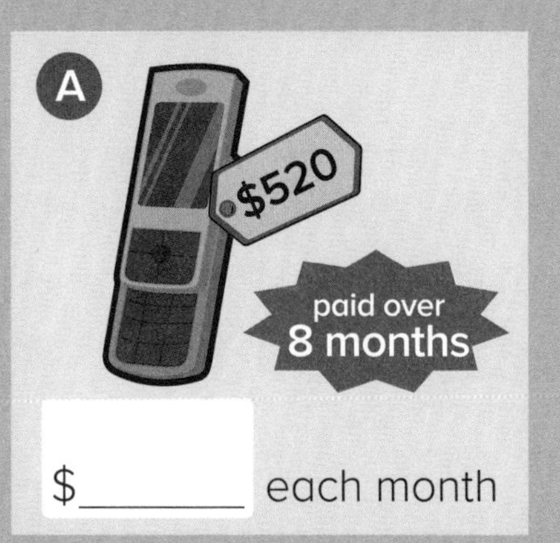

$______ each month

B

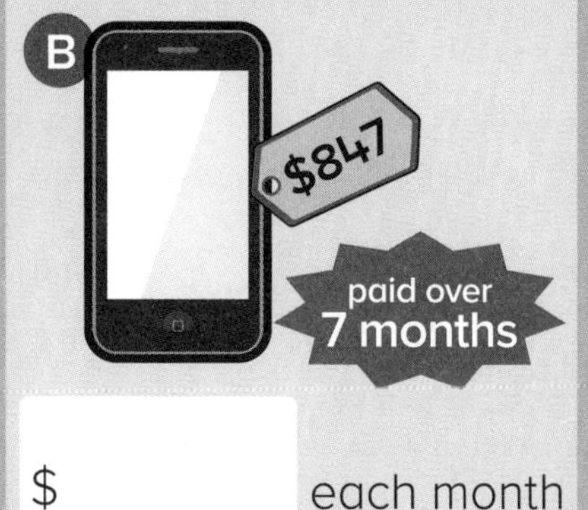

$______ each month

C

$______ each month

Step In Reviewing Customary Units of Length

What unit of measurement would you use to describe the length of a piece of string?

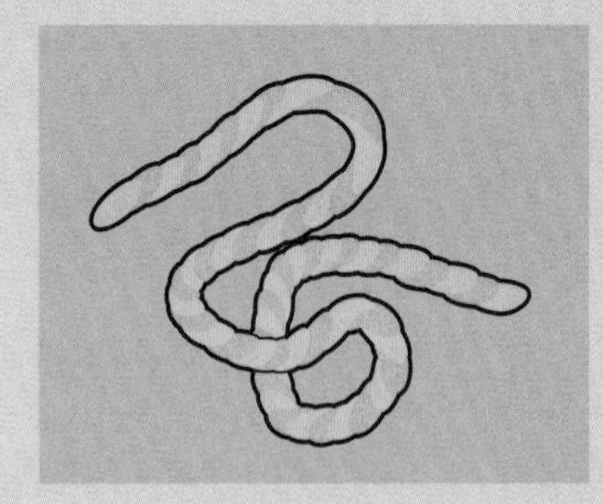

If the string was short, I would describe the length in inches.

What unit do you use to describe the distances that you travel in a car?

There are 5,280 feet in one mile and 1,760 yards in one mile.

A short way to write mile is mi.

Step Up

1. Loop the distance that makes sense.

a. the distance around a sporting field

580 inches	580 feet	580 yards	580 miles

b. the distance of a plane flight

465 inches	465 feet	465 yards	465 miles

c. the length of a baseball bat

32 inches	32 feet	32 yards	32 miles

d. the width of a basketball court

50 inches	50 feet	50 yards	50 miles

e. the length of a school bus

36 inches	36 feet	36 yards	36 miles

2. Write the name of a classroom object to match each length. Then use an inch ruler or yardstick to check the length of each object that you wrote.

Length	Classroom Object or Distance	Measured Length
8 in	pencil case	a little more than 9 in
15 in		
1 ft		
3 ft		
2 yd		
5 yd		

3. Estimate each distance. Then ask your teacher to provide the actual distances.

	Estimate (mi)	Actual Distance (mi)
a. to the nearest movie theater		
b. to the nearest fire station		
c. to the nearest hospital		
d. to the nearest airport		
e. to the nearest train station		

Step Ahead Estimate then investigate each distance.

	Estimate (mi)	Actual Distance (mi)
a. to the nearest shopping mall by road		
b. to the nearest beach by road		
c. to the nearest college by road		

Step In Converting Feet and Inches

A zoo keeper compares the length of two snakes.
The first snake is 2 feet long. The second snake is 21 inches.
Which snake is longer? How do you know?

There are 12 inches in 1 foot.

Complete this table.

Feet	1	2	3	5	10	15	20
Inches	12						

How did you figure out the number of inches in 10, 15, and 20 feet?

The Australian taipan, an extremely poisonous snake, is $2\frac{1}{2}$ feet long.

How many inches is that? How do you know?

I know there are 12 inches in one foot, so there must be 6 inches in $\frac{1}{2}$ foot.

Step Up

The lengths of 20 snakes are shown below.
Use this data to complete the dot plot on page 267.

$23\frac{1}{2}$ inches	26 inches	27 inches	23 inches	26 inches
22 inches	$25\frac{1}{2}$ inches	$27\frac{1}{2}$ inches	25 inches	2 feet
23 inches	26 inches	$23\frac{1}{2}$ inches	26 inches	$23\frac{1}{2}$ inches
26 inches	$25\frac{1}{2}$ inches	$25\frac{1}{2}$ inches	2 feet	25 inches

1. Draw ● on the dot plot to show each length from the bottom of page 266. Cross out each length on page 266 after you record it on the dot plot.

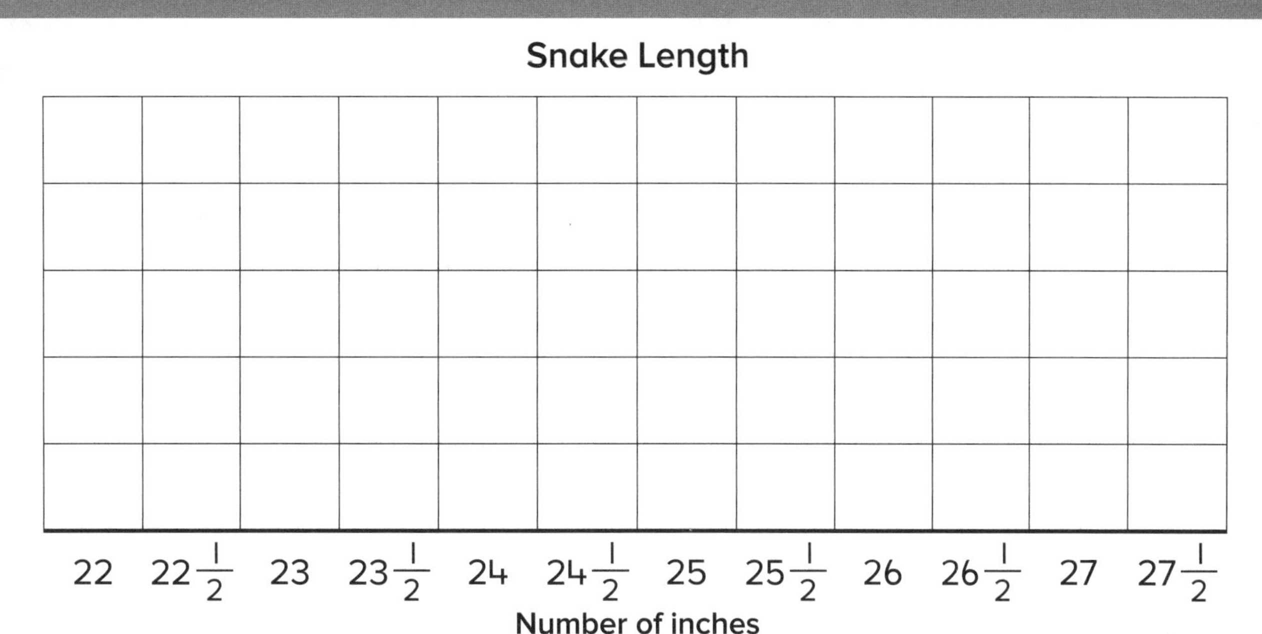

2. Use the dot plot above to answer these questions.

a. What is the most common length of snake? ____________

b. How many snakes are **less than** 26 inches long? ________

c. How many snakes are **longer than** 2 feet? ________

d. What is the difference in length between the shortest and longest snakes? ________ inches

e. If all the snakes grew by $\frac{1}{2}$ inch, how many snakes would be 2 feet long? ________

Step Ahead Write the length of these snakes in inches.

Rattlesnake	King Cobra	Python
7 feet ________ inches	$16\frac{1}{2}$ feet ________ inches	25 feet ________ inches

Step In Converting Yards, Feet, and Inches

Two friends compare their running jumps. Nicole jumped 2 yards. Awan jumped 5 feet.

What is the difference in length between their jumps? How do you know?

Complete this table.

Yards	1	2	3	5	15	20	35
Feet	3						

How did you figure out the number of feet in 15, 20, and 35 yards?

What does this diagram show?

How many inches are in 1 yard?

How many inches in 2 yards? How do you know?

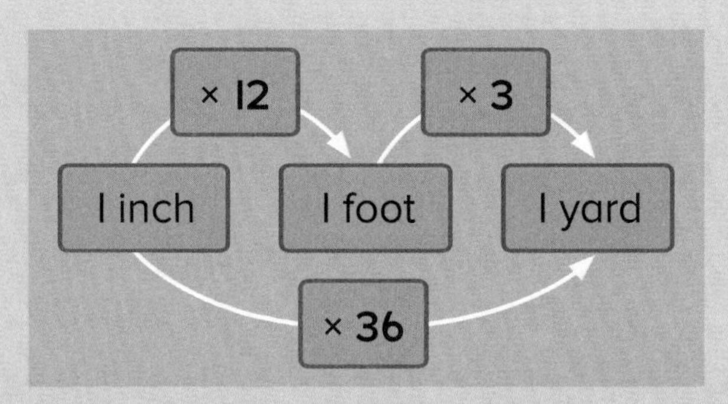

Step Up

1. Convert yards to feet. Show your thinking below.

a. 5 yards is the same length as ______ ft

b. 9 yards is the same length as ______ ft

c. 6 yards is the same length as ______ ft

2. Convert yards to feet and then inches. Show your thinking below.

a. 4 yards

is the same length as

____ feet

is the same length as

____ inches

b. 7 yards

is the same length as

____ feet

is the same length as

____ inches

3. Solve these word problems. Show your thinking.

a. Archie's golf ball is 3 yards from the hole. Jerilene's ball lands 10 feet from the hole. Whose ball is closer to the hole?

____

b. Antonio kicked a ball 42 feet. His dad kicked the ball 3 yards farther. How far did his dad kick the ball?

____ ft

Step Ahead Figure out the length of each jump.

Paul jumped 2 yards. Andrea jumped 1 foot farther than Paul. Kuma jumped 1 yard less than Andrea. How far did each person jump?

Paul ____ ft Andrea ____ ft Kuma ____ ft

Step In Converting Miles, Yards, and Feet

Jadyn rides one mile to school each day. Emily walks 1,200 yards.

Who lives closer to the school? How do you know?

There are 1,760 yards in one mile.

How could you figure out the number of yards in 5 miles? What number sentences could you write?

Ricardo used the standard algorithm for multiplication.

What steps did he follow?

How many yards in 5 miles?

$$\begin{array}{r} {}^{3}\,{}^{3} \\ 1760 \\ \times 5 \\ \hline 8800 \end{array}$$

How could he figure out the number of yards in 7 miles?

What does this diagram show?

How could you figure out the number of feet in 1 mile?

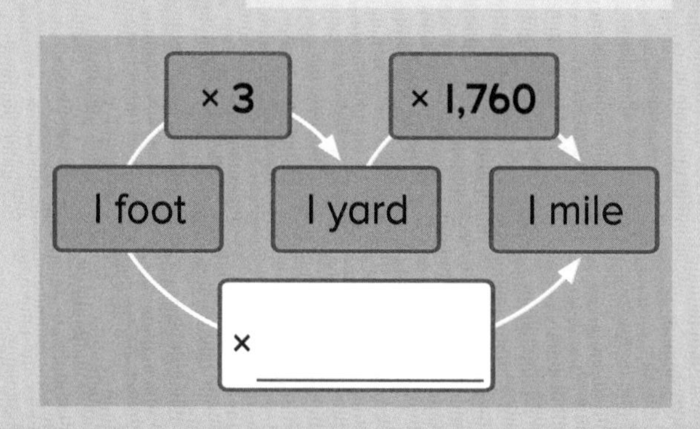

Step Up

1. Figure out the number of yards in each distance. Show your thinking.

a. 4 miles	b. 6 miles	c. 8 miles
______ yd	______ yd	______ yd

2. Use your answers from Question 1 to figure out the number of feet in each distance. Remember there are 3 feet in 1 yard.

a. **6 miles**

_____ ft

b. **8 miles**

_____ ft

3. Solve each of these problems. Show your thinking.

a. Helen is going on a 3-mile hike. She has walked 500 yards already. How much farther does she have to walk?

_____ yd

b. Beatrice's house is 2 miles from school. Aston lives another 100 yards farther away. How many yards does Aston live from the school?

_____ yd

Step Ahead Gracia walked over 7,000 yards as she played 18 holes of golf.

About how many miles did she walk?

_____ miles

Working Space

Step In Partitioning and Regrouping Dividends

Imagine you are planning a vacation.

How can you figure out the cost of one night at this hotel?

Patricia showed the total cost using base-10 blocks.

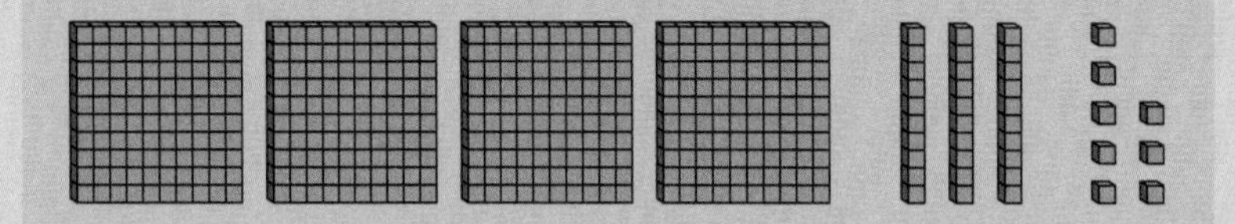

Then she followed these steps to calculate the cost of each night.

	Step 1 Share the hundreds.	Step 2 Share the tens.	Step 3 Share the ones.
3 Nights			

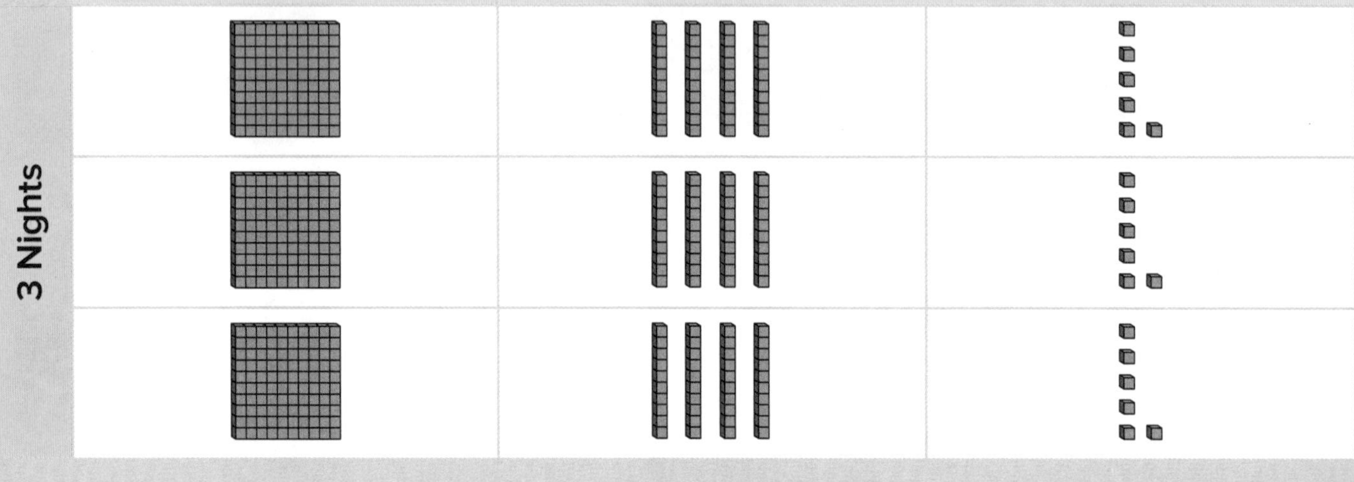

What did Patricia do at each step? What happened to the fourth hundreds block?

What is the cost of each night?

What is another way you could figure it out?

Step Up

1. Draw or write the amount in each share. Use blocks to help you.

a.	456 ÷ 3
Shares	

b.	372 ÷ 3
Shares	

2. Use a strategy of your choice to complete each of these.
You can use blocks to help. Show your thinking.

a. 620 ÷ 5 = ____

b. 375 ÷ 3 = ____

c. 528 ÷ 4 = ____

d. 429 ÷ 3 = ____

e. 4,206 ÷ 3 = ____

f. 3,250 ÷ 5 = ____

Step Ahead

Show how you would split these numbers into parts to make it easy to divide by 4.

a. 708 ÷ 4
is the same as
____

b. 960 ÷ 4
is the same as
____

c. 1,320 ÷ 4
is the same as
____

Step In Recording Division

Three people share the cost of renting this car.

How could you figure out each person's share?

Joe showed the total cost with blocks then followed these steps to figure out each share.

	Step 1 Share the hundreds.	Step 2 Share the tens.	Step 3 Share the ones.
Shares			

Samuru followed these steps to help him write the amount in each share.

	Step 1 Share the hundreds.	Step 2 Share the tens.	Step 3 Share the ones.
Shares	100	100 + 10	100 + 10 + 6
	100	100 + 10	100 + 10 + 6
	100	100 + 10	100 + 10 + 6

How much is each person's share of the car rental?

Step Up

1. Figure out how much two people, then four people would pay to share the same total cost of the car rental above. Use a strategy of your choice.

a.	$348 ÷ 2
Shares	

b.	$348 ÷ 4
Shares	

2. Figure out the amount in each share. You can use blocks to help your thinking.

a. $\$512 \div 4 =$ $ ______

100
100
100
100

b. $\$798 \div 6 =$ $ ______

c. $\$847 \div 7 =$ $ ______

d. $\$732 \div 6 =$ $ ______

e. $\$648 \div 4 =$ $ ______

f. $\$573 \div 3 =$ $ ______

g. $\$4,230 \div 3 =$ $ ______

1,000
1,000
1,000

h. $\$5,631 \div 3 =$ $ ______

Step Ahead For both of these, write a digit to complete a three-digit number that you can divide without any amount left over. Then write the answers.

a. 5 8 ___ ÷ 3 = ______

b. 6 2 ___ ÷ 5 = ______

Step In Developing the Standard Division Algorithm

Four people shared the cost of a restaurant bill for $84.

4 people share $84
2 tens + 1 one
2 tens + 1 one
2 tens + 1 one
2 tens + 1 one

Anya calculated each share and recorded her thinking like this.

How much did each person pay?

Another way to record the calculation is to use a division bracket.

$4\overline{)\,8\quad 4}$

What numbers are written around this division bracket?
What does each number tell you?

What is happening in each of these steps?

How are the steps similar to Anya's method?

Step 1

	T	O
	2	
4)	8	4

Step 2

	T	O
	2	1
4)	8	4

Look at these steps to figure out 906 shared by 3.

Step 1

	H	T	O
	3		
3)	9	0	6

Step 2

	H	T	O
	3	0	
3)	9	0	6

Step 3

	H	T	O
	3	0	2
3)	9	0	6

What is happening in each step?

Why is 0 written above the bracket in Step 2?

I think I could skip Step 1 because I know that 90 tens divided by 3 is 30 tens.

Numbers in equations are arranged in different positions when using division brackets.

$64 \div 2 = 32$ $\quad \begin{array}{r} 3\;\;2 \\ 2\overline{)\,6\;\;4} \end{array}$

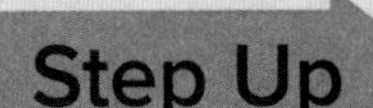

Step Up

1. Rewrite each equation using the division bracket.

a. 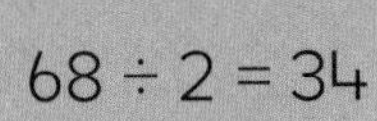

68 ÷ 2 = 34

T O

b. 32 = 96 ÷ 3

T O

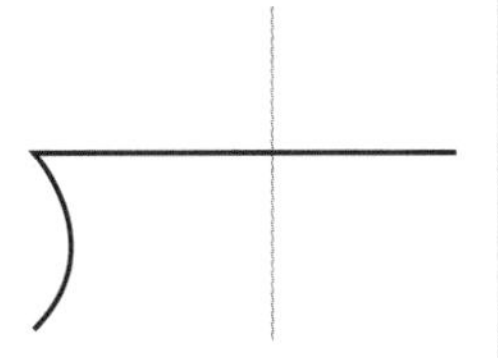

c. 412 = 824 ÷ 2

H T O

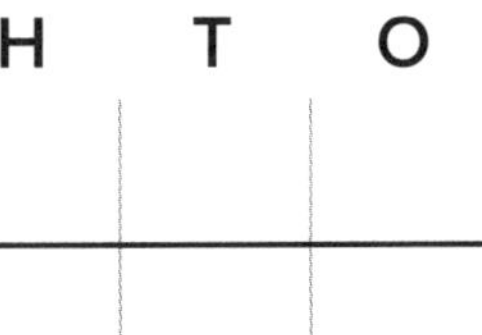

d. 309 ÷ 3 = 103

H T O

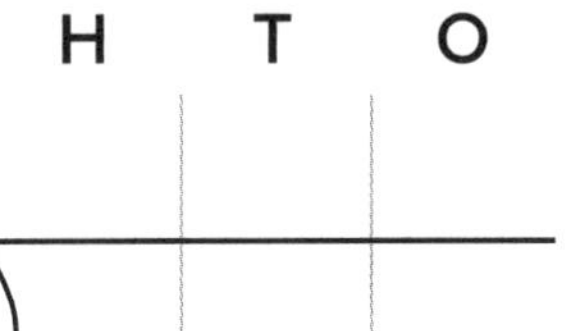

2. Use the steps on page 276 to calculate each quotient.

a. T O
$2\overline{)82}$

b. H T O
$3\overline{)693}$

c. Th H T O
$2\overline{)8626}$

d. T O
$3\overline{)63}$

e. H T O
$4\overline{)804}$

f. Th H T O
$4\overline{)4048}$

g. T O
$4\overline{)84}$

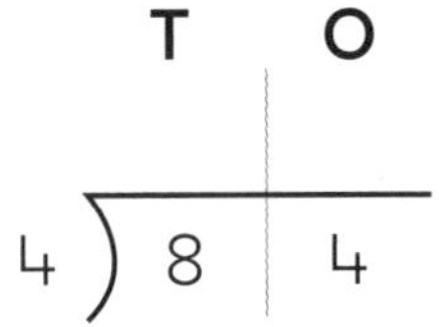

h. H T O
$2\overline{)460}$

i. Th H T O
$3\overline{)9309}$

3. Choose three problems from Question 2. Rewrite each as an equation.

______ ______ ______

Step Ahead

Write digits to complete each problem.

a. Th H T O

	Th	H	T	O
	1	3	2	0
3)		9		

b. Th H T O

	Th	H	T	O
	3	4	0	
)	6	8		2

Step In Introducing the Standard Division Algorithm

Three friends equally share $78.

Ethan used blocks and wrote this to figure out each share.

How much is each share?

What regrouping did Ethan have to do? How do you know?

78 ÷ 3
7 tens ÷ 3 = 2 tens
and 1 ten left over
18 ones ÷ 3 = 6 ones

Abigail tried using the division bracket but did not know how to show the regrouping.

Kevin showed her the standard division algorithm to help.

	T	O
	2	
3)	7	8

Step 1	T	O
Divide	2	
There are 7 tens to share. There are 3 shares. There are 2 tens in each share because 3 × 2 is 6.	3) 7	8

Step 2	T	O
Multiply then subtract.	2	
There are 7 tens to share. There are 6 tens shared. There is 1 ten left over because 7 − 6 is 1.	3) 7	8
	− 6	
	1	

Step 3	T	O
Bring down the next digit.	2	
There is 1 ten left to share. There are 8 ones to share. That makes 18 ones to share.	3) 7	8
	− 6	↓
	1	8

Kevin completed the standard algorithm by repeating the first two steps with 18 ones.

	T	O
	2	6
3)	7	8
−	6	↓
	1	8
−	1	8
		0

How is Kevin's method similar to Ethan's method?

What is another method you could use?

Try using the standard division algorithm to calculate 68 ÷ 4.

Step Up

Use the standard division algorithm to calculate each quotient. Remember to estimate before or after your calculation to check your accuracy.

a. T O

$4\overline{)56}$

b. T O

$3\overline{)81}$

c. T O

$5\overline{)85}$

d. T O

$2\overline{)76}$

e. $6\overline{)84}$

f. $3\overline{)78}$

g. $7\overline{)91}$

h. $3\overline{)54}$

i. $8\overline{)96}$

j. $4\overline{)92}$

k. $5\overline{)75}$

l. $3\overline{)48}$

Step Ahead

Show two different ways to figure out 87 ÷ 3.

Step In Working with the Standard Division Algorithm

A rope of 645 centimeters was cut into three equal parts.

How would you figure out the length of each part?

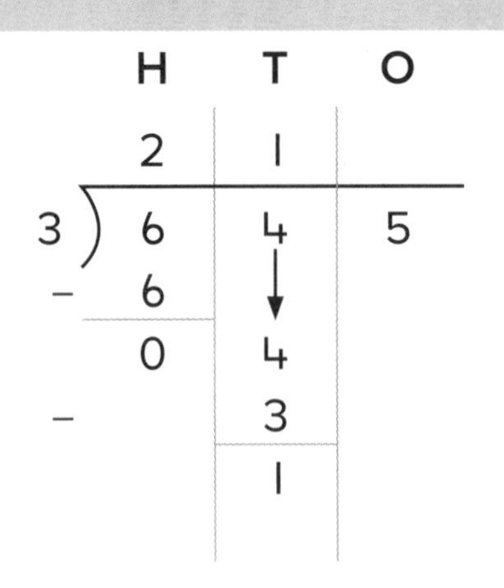

Sara decided to use the standard division algorithm to calculate each length.

What steps has she completed?
What does she need to do next?

Complete Sara's calculation.

Four wheels cost $832. How much does each wheel cost?

Blake followed these steps to figure it out.

8 hundreds divided by	3 tens divided by 4	32 ones divided by 4
2 hundreds	2 hundreds + 0 tens	2 hundreds + 0 tens + 8 ones
2 hundreds	2 hundreds + 0 tens	2 hundreds + 0 tens + 8 ones
2 hundreds	2 hundreds + 0 tens	2 hundreds + 0 tens + 8 ones
2 hundreds	2 hundreds + 0 tens	2 hundreds + 0 tens + 8 ones

Rozene and Benjamin each used the standard algorithm.

Compare their calculations.

What do you notice about the steps Benjamin used?

Why do you think he brought down the 3 tens and 2 ones at the same time?

Did this affect the final answer?

How does each method relate to Blake's method?

Rozene

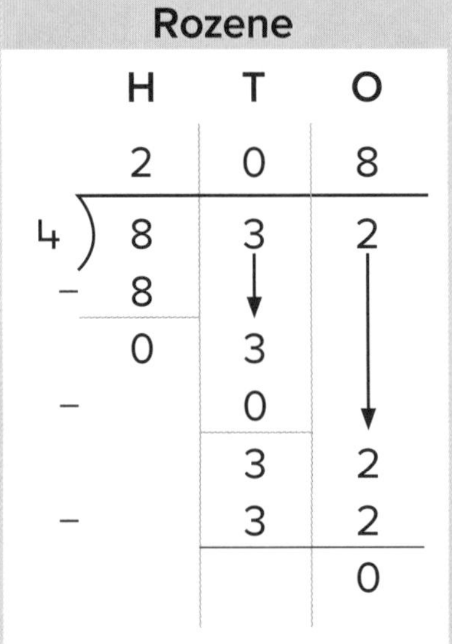

Benjamin

H T O
2 0 8
4) 8 3 2
− 8
0 3 2
− 3 2
0

Five friends ran a carwash. They earned $285 and split the money evenly.

How much was in each share?

How could you use the standard division algorithm to help you?

Step Up

Complete these calculations using the standard division algorithm.

a. H T O

$3\overline{)486}$

b. H T O

$4\overline{)904}$

c. H T O

$5\overline{)415}$

d. Th H T O

$4\overline{)6184}$

e. Th H T O

$6\overline{)1872}$

f. Th H T O

$5\overline{)3205}$

Step Ahead

Choose two problems above that you can solve easily **without** using the standard division algorithm. Show your methods.

Step In — Working with the Standard Division Algorithm (with Remainders)

Muffins are sold in boxes of 5.
There are 267 muffins to pack.

Will there be any muffins left over?
How do you know?

I know there will be some muffins left over because there is no 0 or 5 in the ones place.

How many boxes of muffins can be sold?

Owen used the standard division algorithm.

Describe the steps that he used.

How many boxes are needed?
How many muffins are remaining?
How is the remainder recorded?

	H	T	O	
		5	3	R2
5)	2	6	7	
−	2	5	↓	
		1	7	
−		1	5	
			2	

How could you pack 267 muffins in boxes of a different size so that there are no muffins left over?

Step Up

1. Complete these calculations using the standard division algorithm. Record the remainder.

a.

	H	T	O	
				R
5)	6	3	7	

b.

	H	T	O	
				R
3)	2	0	9	

c.

	H	T	O	
				R
4)	6	5	5	

2. Complete each of these.

a.

Th	H	T	O
			R
5) 7	3	0	8

b.

Th	H	T	O
			R
7) 3	7	4	0

c.

Th	H	T	O
			R
5) 4	8	2	9

d.

			R
6) 3	0	4	5

e.

			R
9) 5	2	1	4

f.

			R
4) 3	0	0	9

Step Ahead Use the standard division algorithm to solve this problem.

A farmer collects 207 eggs in the morning and another 228 eggs later that night. The eggs are packed into cartons of 6. How many eggs are left over?

_____ eggs

Step In Exploring the Relationship between Kilograms and Grams

Look at this balance picture. Each small box has the same mass.

How could you figure out the mass of each one?

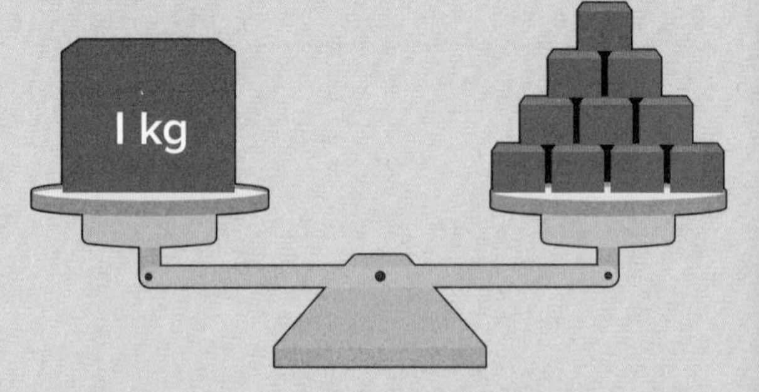

Look at this scale.

How could you write the mass shown?

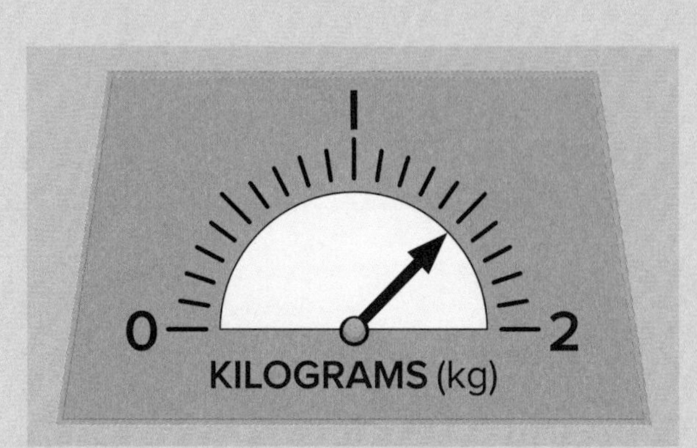

How could you write the same mass in grams?

Complete these statements.

1.5 kg is the same as ____________ g

0.1 kg is the same as ____________ g

What are some other kilogram masses that you can say in grams?

Step Up

1. Read the scales carefully. Write each mass in grams.

a.

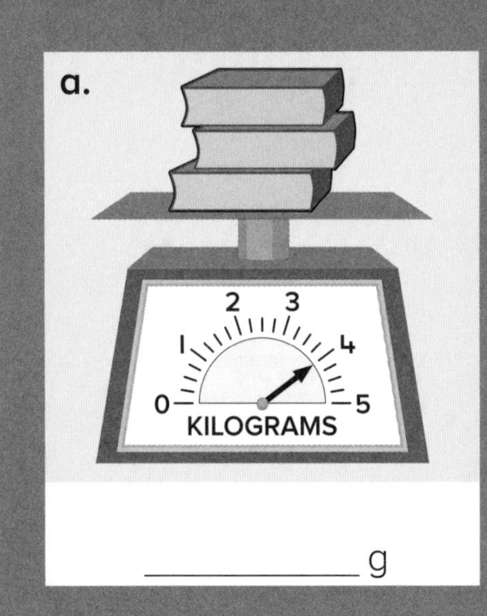

____________ g

b.

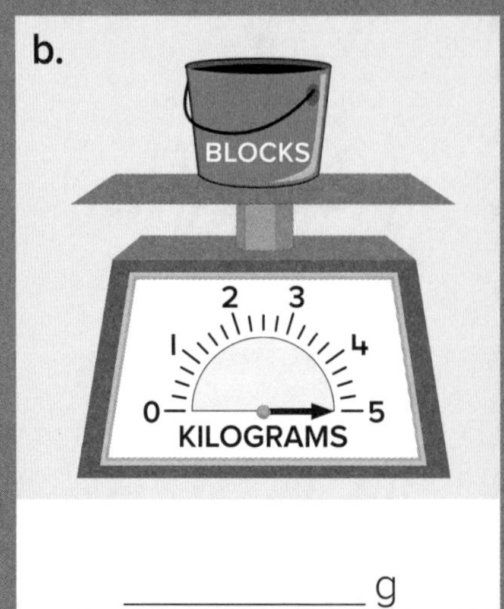

____________ g

c.

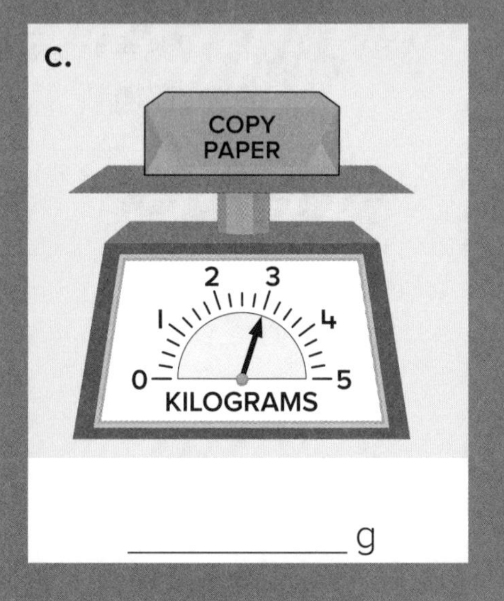

____________ g

2. Read the scales carefully. Then write each mass in grams.

a.

0 KILOGRAMS 1 2

_____________ g

b.

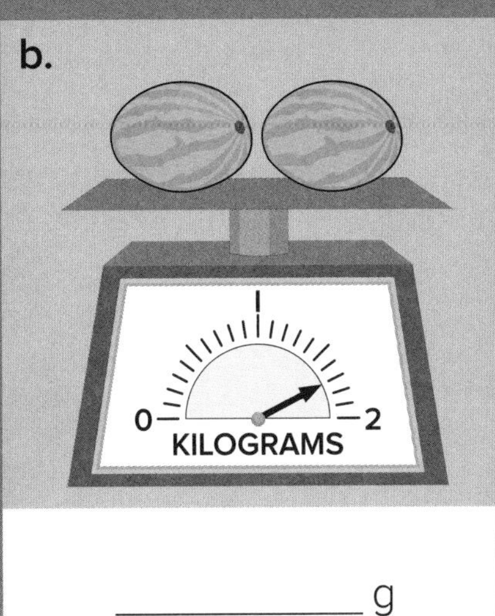

_____________ g

c.

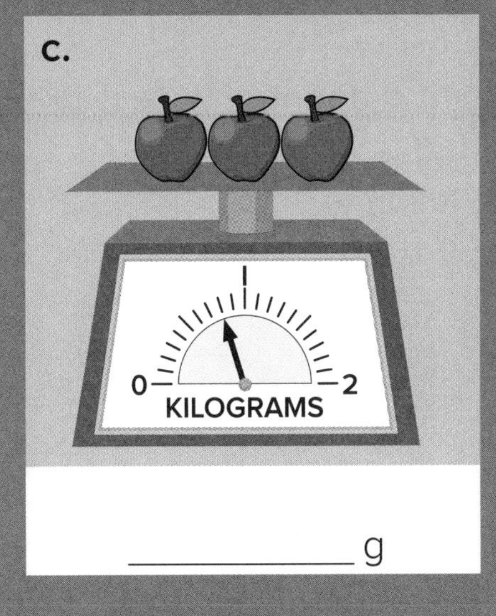

_____________ g

3. Write the missing numbers to show the same mass in each row.
The first row has been done for you.

Grams	Kilograms (common fraction)	Kilograms (decimal fraction)
100	$\frac{1}{10}$	0.1
	$\frac{4}{10}$	0.4
2,600		2.6
	$4\frac{3}{10}$	4.3
		1.8
	$3\frac{7}{10}$	

Step Ahead Look at each balance picture. Write **T** on the picture that is true.

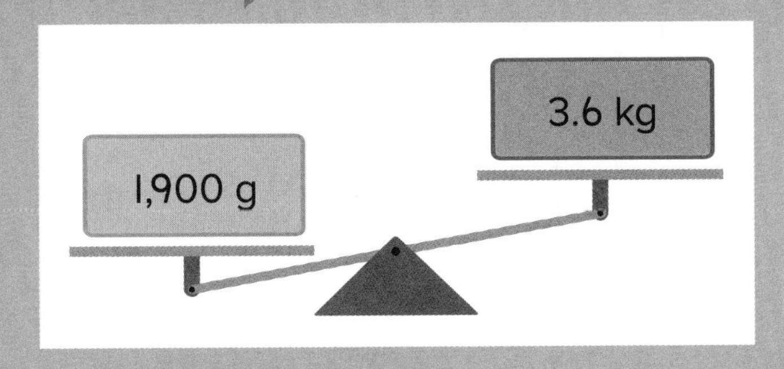

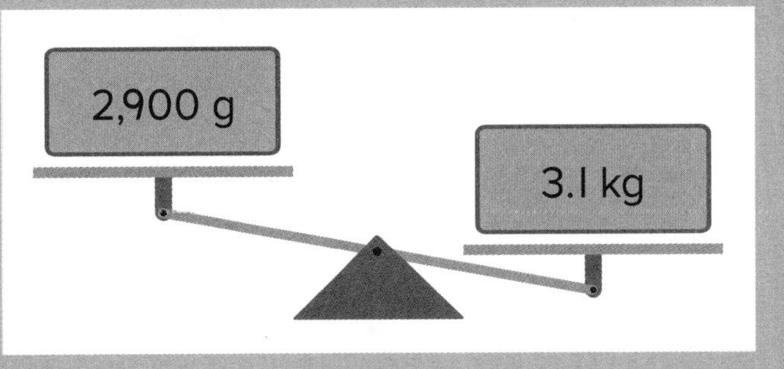

Step In — Exploring the Relationship between Liters and Milliliters

What amount of juice is in this pitcher?

Imagine the juice was poured equally into two containers.
How many milliliters would be in each container?

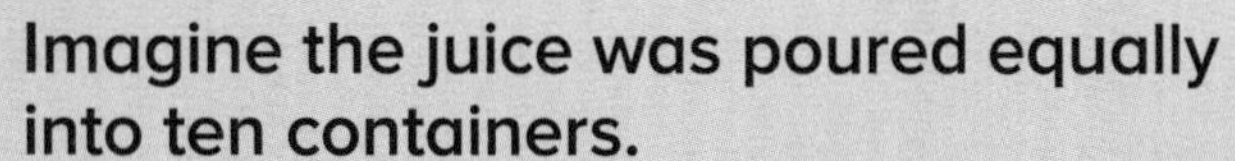

Imagine the juice was poured equally into ten containers.
How many milliliters would be in each container?
How do you know?

This container holds more than one liter.
How much juice is in the container?

Complete these statements.

1.5 L is the same as ______ mL

0.1 L is the same as ______ mL

What are some other liter amounts that you can say in milliliters?

Step Up

1. Look carefully at the scale on each container. Then write the amount of water in each.

a.

______ mL

b.

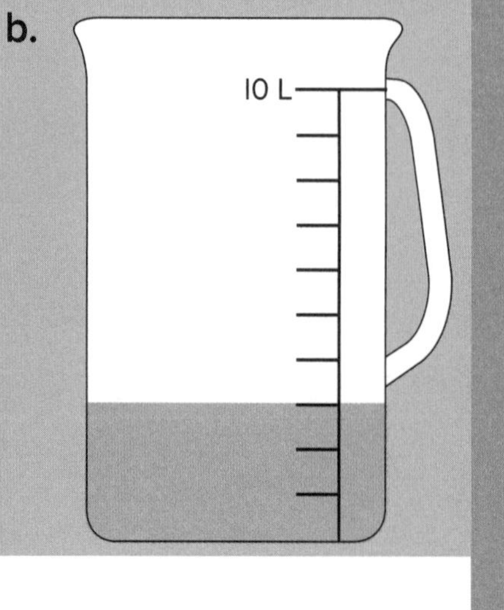

______ mL

c.

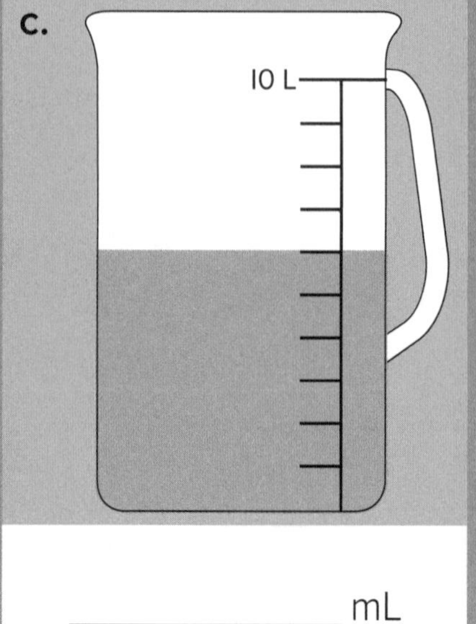

______ mL

2. Look carefully at the scale. Then write the amount in each container.

a.

_____________ mL

b.

_____________ mL

c.

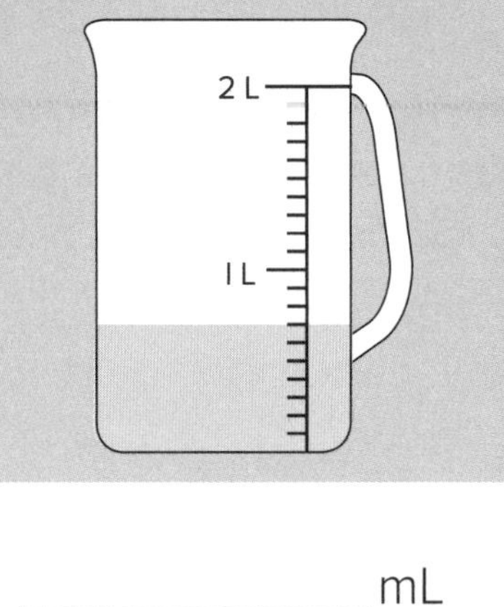

_____________ mL

3. Write the missing numbers to show the same capacity in each row.
The first row has been done for you.

Milliliters	Liters (common fraction)	Liters (decimal fraction)
2,400	$2\frac{4}{10}$	2.4
	$1\frac{7}{10}$	1.7
900		0.9
2,800	$2\frac{8}{10}$	
		3.2
	$\frac{6}{10}$	

Step Ahead For each of these, look at the amount of water in both the containers. Then write an amount that could be in the second container.

a.

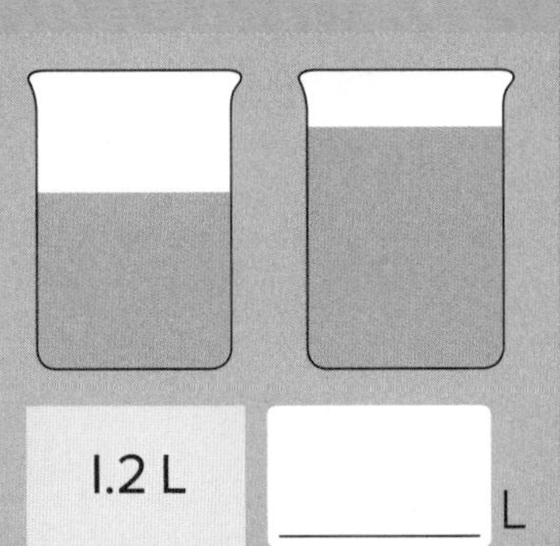

1.2 L _________ L

b.

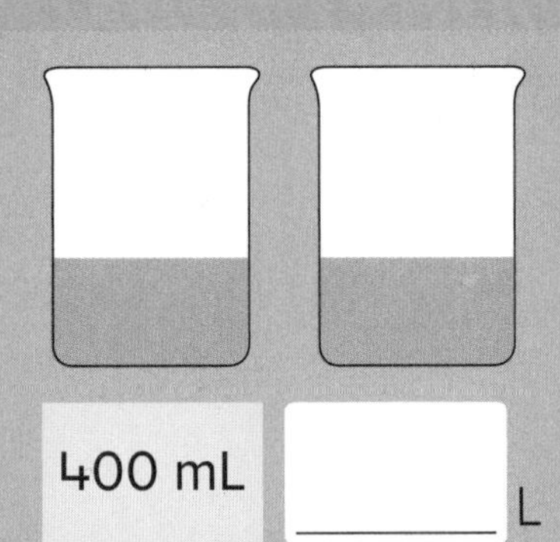

400 mL _________ L

c.

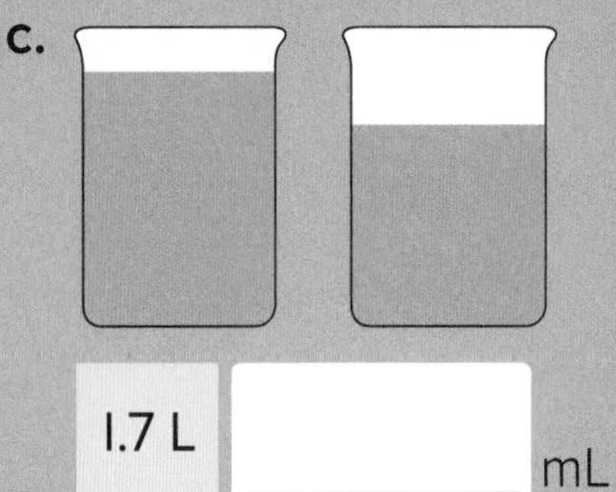

1.7 L _________ mL

Step In Solving Word Problems Involving Metric Units of Mass and Capacity

Two friends are planning a party. Juliana is making the punch.

She has two bowls that she can use to hold this punch. The first bowl holds 4 liters. The second bowl holds 5 liters.

Which bowl should she use? Why?

FRUIT PUNCH

2 L of lemonade

1.5 L of cranberry juice

600 mL of pineapple juice

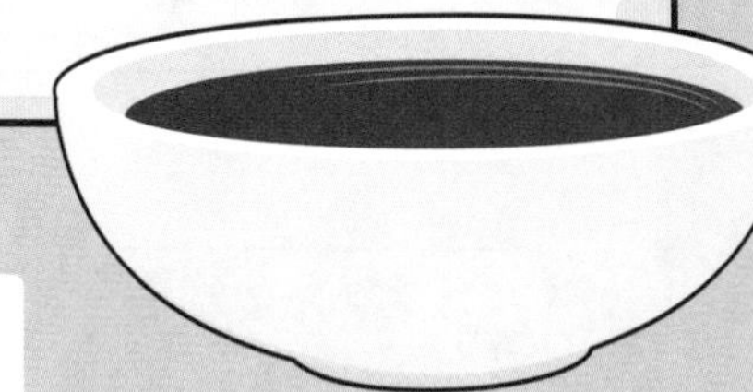

There are 1,000 mL in 1 liter. I can change liters to milliliters to figure out the total amount. That's 2,000 + 1,500 + 600.

Cary is organizing a barbeque. He buys 1.5 kg of sausages, 2 kg of steak, and 700 g of chicken. How much meat did he buy?

Step Up

1. This is another punch recipe. Solve each word problem. Show your thinking.

3 L of cranberry juice

1.2 L of lemonade

700 mL of pineapple juice

100 mL of lemon juice

a. If you follow the recipe exactly, how much punch will you make?

_____ L

b. What is the difference between the amount of cranberry juice and pineapple juice in the recipe?

_____ L

c. If you pour all the punch equally into 10 glasses, how much punch will be in each glass?

_____ mL

2. Solve each problem. Show your thinking.

a. Hailey orders 1.5 kg of ham, 600 g of chicken, and 300 g of turkey. The meat is packed together. What is the total weight?

_____ kg

b. Abraham's dog lost 900 g after an operation. Before the operation he weighed 8.5 kg. How much does the dog weigh now?

_____ kg

c. A box holds 8 identical jars. The jars weigh 2 kg in total. What is the mass of each jar?

_____ g

d. Jennifer needs 2 kg of butter for a baking fundraiser. She has 6 sticks of butter that each weigh 125 g. How much more butter does she need?

_____ kg

Step Ahead

For each of these, look at the amount of water in both the containers. Then write an amount that could be in the second container.

a. 1,900 mL _____ L

b. 900 mL _____ L

c. 2 L _____ mL

Step In — Exploring the Relationship between Pounds and Ounces

How could you figure out the difference in mass between these two bags?

I would change the pounds into ounces to find the difference. There are 16 oz in 1 lb, so that is 32 – 5.

Complete these statements.

1 pound is ______ ounces

$\frac{1}{2}$ pound is ______ ounces

$\frac{1}{4}$ pound is ______ ounces

How could you figure out the difference in mass between these two boxes?

What number sentences would you write?

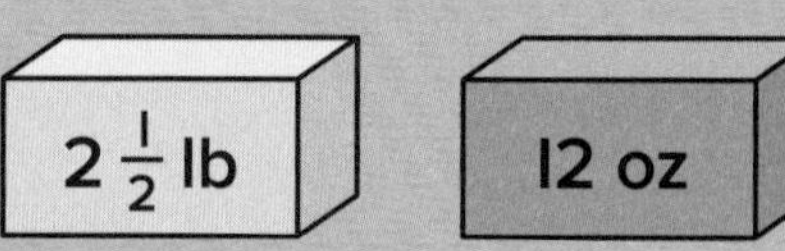

Step Up

1. For each pair of bags, figure out the difference in mass. Write number sentences to show your thinking.

a.

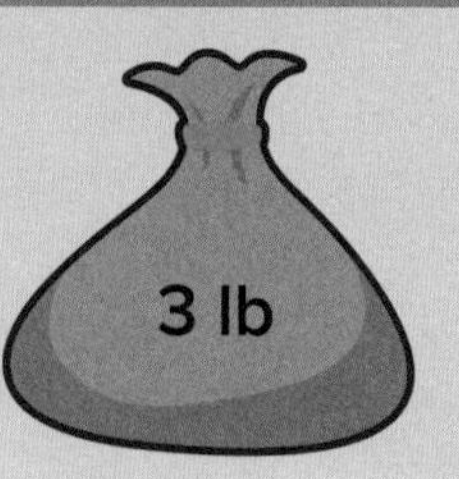

9 oz

______ oz

b.

______ oz

2. Figure out the difference in mass. Show your thinking.

a.

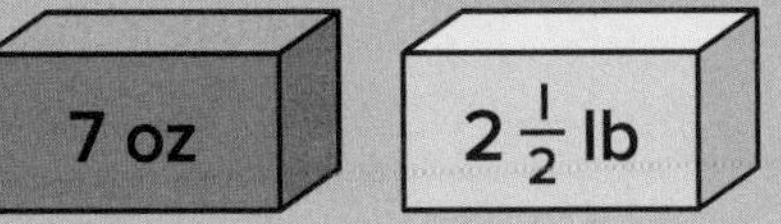

☐ oz

b.

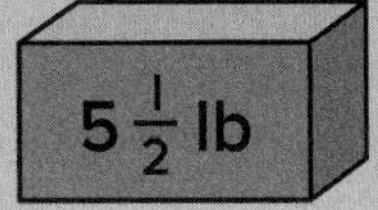

10 oz

☐ oz

3. Solve these word problems. Show your thinking.

a. Six muffins weigh 4 oz less than a cake. The cake weighs $1\frac{1}{2}$ lb. How much do the muffins weigh?

☐ oz

b. $2\frac{1}{2}$ lb of flour is poured equally into 4 containers. How much flour is in each container?

oz

Step Ahead Write the missing mass in each balance picture.

a.

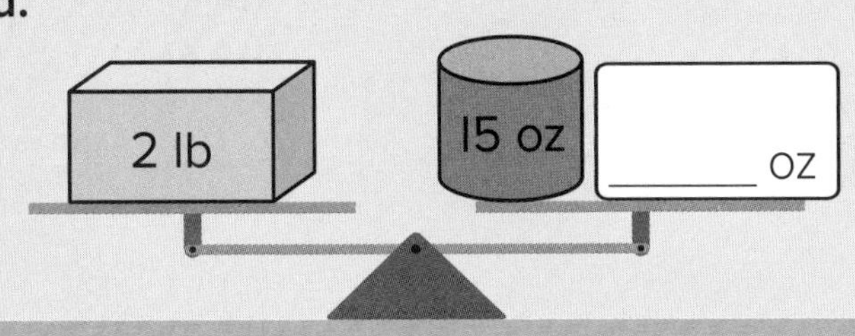

b.

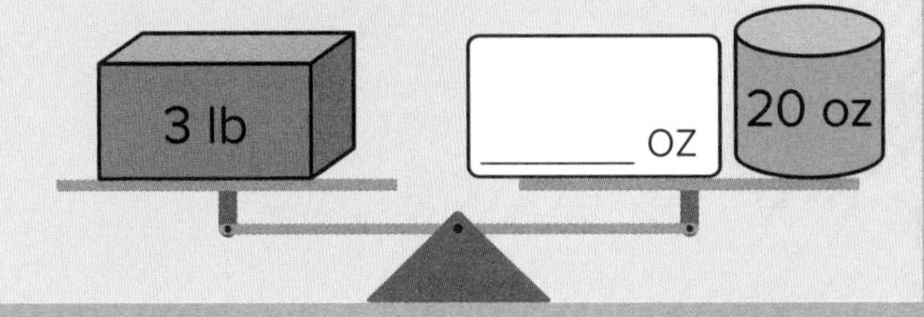

c.

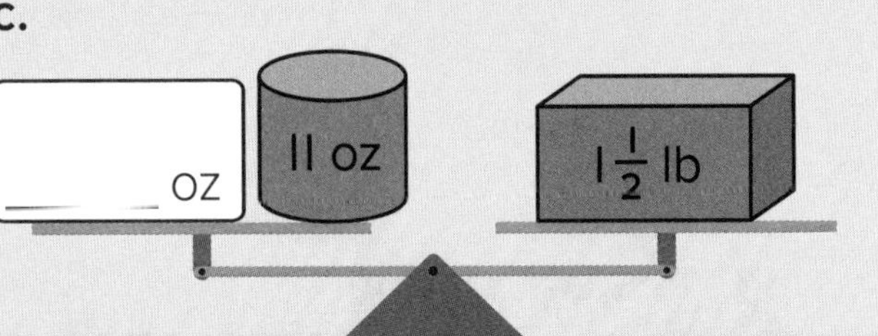

d.

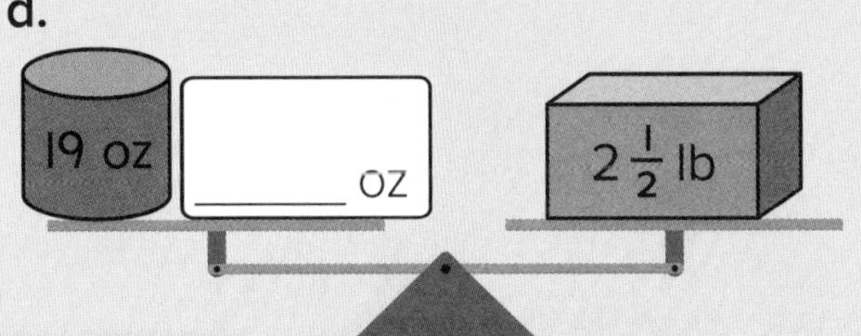

Step In Reviewing Gallons, Quarts, Pints, and Fluid Ounces

This table shows the number of containers that are required to make one gallon.
What do you notice?

Size of Container	Number of Containers
Quart	
Pint	
Cup	

I can see a doubling pattern. I quart is equal to 2 pints or 4 cups.

Complete this statement.

I gallon is ____ quarts or ____ pints or ______ cups.

What is another unit of measure that is less than one cup?

Fluid ounces are less than a cup.

There are 8 fluid ounces in I cup. A short way to write fluid ounce is **fl oz**.

Step Up I. Figure out the number of fluid ounces in each of these units.

I pint = 16 fl oz

I quart = ______ fl oz

I gallon = ______ fl oz

Working Space

2. Solve each word problem. Show your thinking.

a. There is half a gallon of water in a sink. Another quart of water is poured into the same sink. How much water is in the sink now?

b. Betty bought two 1-qt bottles of juice. Nina bought 10 bottles of juice that each held 8 fl oz. Who bought the greater amount of juice?

c. Rodrigo opens a 1-gallon bottle of milk. He fills 4 glasses with milk. Each glass holds 16 fl oz. How much milk is left in the bottle?

Step Ahead Write numbers to make these balance pictures true.

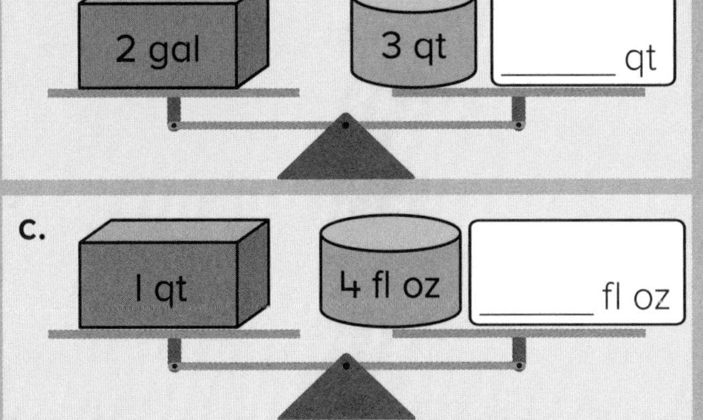

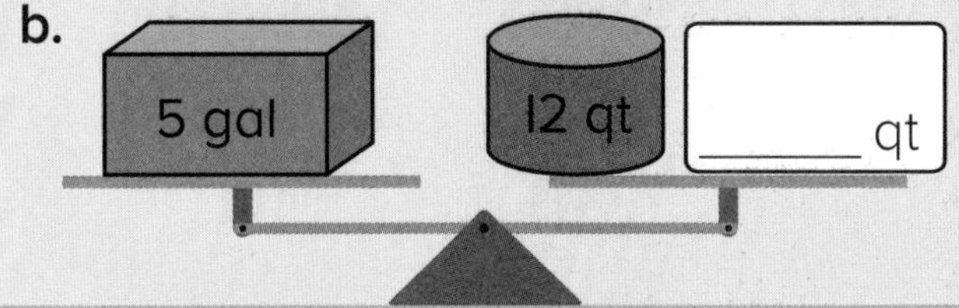

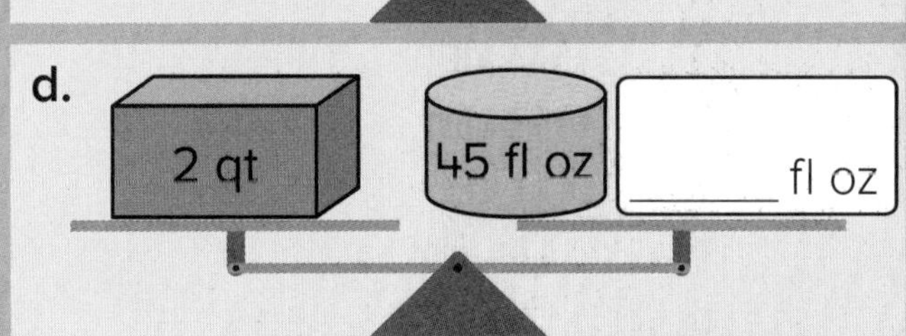

Step In Solving Word Problems Involving Customary Units of Mass and Capacity

What can you see in this picture?

Imagine each small glass holds 8 fl oz.

How many small glasses could you fill from one bottle of soda? How do you know?

How many glasses could you fill with grape juice?

Each muffin weighs about 7 oz. What is the total mass of muffins?

Is the total mass more or less than 2 lb? How do you know?

Step Up

1. Solve each of these problems. Show your thinking.

a. Bottled water is sold in packs of 6. Each small bottle holds about 17 fl oz. About how much water will there be in 2 packs?

_____ fl oz

b. Yuma buys 1 lb of cheese. He cuts the cheese into 4 equal pieces then eats 1 piece. How much cheese is left?

_____ oz

2. Solve each problem. Show your thinking.

a. Each bottle of soda holds 1 qt. Each can holds 12 fl oz. How much soda is in $1\frac{1}{2}$ bottles and 3 cans?

_______ fl oz

b. Raisins are sold in 16-oz boxes. Jose buys 3 boxes then shares the raisins equally among 4 bowls. What is the mass of raisins in each bowl?

_______ oz

c. Ruth buys two 1-gallon bottles of water. She pours all the water equally into 8 pitchers. How much water is in each pitcher?

_______ fl oz

d. Fiona opens a carton of juice that holds 59 fl oz. She fills 4 glasses of juice that hold 8 fl oz each. How much juice is left in the carton?

_______ fl oz

Step Ahead Write numbers to complete the word story. Make sure the story make sense.

Rita buys a carton of juice. The carton holds ________ fluid ounces. She fills ________ glasses with juice from the carton. Each glass holds ________ fluid ounces. There are ____________ fl oz left in the carton.

STEPPING INTO

FINANCIAL LITERACY

CONTENTS

Exploring the Difference between Fixed and Variable Expenses

For A and B:

- Rewrite the monthly expenses into columns that show fixed and variable expenses.
- Calculate the subtotal for each type of expense.
- Write the total monthly expenses.

A

Monthly expenses		Fixed expenses	Variable expenses
Food for home	$478.00		
Movies	$24.00		
Electric bill	$145.50		
TV/internet	$89.95		
Car loan	$195.00		
Jeans and jacket	$57.75	Subtotal $ ______	Subtotal $ ______
Rent	$650.00		
Restaurant	$78.80		Total $ ______

B

Monthly expenses		Fixed expenses	Variable expenses
Rent	$580.00		
TV/internet	$75.00		
Ball park tickets	$38.00		
Cell phone	$49.95		
Personal loan	$124.50		
Food for home	$380.00		
Electric bill	$139.50	Subtotal $ ______	Subtotal $ ______
Heating bill	$115.65		
Dress and shoes	$88.20		Total $ ______

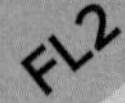

Financial Literacy

Calculating Profit

1. Write **P** on each of these that will show a profit. Then calculate the exact profit for each one with a **P**.

	Income	Expenses	Profit
a.	$450.75	$415.60	$______
b.	$236.40	$216.90	$______
c.	$208.50	$218.40	$______
d.	$1,024.50	$816.40	$______
e.	$1,140.60	$ 814.00	$______
f.	$1,470.00	$1,017.00	$______

2. Solve each of these. Show your thinking.

a. Frida's expenses were $18.50 and her profit was $8.75. What was her income?

$______

b. Kyle's income was $32. He said his profit was $11.50. How much were his expenses?

$______

Financial Literacy

Comparing Savings Options

1. Loop the plan that will save you more from July 1st to September 30th. Then estimate the total savings of that plan.

a.	b.	c.	d.
$2 a day	$5 a day	$150 a month	$30 a month
or	or	or	or
$80 a month	$120 a month	$6 a day	$1.50 a day
Total $__________	Total $__________	Total $__________	Total $__________

2. Loop the plan that will save you more from July 1st to December 31st. Then estimate the total savings of that plan.

a.	b.	c.	d.
$3 a day	$200 a month	$4 a day	$1.50 a day
or	or	or	or
$100 a month	$8 a day	$110 a month	$40 a month
Total $__________	Total $__________	Total $__________	Total $__________

3. Loop the plan that will save you more from July 1st to June 30th. Then estimate the total savings of that plan.

a.	b.	c.	d.
$10 a week	$20 a week	$250 a month	$300 a month
or	or	or	or
$50 a month	$80 a month	$50 a week	$80 a week
Total $__________	Total $__________	Total $__________	Total $__________

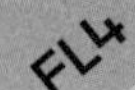

Financial Literacy

Splitting an Allowance between Spending, Saving, and Giving

Look at these diagrams.

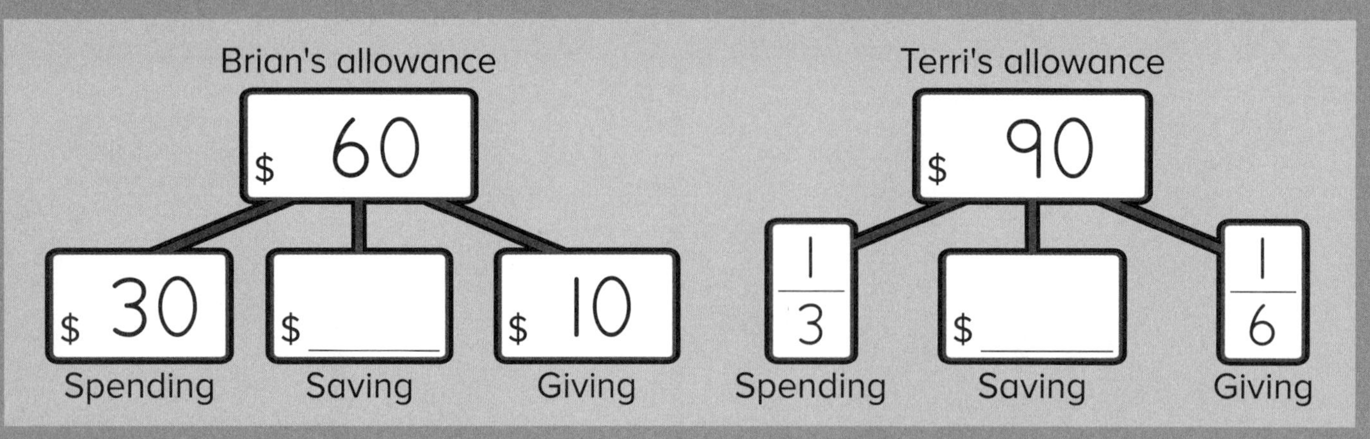

1. a. Compare the amounts they each plan to spend. What do you notice?

   b. What fraction of his allowance is Brian allocating to spending?

   c. Who plans to spend the greater fraction of their allowance?

2. a. Compare the amounts they each plan to give. What do you notice?

   b. How much money does Terri plan to give? $______

3. a. Write each person's savings amount in the diagrams above.

   b. What fraction of each allowance are these savings amounts?

   Brian's fraction　　Terri's fraction

   c. They each allocate half their savings toward college. Write these amounts in dollars.

   Brian's amount $______　　Terri's amount $______

Financial Literacy

Investigating the Purposes of Financial Institutions

1. Conduct research to make a list of banks in your home state.

2. Choose one bank from your list. Research that bank to make a list of products and services that it offers.

Name of bank

Logo of bank

Products and services

INDEX